# NOTE

THE PRESENT VOLUME continues the series produced under the editorship of the Keeper to replace the catalogue of 1929, but dealing, as it does, with a single school within a single century, it is to that extent more restricted in scope than its predecessors. It had originally been intended to issue the catalogue of the sixteenth-century Italian schools as a single volume, but as the work progressed it became clear that the result might well be too bulky for convenient use and that a division into two volumes might be preferable. The sections already complete comprise the schools of Florence, Venice, Ferrara and Parma, but as these would not make up a coherent entity and as the Venetian pictures in the National Gallery greatly outnumber those of any other *cinquecento* school a division into Venetian and non-Venetian seemed the most practical. The present volume, the first of the two to be published, includes those painters whose work, irrespective of the place of their birth, seemed to me to fall properly within the category of the Venetian school. Thus, painters of Bergamasque origin, such as Cariani or Palma Vecchio, are included, while the Brescians are not. Chronologically, all Venetian painters are included who were not covered by the catalogue of the *Earlier Italian Schools* by Martin Davies and who were active up to the end of the sixteenth century. Though certain artists, such as Palma Giovane or Leandro Bassano, continued working until well into the seventeenth century they are included here as being *cinquecento* rather than *seicento* figures.

A great deal of the ground covered by the present volume was explored by two of my predecessors, Mr (now Professor) E. K. Waterhouse and Mr Philip Pouncey. Mr Waterhouse compiled a card index of most of the pictures in question, disclosing a quantity of new information, particularly in respect of provenance. He then wrote draft entries for about half of them. Mr Pouncey's work covered fewer paintings, but he carried his research a stage farther than Mr Waterhouse, and as a result I have usually found it very difficult to add new facts of importance in the case of pictures investigated by him. Though the entries written by these two scholars were too summary to be incorporated into the present catalogue their preliminary notes have been of inestimable value to me, as have various notes left in the Gallery archives by Mr A. E. Popham and Dr (now Professor) Johannes Wilde. Other unpublished material on which I have drawn freely are the notes on costume by Miss Stella Mary Pearce, who carried out research in respect of the majority of the pictures contained in the present volume. Her notes, which are unfortunately too lengthy to publish in full with the relevant entry, have frequently constituted a factor in the dating of a picture and sometimes also in its attribution. In one instance (no. 287, Bartolommeo Veneto) they have even contributed a new element to the biography of the artist in question.

Colleagues abroad to whom I am under an obligation include Dottoressa Paola Della Pergola, Director of the Borghese Gallery, Rome, and Dr Ferruccio Zago, of the Archivio di Stato, Venice, both of whom put themselves to considerable trouble on my behalf, as did Professor Vittorio Moschini, Soprintendente alle Gallerie, Venice, Dr Terisio Pignatti of the Museo Correr and Dr Alessandro Bettagno of the Istituto di Storia dell' Arte (Fondazione Giorgio Cini), Venice. I am also most grateful to the authorities of the Archivio di Stato at Rome and the Archivio di Stato at Modena for facilities and help. Mr John Fleming, resident in Italy, and Mr Hugh Honour were willing and able to comply with innumerable requests for verification and information from local sources, and Mr Patrick Thursfield motored me to some very inaccessible places in both Italy and Germany to study comparative material. Professor Edgar Wind, when the catalogue was already in page proof, shed light on one particularly vexed problem. To all of these, and to my colleagues in the National Gallery—particularly those in the Conservation and Scientific Departments and in the Photographic Section of the Publications Department—I would wish to express my thanks.

CECIL GOULD

NATIONAL GALLERY CATALOGUES

# THE
# SIXTEENTH-CENTURY
# VENETIAN SCHOOL

BY

CECIL GOULD

PUBLISHED BY ORDER OF THE TRUSTEES
PUBLICATIONS DEPARTMENT
THE NATIONAL GALLERY
LONDON
MCMLIX

Made and printed in Great Britain by William Clowes and Sons, Limited, London and Beccles

# EXPLANATIONS

ABBREVIATIONS: As certain books and institutions are repeatedly referred to an abbreviated form is normally used, as follows:

| *Abbreviation* | *Fuller Title* |
| --- | --- |
| B.I. | British Institution. |
| Berenson: *Lists* (with date) | Bernard Berenson: *Italian Pictures of the Renaissance*, 1932. *Pitture Italiane del Rinascimento*, 1936. *Italian Pictures of the Renaissance, Venetian School*, 1957. |
| Buchanan: *Memoirs* | W. Buchanan: *Memoirs of Painting*, 1824. |
| Hill: *Corpus* | G. F. Hill: *A Corpus of Italian Medals of the Renaissance*, 1930. |
| Lugt | F. Lugt: *Répertoire des Catalogues de Vente*, 1938– |
| Morelli: *Munich and Dresden* | Giovanni Morelli: *Italian Painters, The Galleries of Munich and Dresden*, London, 1893. |
| Prussian *Jahrbuch* | *Jahrbuch der (Königlich) Preuszischen Kunstsammlungen*, Berlin. |
| R.A. | Royal Academy. |
| Redford | George Redford: *Art Sales*, 1888. |
| Ridolfi/Hadeln | *Le Maraviglie dell' Arte*, by Carlo Ridolfi, edited by Detlev, Freiherr von Hadeln, 1914–24. |
| Thieme–Becker | U. Thieme and F. Becker: *Allgemeines Lexikon der bildenden Künstler . . .*, 1907–50. |
| Vasari/Milanesi | *Le Vite de' più Eccellenti Pittori Scultori ed Architettori*, by Giorgio Vasari, edited by Gaetano Milanesi, 1878–85. |
| Venturi: *Storia* | Adolfo Venturi: *Storia dell' Arte Italiana*, 1901–39. |
| Vienna *Jahrbuch* | *Jahrbuch der Kunsthistorischen Sammlungen (des Allerhöchsten Kaiserhauses)*, Vienna. |

| *Abbreviation* | *Fuller Title* |
| --- | --- |
| Waagen | Dr Waagen: *Treasures of Art in Great Britain*, 1854. *Galleries and Cabinets of Art in Great Britain*, 1857. |

ATTRIBUTIONS: No claim to completeness is made in listing the suggestions that may at one time or another have been published, but an attempt has been made to quote or discuss those for which serious evidence has been brought forward.

CONDITION: All pictures are on canvas and have been lined unless the contrary is stated. The brief notes on the pictures' state at the time of writing may require modification in the event of subsequent cleaning.

DRAWINGS: A few are noted which are unpublished, but in general only published drawings have been taken into account.

ENGRAVINGS AND COPIES: No attempt has been made to record engravings and copies which date from the nineteenth and twentieth centuries.

MEASUREMENTS: Unless the contrary is stated the dimensions given refer to the area of the original painted surface now visible—i.e. exclusive of bindings. In some cases the word 'circa' is used, since in many pictures the two sides are not of precisely the same dimensions, nor the top and the bottom.

PROVENANCE: In many of the entries it will be seen that the names of successive owners are not recorded in chronological order and sometimes are given in reverse order. This results from an attempt to specify precisely the evidence on which such statements rest and thereby to distinguish between differing shades of certainty and uncertainty. An hypothetical (simplified) example would be: 'No. 4 ("the Pietà") in the Brown sale, 1857, as from the "Jackson collection" and therefore probably identical with no. 8 ("the Dead Christ") in the catalogue of 1795 of the collection of Edward Jackson'. It is to be hoped that some increase in factual clarity resulting from this method may offset any decrease in clarity of presentation.

# BARTOLOMMEO VENETO
## Active 1502, still active 1546

A shadowy figure, not mentioned by Vasari or Ridolfi. His usual form of signature on pictures is 'Bartolommeo' (various spellings), 'Venetus' or 'de Venetia' but the earliest example (1502) is in the unique form 'Bartolamio mezo venizian e mezo cremonexe' (picture formerly in the Donà dalle Rose collection).[1] A 'Bartolomeo da Venezia, pittore', mentioned several times in contemporary documents as engaged, between 1505 and 1508, on decorative and other work in the apartments of Lucrezia Borgia and elsewhere at Ferrara,[2] is usually identified with the author of the signed pictures already referred to. Nevertheless there is a possibility of confusion, since another painter by the name of Bartolomeo da Venezia had been active at Ferrara since at least 1473 and is described as son of 'fu Filippo, cittadino ferrarese'.[3] Some measure of confirmation, however, of the traditional view—that the Bartolommeo Veneto of the signed pictures was active for a time at Ferrara early in the sixteenth century—may perhaps be provided by the Ferrarese element in the costume of no. 2507 below.

Periods in Bergamo and also in Milan have likewise been postulated in respect of the artist of the signed pictures, but though these would not be impossible there is no firm evidence in their favour. The signed works of 1502–6 are religious pictures which are little more than pastiches of Giovanni Bellini. Thereafter Bartolommeo seems to have specialised in fashionable portraiture of which a number of signed examples survive. Of these, one in the Rosebery collection bears the date 1530, and this year was hitherto the last definite date in his career. But since it has been established that the same date formerly read on no. 287 of this Gallery should in fact be read as 1546 his active career must henceforth be extended accordingly.

REFERENCES: (1) Inscription and date as given in the Donà dalle Rose catalogue. The date was inaccurately given as 1503 by André De Hevesy (*Art Quarterly*, vol. II, 1939, p. 233), where the picture was also erroneously said to be in the Museo Correr. (2) Documents published by A. Venturi: *Archivio Storico dell' Arte*, vol. VII, 1894, pp. 297–8. (3) L. N. Cittadella: *Notizie Relative a Ferrara*, 1864, pp. 579 and 596, and *Documenti ed Illustrazioni risguardanti la Storia Artistica Ferrarese*, 1868, p. 146.

## 287 PORTRAIT OF LUDOVICO MARTINENGO

Panel, $41\frac{1}{2} \times 28$ ($1 \cdot 055 \times 0 \cdot 71$).

The face and right hand somewhat retouched. The most conspicuous areas of the dress—the sleeve projecting from the coat and the three rows of satin on the latter—are well preserved. The red of the coat, the waistcoat and, to a lesser extent, the dark background to the left of the curtain are very worn and retouched.

The *cartellino* has suffered damage in a number of places. Original letters remaining are as follows:

– v (only lower half of letter remains) D O (right half) V I | – V M (left half) | M (left half) A (upper half) R T (upper half) | A (left half) T A – – S | S V Æ | A N – – | B – – T O L – (probably small o above the line) M | V (left half) – N (right half) E T V S | F A C I E B A T | M.D.XXX | XVI I (or Z) V N

This had been restored to read as follows:

LVDOVI | CVM | MARTI | –TATIS | SVÆ | ANN– | BARTOL– M| VENETVS | FACIEBAT | M.D XXX | XVI I (or Z) VN

The fact that the picture came from the Martinengo family is a fairly reliable indication that the fragmentary letters remaining of the sitter's name originally spelt Ludovico Martinengo. Enough, likewise, remains of the signature to leave no doubt of its having been that of Bartolommeo Veneto. The date has hitherto been read as 1530, 16th June, but the sitter's costume (which clearly marks the height of fashion) would absolutely exclude so early a date.[1] There can thus be no reasonable doubt that the date is really 1546, June—with which date the costume accords well. The space available to be occupied by the *cartellino* evidently dictated a narrow format for the latter in which there was no room for all the letters MDXXXXVI on the same line. As explained in the biographical notes on Bartolommeo Veneto this new reading extends the period of his working career by sixteen years.

The suggestion, made in the National Gallery Report of 1856, that the sitter is wearing the dress of the *Compagnia della Calza* is untenable, since he is not shown wearing the distinguishing badge.[2] Even without the remains of the signature no. 287 would be immediately recognisable as a characteristic work of Bartolommeo Veneto. The motive, in particular, of the curtain looped over a rod is also found in the Dresden *Salome* and in a female portrait in the Contini Bonacossi collection.

PROVENANCE: Purchased in Venice, 1855, from the representatives of Conte Girolamo Michiel Pisani, heir of Conte Girolamo Martinengo.

REPRODUCTION: *Illustrations, Italian Schools*, 1937, p. 377.

REFERENCES: (1) Notes by Stella Mary Pearce in the Gallery archives. The distinguishing features of the fashion as shown include the small hat and the short coat. These features recur in the costume of the smart young men in Niccolò dell' Abate's frescoes of 1547–51 in the university at Bologna where the costume in general is closely comparable with that in no. 287. Many other parallels among dated pictures could also be quoted. (2) A reference was made to the illustration facing p. 50 of Cesare Vecellio's *Habiti Antichi et Moderni* (1589), but such resemblance as there is is purely superficial.

2507  PORTRAIT OF A LADY

Panel, 22 × 17¼ (0·55 × 0·44).

Thin, and retouched in many places. A biggish patch of repaint, in particular, on her left shoulder.

The beads worn by the lady are ornamented with the emblems of the Passion. One of them is inscribed S A P.

The somewhat unsatisfactory appearance of the picture is probably due in great part to the messy remains of old varnish and engrained dirt. Datable to the early years of the sixteenth century from the costume, which bears a strong resemblance to some in frescoes in Palazzo Costabili, Ferrara.[1] A Ferrarese origin seems therefore probable. A certain divergence, which no. 2507 seems to show, from Bartolommeo Veneto's normal style in portraiture could be explicable on the grounds of its being a relatively early work.

VERSION: Rouen, copy on canvas, 0·49 × 0·38.[2]

PROVENANCE: From the collection of Conte Alessandro Castellani.[3] Salting Bequest, 1910.

REPRODUCTION: *Illustrations, Italian Schools*, 1937, p. 378.

REFERENCES: (1) Reproduced in A. Venturi: *Storia* . . ., VII, III, pl. 849–55, particularly pl. 850. (2) Letter in the Gallery archives from the Director of the Rouen museums. (3) Salting MS. in the Gallery archives.

# FRANCESCO (II) BASSANO
## 1549–1592

Francesco dal Ponte. He committed suicide in July, 1592. The inscription on his grave says he was 43 years old at the time.[1] He was the eldest surviving son of Jacopo Bassano (q.v.) and is called Francesco II to distinguish him from his grandfather. His three younger brothers, Giambattista, Leandro (q.v.) and Gerolamo, were also painters. Ridolfi says that Francesco was the best of the four.[2]

Francesco's art was closely modelled on that of his father, and altarpieces at Marostica (*S. Paul Preaching*: 1574), Civezzano (*Meeting of Joachim and Anna*) and the Bassano museum (*Circumcision*: 1577) are signed as being their joint work. By 1581[3] Francesco was settled in Venice where he participated in the re-decoration of the Doge's Palace.

REFERENCES: (1) See W. Arslan: *I Bassano*, 1931, p. 219, note 3, for the question of the exact day of his birth, and Hadeln (Ridolfi/Hadeln, I, p. 409, note 5, and p. 410, note 1) for that of his death. (2) Ridolfi/Hadeln, I, p. 403. (3) Letter of 25th May, 1581 from Venice, printed in Bottari-Ticozzi: *Raccolta di Lettere* . . ., III, 1822, pp. 265–6. G. Gerola (article on Bassano, Francesco, il Giovane, in Thieme-Becker) says Francesco was in Venice from 1580 but does not state his source.

## (?) After FRANCESCO BASSANO

2148 THE DEPARTURE OF ABRAHAM

$33\frac{1}{2} \times 46\frac{1}{2}$ (0·85 × 1·19).

Much damaged near the edges. Paint in centre seems in good state.

In the 1929 catalogue ('withdrawn from exhibition') as 'School of Jacopo Bassano'.

Studio version of a Bassanesque design of which two examples are at Vienna.[1] Another (attributed to Leandro and closer to no. 2148 in design than to the Vienna pictures) was lot 4, Lord Clinton sale, Sotheby's, 19th July, 1950.

VERSIONS: See above. Others are recorded in the Palazzo Camuccini at Cantalupo in Sabina and (formerly) in the Vom Rath collection, Amsterdam.

PROVENANCE: Bought with the Galvagna collection (Venice), 1855. Said to have been earlier in Casa Savorgnan.[2] On loan to Dublin, 1857 to *c.* 1926. Not catalogued until 1915.

REPRODUCTION: Negative in the possession of the Gallery.

REFERENCES: (1) One reproduced by W. Arslan: *I Bassano*, 1931, pl. LXVI. They figure as nos. 266 and 325 in the catalogue of 1907, attr. Francesco Bassano. A third comparable picture at Vienna is no. 294 in the 1907 catalogue. None of these pictures is included in the catalogue of 1938. (2) National Gallery Report, 1856.

## JACOPO BASSANO
### Active *c.* 1535, died 1592

His name was Jacopo dal Ponte, called Jacopo Bassano from his home city of that name. His father, Francesco I, was also a painter. A census of 1561 gives his age as 45; another, of 1589, as 70.[1] Ridolfi says he was born in 1510[2] and Borghini that 'hoggi' he was 66 years old.[3] There is no reliable guide to which, if any, of these four birth dates (1510, 1516, 1519 and *c.* 1518) is correct. Of his earliest works, Verci mentions a picture as dated 1531, but it is no longer identifiable; also a further painting which he says was dated 1534.[4] The latter work—*Flight into Egypt* (Bassano, Museo Civico, from the church of S. Girolamo)—is not dated now. The earliest surviving approximately datable paintings are, in fact, three oblong religious pictures from the Sala dell' Udienza of the Palazzo Pretorio, Bassano. In one of these—*Shadrach, Meshach and Abednego in the Fiery Furnace*—the Navagier arms are displayed, and since Luca Navagier was *Podestà* of Bassano from October, 1534 to February, 1536[5] it can be deduced that the pictures were probably commissioned during that period.

In addition to training which he would have received from his father Jacopo probably had some in Venice where, in 1535, he was given a patent for an invention.[6] Ridolfi says that according to one version he was a pupil of Bonifazio for a short time. Early paintings such as the three already mentioned would bear this out, as showing marked influence of Bonifazio. The influence of Lotto is also strong. Nevertheless, even in his early work Jacopo shows an individual style which at this period was rustic in character and relatively primitive. Later his art was refined by the influence of engravings after Raphael and, more particularly, by that of Parmigianino's etchings.

Despite the scarcity of dated pictures it is certain that Jacopo's art continued to evolve until an unusually late period of his life and that his most individual and characteristic style was not fully developed before a point within about twenty years of the end of his active career.[7] This late style, though extremely original, in outlook, design and technique alike, was able to be canalised into the work of Jacopo's sons whose activities both as collaborators during their father's old age and later as plagiarists have contributed to obscuring his achievement.

Both Vasari[8] and Borghini,[9] each of whom was writing within Jacopo's life-time, draw attention to his excellence as a painter of animals.

REFERENCES: (1) For both documents see *Bollettino del Museo Civico di Bassano*, II (1905), pp. 67 and 104, note. (2) Ridolfi/Hadeln, I (1914), p. 385. (3) *Il Riposo*, 1584, p. 563. (4) Giambatista Verci: *Notizie . . . della Città di Bassano*, 1775, pp. 86 and 79. (5) Ridolfi/Hadeln, op. cit., p. 388, note 8. (6) W. Arslan: *I Bassano*, 1931, p. 46. (7) By 1581 it seems that Jacopo had more or less retired from active work (letter from Francesco II, quoted by Arslan, *op. cit.*, p. 141). (8) Ed. Milanesi, VII, p. 455. (9) *Loc. cit.*

## 228 THE PURIFICATION OF THE TEMPLE

$62\frac{1}{2} \times 104\frac{1}{2}$ ($1 \cdot 587 \times 2 \cdot 65$).
In general in very fair condition.

The youth, top right, was probably an afterthought. His right arm is painted on top of the pillar which he holds and his head on top of the moulding over the door.

The figures left and right appear truncated: some cutting is probable. No. 228 is related to a number of large Bassanesque upright altarpieces characterised by dark tone, summary handling and a background composed of diverse architectural elements seen in sharply receding (and usually faulty) perspective. Other pictures of this type are the *S. Valentino baptising S. Lucilla* (Bassano, Museo Civico), *S. Roche blessing the Plague Victims* (Milan, Brera), *Martyrdom of S. Lawrence* (1571) (Belluno), *Preaching of S. Paul* (1574) (Marostica)[1] and *Meeting of Joachim and Anna* (Civezzano). The last two of these pictures are signed as being the joint work of Jacopo and his son, Francesco, and it may be noted that this type of design also became a favourite with Jacopo's son, Leandro (an example is no. 60 of this Gallery). A possibility of some collaboration should therefore be considered in the case of no. 228, but though it may in fact have occurred its extent, if any, cannot be established. In the present writer's opinion it would have been the minimum: the handling is much more forceful than in any of the acknowledged works of any of the sons, while all the proto-Impressionist devices which are apparent can also be paralleled in the most admired of Jacopo's productions, namely the *S. Valentino baptising S. Lucilla*.[2] The money-changer seated on the right at the table has been thought to be a portrait of Titian. While the context would conform with his widespread reputation for avarice the likeness is in fact non-committal and is a facial type which occurs frequently in Jacopo's late works.[3]

VERSIONS: Several pictures of this subject are recorded in the inventory of Jacopo's pictures made after his death.[4] A variant (bearing the remains of Leandro's signature) is at Lille, another (closer to the latter than to no. 228) in the Doria collection, Rome (no. 91 in the 1942 catalogue by Ettore Sestieri where attributed to Gerolamo Bassano). Another (attributed Francesco Bassano) is at Vienna (no. 267 in the 1907 catalogue). Another was lot 2 in the Henry Reitlinger sale, Sotheby's, 9th December, 1953. Distant derivatives are in the Museo Correr, Venice and Palazzo Spada, Rome.[5] Pictures of this description recorded in the collection of the Earl of Arundel,[6] in Palazzo Raggi, Genoa,[7] the Lansdowne sale, 2nd day, 20th March, 1806 (26) and the James Cooke sale, 2nd day, 27th February, 1813 (42).

PROVENANCE: Presented, 1853, by Philip L. Hinds. At a sale (Christie's, 11th June, 1870) of pictures belonging to the latter, two (nos. 81 and 96) are specified as from the collection of the Earl of Shaftesbury and are thus identifiable with lots 37 and 56 in the Earl of Shaftesbury's sale, Christie's, 15th May, 1852. The fact that both pictures were bought at the Shaftesbury sale by Hickman, who also bought lot 48[8] ('Giacomo Bassano. Christ driving the money changers from the Temple. *A grand gallery picture*'), is a good indication that the latter was identical with no. 228. Stated in the National Gallery catalogue of 1859 to have been 'brought to England by Mr A. Wilson in 1806' and therefore identifiable with lot 22, Andrew Wilson sale (by Peter Coxe), 6th May, 1807, in the catalogue of which stated to have been bought at Leghorn.

REPRODUCTION: *Illustrations, Italian Schools*, 1937, p. 23.

REFERENCES: (1) Like no. 228 this picture includes the motive of a boy looking down, with his arm round a pillar. (2) W. Arslan (in *Dedalo*, February–May, 1930, p. 564 and *I Bassani*, 1931, p. 304) proposed an attribution of no. 228 to Gerolamo, or to Jacopo and Gerolamo combined, after a design by Jacopo. (3) Examples are the most prominent member of the congregation in the *Paul Preaching* (Marostica), the bearers at Christ's head in the *Entombment* and *Deposition* (Padua, S. Maria in Vanzo and Lansdowne collection) and several figures in the *Gloria* (Bassano, Museo Civico). (4) See Giambatista Verci: *Notizie Intorno . . . alle Opere . . . della Città di Bassano*, 1775, pp. 92–100, nos. 34, 96 and 187. (5) The Palazzo Spada picture was, in 1957, hanging in the private rooms on the *piano nobile* and not in the Gallery. It does not figure in F. Zeri's catalogue of the latter. (6) Mentioned by Ridolfi (Ridolfi/Hadeln I, p. 399) and figuring in the 1655 Arundel inventory (Mary F. S. Hervey: *Thomas Howard, Earl of Arundel*, 1921, p. 475). (7) Ratti's guide to Genoa of 1780, p. 236. (8) Marked copy of the sale catalogue in the Gallery library.

## 277  THE GOOD SAMARITAN

40 × 31¼ (1·015 × 0·794).

The flesh of the two main figures, and more particularly the sky, fairly extensively damaged and retouched; the Samaritan's clothes, rock, ass, dogs and bottle rather less so.

The priest and the Levite are shown in the middle distance, left. In the background, the city of Bassano.

Attributed by Waagen to Francesco Bassano.[1] Otherwise the attribution to Jacopo has been general and is acceptable.

VERSIONS: Two pictures, variants of each other rather than of no. 277 and both apparently earlier than it—Hampton Court (ex-coll. Charles I—oblong) and Rome, Capitoline (upright) [2]—show a different moment in the story; the Samaritan is not carrying the man to his ass but binding his wounds. Derivatives of these pictures are at Vienna (no. 283 in the 1907 catalogue) and Berlin (no. 314 in the 1931 catalogue). A picture of this subject is listed on pp. 116–17 of the 1734 catalogue of the collection of Cardinal Tommaso Ruffo at Ferrara.

DRAWING: London, Courtauld Institute (Witt Collection). No. 2235. Black chalk sketch of the two main figures and the ass. Oblong format, extensively retouched.

ENGRAVING: No. 277 (or a hypothetical identical replica) engraved as no. 34 in P. Monaco: *Raccolta di Cento e Dodeci Quadri . . .*, Venice, 1772.

PROVENANCE: No. 54 in the sale (18th May, 1821) of pictures in the estate of the Dowager Marchioness of Thomond, niece and heiress of Sir Joshua Reynolds. Therefore identifiable with lot 36 in the Reynolds sale of 9th May, 1798 and with lot 48 in the Reynolds sale of 17th March, 1795 (catalogue dated 8th March, 1794)—presumably bought in on both occasions. On the strength of the engraving in Monaco's *Raccolta* (see ENGRAVING above) almost certainly identical with the picture in the Pisani collection in the eighteenth century.[3] Bought at the Thomond sale by 'Mr Rogers' (Samuel Rogers)[4] by whom exhibited, B.I., 1823 (142)[5] and at whose sale (3rd May, 1856) purchased (lot 709).

REPRODUCTION: *Illustrations, Italian Schools*, 1937, p. 23.

REFERENCES: (1) *Treasures . . .*, vol. II, p. 77. (2) Reproduced by W. Arslan: *Contributo a Jacopo Bassano* in *Pinacotheca*, 1928–9, pp. 194–6. (3) Therefore, as pointed out by Hadeln (Ridolfi/Hadeln, vol, I, p. 395, note 6), not identical with Ridolfi's mention of the 'Samaritano . . . tra le cose . . . che passarono in Inghilterra'. (4) The name is printed in one copy of the catalogue in the National Gallery library and written in another. (5) Samuel Rogers' name is (apparently) misprinted 'Henry Rogers' in the exhibition catalogue.

# LEANDRO BASSANO
## 1557–1622

Leandro dal Ponte. The third of Jacopo Bassano's sons to reach maturity.[1]

Ridolfi[2] says he stayed with his father in Bassano after his elder brother, Francesco, settled in Venice. He himself seems to have settled in Venice by 1588[3] and he completed a number of Francesco's pictures after the latter's premature death in 1592.[4] His active and successful career included work at the Doge's Palace, but Ridolfi stresses that his fame rested chiefly on his skill as portraitist and that it was this which procured him a knighthood from the Doge, Marin Grimano.[5] Thereafter the word 'eques' after his signature is normally added.

In his subject-pictures Leandro's point of departure was the late work of his father; in portraiture, probably Tintoretto.

REFERENCES: (1) For dates of birth and death cf. Hadeln (Ridolfi/Hadeln, II, pp. 167–71) and W. Arslan: *I Bassano* (1931, pp. 247–73). (2) Ridolfi/Hadeln, II (1924), p. 165. (3) Ridolfi says that it was on Francesco's death that Leandro removed to Venice. But Hadeln (*op. cit.*, p. 166, note 2) produces evidence for the earlier date. (4) Ridolfi/Hadeln, I, p. 409, and II, p. 166. (5) Ridolfi, *op. cit.*, p. 166.

## 60  THE TOWER OF BABEL

$53\frac{3}{4} \times 74\frac{1}{2}$ ($1\cdot39 \times 1\cdot892$).

Signed, on the block of stone bottom left, LEANDER A PONTE B... The last letters may be B ES$^F$, but the letters are indistinct, and the abbreviation 'es' for 'eques' would be unusual. An alternative reading would be BASS, but it is far from certain whether there is any letter immediately after the B, while the letter before the s looks more like an E than another s.

Good condition.

In earlier editions of the catalogue as 'School of Leandro', but the signature, which has not been recorded hitherto, seems genuine, and the style of the picture characteristic of Leandro. Some of the costumes are apparently intended to be oriental.[1] That of the horseman, left, seems contemporary and suggests a dating soon after 1600.[2]

VERSION: Prague, square format (photograph in the Gallery archives). If this was the version engraved in the *Theatrum Pictorium* (see below), it has since been considerably truncated on the right and slightly on the left.

ENGRAVING: The design, but not necessarily this version, engraved in the *Theatrum Pictorium* of Teniers (pl. 154).

PROVENANCE: Bequeathed by Lt.-Col. Ollney, 1837. On loan to Dublin, 1862 to *c.* 1926.

REPRODUCTION: *Illustrations, Italian Schools*, 1937, p. 24.

REFERENCES: (1) There was some tradition for this in representations of the Tower of Babel. Examples are Giusto de' Menabuoi, Padua, Baptistery (pl. 76 in Sergio Bettini's monograph, 1944), Benozzo Gozzoli, Pisa, Campo Santo; also Martin van Valckenborch, Dresden (no. 832 in 1902 catalogue). The writer is grateful to Stella Mary Pearce for drawing his attention to these examples. (2) Notes by Stella Mary Pearce in the Gallery archives.

## Style of LEANDRO BASSANO

## 2149  PORTRAIT OF A MAN

$25\frac{1}{2} \times 21$ ($0\cdot647 \times 0\cdot533$).

Inscribed: HIC SATVS EST | CVLTOR PHÆB– | ORPH– | GRATVS PRINC – | PROMPTVS IN |

Somewhat rubbed. To judge from the truncated form of the inscription, evidently cut on the right. The inscription (more easily legible in an infra-red photograph than to the naked eye and not hitherto recorded) may be part of a couplet with reference to the sitter.

In the 1929 catalogue as 'School of Leandro Bassano'.

An inferior example of a type of portraiture associated with Leandro Bassano.

PROVENANCE: Purchased with the Galvagna collection (Venice), 1855. On loan to Dublin, 1857 to *c.* 1926. Not catalogued until 1915.

REPRODUCTION: *Illustrations, Italian Schools*, 1937, p. 24.

## Follower of the BASSANO

### 1858 ADORATION OF THE SHEPHERDS

$25\frac{1}{4} \times 35\frac{1}{2}$ (0·645 × 0·901).
Some wearing, particularly in the back of the foreground shepherd. Otherwise in good state.

A later derivative, perhaps via Leandro, of a design by Jacopo of which the best version is probably that in the Galleria Nazionale, Rome. Others in the Reinhart collection (Winterthur), in the Accademia, Venice, at Nancy (no. 16), and in the collection of Viscount Allendale.

In the 1929 catalogue ('withdrawn from exhibition') as 'School of Jacopo Bassano'.

PROVENANCE: Bequeathed by Sir John May, 1847, but apparently never exhibited.

REPRODUCTION: Negative in the Gallery's possession.

## BONIFAZIO DI PITATI
### 1487–1553

A Veronese who settled at Venice. The confusion which long persisted concerning him started with G. Moschini[1] (who postulated two painters of this name), was aggravated by Bernasconi[2] (who produced a third) and culminated with Morelli[3] (who divided the existing Bonifazian *œuvre* stylistically into three groups and called them Bonifazio I, II and III). The ground was then cleared by G. Ludwig,[4] who showed from archival research that the Pitati family had been established at Verona since the fourteenth century but that only one of them was a painter, that the second painter called Bonifazio bore the surname Pasini and that the third was a phantom. The unequal quality of many of the existing pictures in a Bonifazian style was explained by Ludwig's discovery of documents which showed that Bonifazio kept an abnormally large studio.

Ludwig produced indications which suggested that Bonifazio's father moved in 1505 from Verona to Venice, but the first record of the painter at Venice is of 1528, while the earliest dated picture by Bonifazio which survives (and the only one which is both signed and dated) is of 1533 (Venice, Palazzo Reale, lent to the Accademia, *Madonna and Child with SS. John the Baptist, Homobono and Barbara*)[5]. . . . In addition a number of surviving paintings are reasonably associated with him, notably a large series of (partly documented) decorations dating from 1530 onwards, painted for the Palazzo Camerlenghi at Venice and now dispersed.

If, as is probable, pictures such as no. 1202 of this Gallery are in fact early works of Bonifazio it would be an indication that his earliest work was modelled on Palma. But in default of further firm evidence as much must remain obscure in the career of the one as in that of the other.

REFERENCES: (1) *Guida per la Città di Venezia*, 1815. (2) *Studj sopra la storia . . . della scuola pittorica Veronese*, 1864. (3) *Munich and Dresden*, 1893. (4) Prussian *Jahrbuch*, vols. XXII and XXIII. (5) Signature and date have not, apparently, been questioned. The inscription containing the signature, however, is in the same kind of paint as the other inscription (containing the date), and this is demonstrably superimposed on an earlier inscription. As the date in the latter is still legible, however, and is the same as that in the former (MDXXXIII) the status of the existing signature may not be of great significance. In any case the attribution to Bonifazio is acceptable.

1202 MADONNA AND CHILD, WITH SS. JAMES THE GREATER, JEROME, INFANT JOHN THE BAPTIST AND CATHERINE OF ALEXANDRIA

Panel, painted surface $28\frac{3}{4} \times 46$ ($0.73 \times 1.168$).
Good condition.

S. James has thrown his pilgrim's hat (decorated with his shell and cross and with Veronica's veil) over his shoulders.[1] S. Jerome, next him, is without his lion but identifiable by his scarlet robes.[2] The coat of arms above the door in the background appears indecipherable. There are also traces of cabalistic characters on the wall below it to the right.

This type of *Santa Conversazione* is pre-eminently associated with Palma Vecchio to whom, indeed, no. 1202 was long ascribed.[3] Nevertheless the handling is coarser than Palma's and more summary, and the picture, with others of similar kind, is generally attributed to a relatively early (and still Palmesque) phase of Bonifazio's career.[4]

VERSION: Venice, Accademia (no. 275), where catalogued as a copy.

PROVENANCE: From the Terzi[5] and Andreossi collections at Bergamo. Purchased, 1886, from the heirs of Enrico Andreossi, Walker Fund.

REPRODUCTION: *Illustrations, Italian Schools*, 1955, p. 45.

REFERENCES: (1) He is shown wearing a similar hat in a painting reproduced by Kaftal: *Iconography of the Saints in Tuscan Painting* (1952), fig. 595. (2) It is possible that the lion shown attacking a sheep in the background (to the consternation of the—presumably hireling—shepherds) is meant to be S. Jerome's which has got out of hand. (3) E.g. by the former owner and by Crowe and Cavalcaselle (*Painting in North Italy*, III, 1912, pp. 367–8). Morelli (*Munich and Dresden*, 1893, p. 41) first put forward the Bonifazio attribution. This has found almost general favour since, but cf. Venturi's whim of including no. 1202 under both Jacopo and Antonio Palma (*Storia*, IX, III, pp. 436 and 1059), in the former reference as "Andreossi coll., Milan". (4) Notes by Stella Mary Pearce in the Gallery archives on the costumes in no. 1202 favour a dating around 1529–32. (5) Information from Crowe and Cavalcaselle, *loc. cit.* Morelli (*loc. cit.*) mentions that no. 1202 was exhibited at Bergamo as Palma.

## Studio of BONIFAZIO

### 2145 A HUNTSMAN

46 × 25½ (1·169 × 0·648).
Fair condition.

In the Galvagna collection, Venice, as Giorgione. Lent to Dublin from 1857 to 1926 and not catalogued until 1915 ('School of Giorgione'). In the 1920 edition as 'Venetian School'. As Bonifazio in the edition of 1929, and this attribution supported by Berenson[1] and by Westphal.[2] In point of fact no. 2145 would seem a routine production of Bonifazio's large studio. Westphal[3] suggests it was one of a series of Labours of the Months (cf. nos. 3109 and 3110 of this Gallery).

PROVENANCE: Collection Baron Galvagna, Venice, with which purchased, 1855.[4] Said to have been in Casa Savorgnan.[5]

REPRODUCTION: *Illustrations, Italian Schools*, 1937, p. 46.

REFERENCES: (1) *Lists*, 1932, 1936 and 1957. (2) *Bonifazio Veronese*, 1931, pp. 54–5. (3) *Loc. cit.* (4) Noted by Mündler (note book in the Gallery archives) in October, 1855 in Baron Galvagna's possession. (5) National Gallery Report, 1856.

## Style of BONIFAZIO

### 3109 THE LABOURS OF THE MONTHS—JANUARY TO JUNE

Canvas, mounted on wood. Each painting *c.* 5¼ × 4 (0·133 × 0·102). Apparently in good condition for the most part.

1. An old man asleep by a stove.
2. A youth asleep on a rampart.
3. Pig-killing.
4. A falconer with hounds.
5. A man cutting corn.
6. Ploughing.

For commentary see no. 3110.

### 3110 THE LABOURS OF THE MONTHS—JULY TO DECEMBER

Canvas, mounted on wood. Each painting *c.* 5¼ × 4 (0·133 × 0·102). Apparently in good condition for the most part.

1. Threshing.
2. Squeezing grapes.
3. Coopering wine-casks.

2—V.S.C.

4. Pointing vine-poles.
5. Making vine-trellises.
6. Vine dressing.

The Labours of the Months was a subject which had been extremely common in mediaeval art and which became popular again in a somewhat altered form around the middle of the sixteenth century in northern Italy, particularly with the Bassano and their followers. The present set (nos. 3109 and 3110) has been attributed to Bonifazio since Layard's time.[1] There is some generic resemblance to works such as no. 2145 of this Gallery which is acceptable as a product of Bonifazio's studio, but the erratic draughtsmanship of nos. 3109 and 3110 presupposes an even more distant connection with the master.

PROVENANCE: Bought by Sir A. H. Layard from Marini.[2] Layard Bequest, 1916.

REPRODUCTION: *Illustrations, Italian Schools*, 1937, pp. 47–8.

REFERENCES: (1) Admitted as Bonifazio by Berenson (1897) and by Hadeln (article in Thieme–Becker). An oral communication from P. Toesca (October, 1930) favoured Andrea Schiavone. D. Westphal (*Bonifazio Veronese*, 1931, p. 97) says 'die Bilder gehören gewiss dem Kreise des Bonifazio an'. (2) Layard MS. in the Gallery archives. The entry comes almost at the end of Layard's note book, in consequence of which it would have been among his latest purchases.

3536 MADONNA AND CHILD WITH SS. JOHN THE BAPTIST, ELIZABETH AND CATHERINE OF ALEXANDRIA

$28\frac{3}{4} \times 47$ (0·73 × 1·194).
Fair state. Some damage due to flaking.

Traces of scribbled characters, probably always devoid of meaning, on the pier behind S. Catherine.[1]

Probably as Bonifazio when in the Manfrin collection, thereafter ascribed to Palma Vecchio until entering the Gallery. As Bonifazio in the 1929 catalogue.

The type of the figures, particularly that of S. Catherine, is much closer to that of acceptable Bonifazio's than to Palma. But the poverty of the execution militates against assuming his active participation, while the tameness of the design suggests rather a pastiche of Bonifazian motives put together by a follower.[2] The costumes accord best with a dating in the early 1530's.[3]

PROVENANCE: From the Manfrin collection, Venice (label on the back).[4] In the collection of the Earl of Dudley by 1868 when exh. by him at Leeds (label on the back).[5] Exh. R.A., 1871 (335) ('Palma Vecchio'), by Lord Dudley. Dudley sale, 25th June, 1892 (probably lot 72).[6] Exh. New Gallery ('Venetian Art'), 1894–5 (92) ('Palma Vecchio'), lent by Wickham Flower. No. 54 in the latter's sale, 17th December, 1904 ('Palma Vecchio') as ex-Manfrin and ex-Dudley,[7] where bought Colnaghi by whom sold to Alfred A. de Pass. Presented by the latter, 1920.

REPRODUCTION: *Illustrations, Italian Schools*, 1937, p. 47.

REFERENCES: (1) Cf. similar characters on no. 1202. (2) The S. Catherine in no. 3536, as already indicated, is of a usual Bonifazian type, comparable with several figures in the Brera *Finding of Moses* and to some extent with the same saint in no. 1202 of this Gallery. The infant S. John in no. 3536 is almost a repetition of the same figure in the *Santa Conversazione* in the Gardner Museum, Boston. Berenson (*Lists*, 1936 and 1957) gives no. 3536 to Bonifazio 'in great part'. (3) Notes in the Gallery archives by Stella Mary Pearce who points out that the costumes alone in no. 3536 suggest a different hand from no. 1202; also, that while S. Catherine's costume is consistent with the fashion of the early 1530's, that of the Virgin and S. Elizabeth is unusually archaic, which seems to support the theory of a pastiche. (4) Probably no. 417 in the Manfrin catalogue of 1856—'Bonifazio, Madonna, Bambino e Santi, tela, larghezza 1.22, altezza 0.77'. The latter picture no longer figures in the 1872 Manfrin catalogue. (5) Could be any of nos. 2912 ('Bonifazio'), 2913 ('Bonifazio') or 2916 ('Palma Vecchio') in the exhibition catalogue. (6) Lots 72 and 73 are given in the sale catalogue as of identical dimensions, both as 'Palma Vecchio' and both as 'exh. R.A., 1871' and as 'ex-coll. Alexander Barker, 1874'. There therefore seems to be some confusion. If no. 3536 was the property of Lord Dudley in 1868, 1871 and 1892 it is most unlikely to have been in the Barker collection in 1874. The latter date was that of the Barker sale, in which no. 3536 certainly did not figure. Barker, however, had bought pictures from the Manfrin collection, and a '*Holy Family* by Palma Vecchio', listed in the National Gallery Board minutes of 9th June, 1856 as one of the pictures recently sold from the Manfrin collection could be no. 3536 and could have been bought by Barker. (7) Also as ex-Alexander Barker, 1874, evidently copying the Dudley sale catalogue.

## After BONIFAZIO

### 3106  DIVES AND LAZARUS

Panel, $18\frac{1}{2} \times 33\frac{1}{3}$ (0·47 × 0·845).
Much damaged, and disfigured by engrained dirt.

The textual source is Luke xvi, 19 ff: *There was a certain rich man which was clothed in purple and fine linen, and fared sumptuously every day: And there was a certain beggar named Lazarus, which was laid at his gate, full of sores, And desiring to be fed with the crumbs which fell from the rich man's table: moreover the dogs came and licked his sores.*

A MS. note by Layard[1] says that the following information was on the back of no. 3106 before it was cradled; *Di mano di Bonifatio— Originale et modelo del quadro famoso delle Nozze del Ricco Epulone in Casa Giustinian a Stae per cui il Zanetti vuolse pagar doppie di Spagna No. mille e cinquecento a Marco.*

There is no indication of the date when this notice was written, but it may be deduced from the reference to Zanetti that it could not have been earlier than the 18th century, and therefore too late to be of any documentary value for the origin of the picture. The same objection applies to a further MS. note by Layard quoting a letter written to him in 1868 by Rawdon Brown. According to this, a former owner, Signor Vason of Venice, had deduced that no. 3106, like the large picture in the Accademia at Venice, had been painted for the Giustiniani family.

Even if this was the case it would still not prove that no. 3106 was a study for the big picture and not a copy after it. The main differences between the two are as follows:

1. No. 3106 shows more space at the right and at the base than the Accademia picture and less on the left hand side. This could be explained by assuming that no. 3106 had been cut on the left and the Accademia picture at the base and on the right.

2. Several features in the middle distance of the Accademia picture are omitted in no. 3106, viz. the shield or banner on the wall behind the falconer (left centre), the figures under the arch in the central perspective and those on the extreme right (running up to the horse).

3. Details of the foreground group are simplified in no. 3106, viz. the unpatterned tablecloth, the lack of a bowl on it, the plain right sock of the negro page, centre (in the Accademia picture he has a striped one) and the details of the rich man's hat and lapels. The second and third of these differences (as well as the fact that the dog in no. 3106 who licks Lazarus is only lightly outlined) would be by no means incompatible with a copy on so greatly reduced a scale. A further difference, arising from the fact that Lazarus is nearer to the pillar in the Accademia picture than in no. 3106, on the other hand, would be more natural in a study than a copy. The present condition of no. 3106 precludes a confident verdict, but the apparent feebleness of the execution seems to the present writer to be the deciding factor in favour of the theory of a copy.[2]

PROVENANCE: Purchased by Sir A. H. Layard, February, 1868, from Vason, Venice. According to a note already quoted from Rawdon Brown (which cannot be confirmed) no. 3106 was among property which passed from a branch of the Giustiniani family to the Donà family and was presented by Marina Donà (who had married Piero Grimani in 1796) to Vason about 1845. Exh. South Kensington, 1869 (no. 29, lent Layard). Layard Bequest, 1916.

REPRODUCTION: Westphal: *Bonifazio Veronese*, 1931, pl. 17.

REFERENCES: (1) In the Gallery archives. (2) No. 3106 is considered an autograph study by Westphal (*op. cit.*, pp. 47–8).

## PARIS BORDON
### 1500–1571

The notice of his death is dated 19th January, 1571 (1570 in the then Venetian style), and gives his age as 70. As the entry of his baptism is dated 5th July, 1500 the latter is the year of his birth. He was from Treviso but spent most of his life at Venice where he was living by 1518. Vasari, who is probably reliable, mentions, *inter alia*, visits by Bordon to Vicenza and Milan and apparently also to Augsburg.[1] He also speaks of a journey to France made in 1538 at the instance of 'Re Francesco'. If the date is correct, the king would be François I. But a local Trevisan tradition, reported by Federici,[2] gives the date as

1559 which was during the short reign of François II, and this seems, on the whole, the more probable.

Vasari says that Bordon was apprenticed for a time to Titian and that he then set himself to follow the manner of Giorgione. While both these statements are probable, insufficient of Bordon's early work has been identified to permit of an analysis of his development. Probably his earliest acceptable work is an altarpiece from Crema (now Lovere, Accademia Tadini). This is mentioned as Bordon's by the Anonimo Morelliano and incorporates, according to Vasari, a portrait of Giulio Manfron who was killed in 1526. It probably dates from shortly before then.[3] There are enough signed works to define Bordon's strongly individual style, but as hardly any are dated and as he seems to have evolved very little the chronology of his *œuvre* is uncertain.

REFERENCES: (1) Vasari seems to imply (Milanesi ed., vol. VII, p. 464) that Bordon actually worked at Augsburg, rather than merely sending pictures there (as he is reported to have done in the case of Flanders and for the King of Poland) but the wording is less unequivocal than in the case of the visits to Vicenza, Milan or France. A portrait in the Louvre, signed by Bordon and dated 1540, includes the word 'Augusta' in the inscription and was most probably painted at Augsburg. But the possibility would remain that it was painted at Venice though of an Augsburg resident. (2) Domenico Maria Federici: *Memorie Trevigiane*, vol. II (1803), pp. 41–2. Bailo and Biscaro: *Paris Bordon* (1900), pp. 41–4, discuss the problem of the French journey in full. (3) Bailo and Biscaro, *op. cit.*, pp. 45–6 and 132–3.


637 DAPHNIS AND CHLOE

$53\frac{1}{3} \times 47\frac{1}{2}$ ($1 \cdot 359 \times 1 \cdot 206$).

Flesh and hair in good condition. In Chloe's dress, the foliage behind her, the tree trunks on the right and elsewhere a good deal of wearing is apparent, probably caused by pressure at the time of lining.

The source of the Daphnis and Chloe story is the Greek pastoral romance of Longus.

The attribution of no. 637 to Bordon is acceptable, probably somewhat earlier than no. 674.[1]

VERSION: Vienna, Kunsthistorisches Museum (no. 253 in the catalogue of 1907; not in the 1928 or 1938 catalogues). The design is given an oblong format. The female figure holds a bow and arrows instead of the reed pipes. Called 'Venus and Adonis'.[2] A third version (Dubrovnik)[3] is of the same format as no. 637 but with the bow and arrows as in the Vienna picture, though arranged differently.

PROVENANCE: Purchased with the Beaucousin collection, Paris, 1860.

REPRODUCTION: *Illustrations, Italian Schools*, 1937, p. 50.

REFERENCES: (1) In notes (in the Gallery archives) on the hair styles shown in no. 637 Stella Mary Pearce favours a dating around 1540. (2) No. 637 is said to have been called 'Mars and Venus' when in the Beaucousin collection. (3) Photograph in the Gallery archives.

### 674 PORTRAIT OF A YOUNG LADY

42 × 33¾ (1·067 × 0·857).

These dimensions include strips *c.* 3″ wide at the top of the picture, *c.* 2″ wide at the sides and *c.* 1″ wide at the base which are later additions.[1] As the strip on the left hand side of the picture includes part of the lady's right sleeve it is probable that the picture had been cut down at some stage before the additions were made.

The hair and nearly all of the dress in good condition, the face and hands fair. The area of flesh within the pearl necklace a good deal retouched.

Inscribed: . ÆTATIS. SVÆ | ANN. XVIIII.

In earlier editions of the National Gallery catalogue it is said to be signed PARIS .B.O., but only faint indications of some of these letters are now visible. Nevertheless no doubt can be entertained regarding the attribution.

Hitherto called 'A Lady of the Brignole Family, Genoa'. As there is no coat of arms or inscription to this effect such a title was presumably that used by the former owner, the Duca di Cardinale. There is otherwise no evidence in its favour.[2] Another suggestion—made by Bailo and Biscaro[3]—that no. 674 is identical with the picture of a '*donna lascivissima*' painted by Bordon, according to Vasari,[4] for Ottaviano Grimaldi of Genoa, seems questionable, since Ridolfi refers to what is clearly the same picture as a '*Venere ignuda*'.[5] The costume of no. 674— which is fashionable—suggests a dating in the late 1540's or early 1550's.[6] This dating is also applicable to the costume of a young man in a portrait by Bordon in the Uffizi (no. 929). The sitter rests his right hand on a table containing his helmet and lance, together with a floral crown and a ring. In the top right hand corner there is a view of steps and columns similar to that shown in the top left corner of no. 674, but with a female figure (greeting an *amorino*) instead of the young man. The complementary arrangement of the arms in the two pictures and of the direction of the eyes would also support a theory that the two were painted as pendants—very possibly on the occasion of a betrothal.[7] While this seems reasonable to the present writer it cannot be finally established on the basis of identity of size owing to the changes undergone by no. 674 in this respect.

PROVENANCE: Said to have come from Genoa (letter from Sir Charles Eastlake, quoted in reference 1). Purchased in Naples from the Duca di Cardinale, 1861.

REPRODUCTION: *Illustrations, Italian Schools*, 1937, p. 50.

REFERENCES: (1) Writing from Naples on 20th September, 1861, Sir Charles Eastlake, then Director of the National Gallery, says (letter in the Gallery archives): 'I have purchased here a portrait of a lady by Paris Bordone—about half length, but enlarged. It came originally from Genoa, where it was the fashion to increase the size of pictures. It will be a question when it reaches England how far to cut it down. I think the original boundary, at least above, would be too close to the head.' Evidently for that reason nothing was done.

(2) In the Brignole-Sale catalogue of 1813 a similar picture is listed (no. 97—*Ritratto di Signora con abito ricamato, di Paris Bordone*) but this was probably the one still in Palazzo Rosso, since attributed to Parrasio Micheli (N.I.42). (3) *Paris Bordon*, 1900, pp. 128–9. The authors also claim that the sitter of no. 674 is identical with that of a Bordon portrait at Vienna (no. 231). As she is there shown décolletée this is used to support their theory. In point of fact Bordon's female portraits often tend to approximate to a type—for example, a third portrait (Vienna no. 248) shows a lady similar to both the other two. In the present instance identity of the sitters cannot necessarily be assumed. (4) Vasari/Milanesi, vol. VII, p. 465. (5) Ridolfi/Hadeln, vol. I, p. 233. If, as is possible, Ridolfi was merely paraphrasing Vasari, this argument has less force. (6) Notes in the Gallery archives by Stella Mary Pearce. (7) A third portrait by Bordon—of a bearded man (Genoa, Palazzo Rosso)—also has a similar architectural background, the small figures in this case being apparently a lady distributing alms to a beggar. The design of this picture would preclude its having been intended as pendant to no. 674. Since the costume seems somewhat later than that in the National Gallery or Uffizi pictures it might in theory represent the sitter of the latter some years later, but there is no positive evidence in favour of this.

## 1845 CHRIST AS THE LIGHT OF THE WORLD

$35\frac{1}{4} \times 28\frac{3}{4}$ (0·908 × 0·73).
Good condition.
Traces of signature, centre of base of pilaster, top left: O [ ?] PARIDIS. bor-on-.[1]
Inscribed on the scroll: EGO. .SVM. LVX. MVD(I) (*Ego sum lux mundi; qui sequitur me non ambulat in tenebris, sed habebit lumen vitae,* John, VIII, 12).

A comparable picture at The Hague (Mauritshuis no. 310) is signed PARIS. BD O. and there are various early references to pictures of this subject by Bordon.[2] Even irrespective of the remains of the signature on no. 1845 the style and handling alike are eminently acceptable as Bordon's.

VERSIONS: See above. A fairly close replica is at S. Benedetto Po.[3]

PROVENANCE: Presented, *c.* 1829, to Dr Henry Greenwood by a member of the Sicilian embassy in London who stated that it had been painted as the altarpiece of a private chapel of his family and had never been out of their possession.[4] Passed by inheritance to Dr Greenwood's daughter, Mrs Mary A. Wood, by whom presented, 1901, through her brother, the Rev. G. Greenwood.

REPRODUCTION: *Illustrations, Italian Schools*, 1937, p. 51.

REFERENCES: (1) More clearly visible in an infra-red photograph than to the naked eye. The form of Bordon's signature on his pictures varies, the most common being O. PARIDIS BORDONI (BORDONVS, BORDONO, etc.). (2) See Bailo and Biscaro: *Della Vita e delle Opere di Paris Bordon* (1900), p. 110, no. I. A picture of similar design at Ravenna (Istituto di Belle Arti, ex-coll. Rasi) attributed to Bordon by Bailo and Biscaro (*op. cit.*, pp. 146–7) is doubtfully his work (see Andrea Moschetti in *L'Arte*, 1901, pp. 280 ff). (3) Reproduced in *Inventario degli Oggetti d'Arte d'Italia*, VI, p. 148. (4) Document in the Gallery archives.

3122 CHRIST BAPTISING S. JOHN MARTYR, DUKE OF ALEXANDRIA

Painted area 24¼ × 26¾ (0·615 × 0·68).

The original turn-over of the canvas is preserved at the base and at both sides.

Thinly painted and probably somewhat rubbed in places, but the paint on the whole seems in fair condition.

Traces of *pentimenti* in Christ's right foot. Above the latter are some marks which may have been an inscription. If so, it is unlikely to be original.

In Layard's MS. catalogue[1] as 'Christ . . . baptising a Doge in Prison' and published as such by Sir Charles Holmes[2] and in the National Gallery catalogue of 1920. The title was changed in the 1925 catalogue from 'baptising' to 'anointing'—presumably on the assumption that the kneeling figure was a Doge of Venice who would therefore be in no need of baptism. Nevertheless the action seems to be baptism and not anointing (which in any case would be unusual in prison) and in consequence the ducal cap (*corno*) shown on the ground would indicate a potentate with a ducal title but not a Doge of Venice. In point of fact no. 3122 corresponds so closely with a picture described by Ridolfi (in the biography of Paris Bordon, under the heading 'Venetia') that identity can be assumed[3]: *Due piccioli quadretti sono in oltre appresso la Signora Gradenica Gradenico, Monaca in San Daniele . . . nell' altro è San Giovanni Duca di Alessandria nella prigione battezzato dal Salvatore, e vi sono due Angeli con sciugatoi in mano.* The church of San Daniele held the body of S. John Martyr, Duke of Alexandria (Alexandretta), which had arrived at Venice in 1214 from Constantinople. He was said to have been miraculously baptised by Christ in prison, but his cult was local and unofficial as his legend had been taken over from that of S. Procopius of Caesarea.[4]

The attribution of no. 3122 to Bordon seems not to have been questioned and is acceptable.

PROVENANCE: In the mid-seventeenth century in the possession of Gradenica Gradenico, S. Daniele, Venice (see above). Bought by Sir A. H. Layard from 'Signor Marcato'.[5] Layard Bequest, 1916.

REPRODUCTION: *Illustrations, Italian Schools*, 1937, p. 51.

REFERENCES: (1) No. 75—with the Layard papers in the Gallery archives. (2) *Burlington Magazine*, vol. XXXII (1918), p. 107. (3) Ridolfi/Hadeln, I, p. 234. (4) The present writer's grateful thanks are due to Miss Rosalie B. Green, Director of the Index of Christian Art at Princeton, who drew his attention to this. Further references are the *Acta Sanctorum*, May, vol. IV, p. 304, 19th May; also G. B. Tomaselli: *Memorie spettanti alla Vita di S. Giovanni Martire Duca d'Alessandria ed alla Traslazione del suo Corpo che si venera nella chiesa delle Canonichesse lateranensi di San Daniele di Venezia*, 1776, and *Leggenda di S. Zuane martire . . .*, 1543. The present writer has not been able to consult a copy of the last-mentioned work. (5) Layard MSS.

## Imitator of BORDON

2097 A YOUNG WOMAN WITH CARNATIONS

$38\frac{1}{2} \times 29\frac{1}{4}$ (0·978 × 0·743).

Some retouching in the face (notably the eye-lids and eye-brows) and in the sitter's left arm.

Hitherto as 'School of Bordon', but the technique and costume alike are unacceptable as of the sixteenth century. Probably a deliberate and not very skilful imitation of Bordon dating from the seventeenth or eighteenth century.[1]

PROVENANCE: From the John Samuel collection (no. 23 in the catalogue of 1895), which passed to the Misses Cohen, by whom exh., New Gallery, 1894–5 (207). Bequeathed by the Misses Cohen, 1906.

REPRODUCTION: *Illustrations, Italian Schools*, 1937, p. 52.

REFERENCES: (1) Stella Mary Pearce, in a note on the costume in the Gallery archives, is inclined to prefer a dating in the eighteenth century to one in the seventeenth. The technique, however, could well be that of the seventeenth.

## GIOVANNI BUSI, called CARIANI
### Active 1509, still alive 1547

His family was from the Bergamo area. He himself adds the word 'Bergomeus' to his signature on several occasions, but he is first recorded in Venice, and subsequent documentary references confirm his residence there over a period of years.

Only three surviving pictures by Cariani are signed and dated—a group portrait of 1519 (Roncalli collection, Bergamo), an altarpiece of 1520 of the Resurrection (Milan, Brera, ex-Gerli collection) and a Madonna and Child with Donor, also of 1520 (Bergamo, Accademia Carrara). A signed portrait of an old man (Vienna, published by Baldass, Vienna *Jahrbuch*, 1929, p. 108) is datable from an inscription 1536–40. Two signed but undated male portraits (Bergamo and Ottawa Galleries) are similar in style to the 1519 group portrait and with them may be associated a group of further portraits (including no. 2494 of this Gallery) some of which are not signed but which are obviously by the same hand. Cariani's style, indeed, as it was around the year 1520, is easily recognisable from these few works. The chief influences seem to be Titian and Palma Vecchio, but the touch is much coarser and the colours tend to approximate towards pink. The fact that the dated works only define Cariani's style at isolated periods in what was apparently a long career and that he seems to have been something of a chameleon has caused the utmost confusion in attempting to define his *œuvre*.

For the documents concerning Cariani's career see G. Ludwig in Prussian *Jahrbuch*, vol. XXIV, 1903, *Beiheft*, pp. 33–41, and vol. XXVI, 1905, *Beiheft*, p. 153.

## 2494 A MEMBER OF THE ALBANI FAMILY

$42\frac{3}{4} \times 32\frac{3}{4}$ ($1\cdot06 \times 0\cdot8$).

The robe and most of the face in good condition. Retouching covers old slits in the canvas in the landscape and in the beard. The identification of the sitter's family is due to the presence of the Albani arms on another version of the picture, in Casa Suardi, Bergamo.[1] The handling of no. 2494 is clearly the same as that of several signed portraits by Cariani and its authenticity need therefore not be questioned.

The identity and status of the sitter is more conjectural. Morelli referred to him as Francesco Albani but gave no evidence.[2] The costume also is not certainly identifiable.[3]

VERSION: Bergamo, Casa Suardi (see above).

PROVENANCE: Said to have been in the Noli collection, Bergamo, then Luigi Albano in the same town.[4] Before 1883 in the possession of George Salting,[5] by whom exh., New Gallery, 1894–5 (144) and Glasgow International Exhibition, 1901.[6] Lent National Gallery, 1902. Salting Bequest, 1910.

REPRODUCTION: *Illustrations, Italian Schools*, 1937, p. 83.

REFERENCES: (1) The proportions of the Suardi picture are slightly different from those of no. 2494—there is more space at either side (permitting, on the sitter's right, on the parapet behind the table, the inclusion of a coat of arms) and slightly more at the top. Otherwise the two versions are almost identical. While it is not possible to decide on visual evidence whether or not no. 2494 has been cut it is unlikely that this was the case since in the Suardi picture the coat of arms immediately adjoins the sleeve (which indeed slightly breaks the outline of the shield). It may therefore perhaps be deduced that no. 2494 was painted first, that the sitter objected to the non-inclusion of his arms and that as there was no room for them the Suardi replica was made. (2) *Munich and Dresden*, English edition, 1893, p. 25. (3) Notes by Stella Mary Pearce in the Gallery archives. The costume would accord best with a dating around 1520. (4) Crowe and Cavalcaselle, *North Italian Painters*, III, p. 453. (5) Salting MSS. in the Gallery archives. (6) Page 106 (no number) in the catalogue of the Fine Art Section.

## 1203 MADONNA AND CHILD WITH SS. JOSEPH, LUCY, ANOTHER FEMALE SAINT AND A YOUTHFUL DONOR

$33\frac{3}{4} \times 46\frac{1}{2}$ ($0\cdot85 \times 1\cdot18$).

Extensively damaged and repainted.

The arrangement, and to some extent also the types, are comparable with those in a similar picture, formerly in the Frizzoni collection, Bergamo.[1] The latter is a signed work of Cariani. The coarseness of the execution of no. 1203 is marked, even for Cariani, but some, at least, of this effect may be due to the fact that the picture is, apparently, unfinished.[2] For the rest, the attribution to Cariani seems justifiable.

For some reason unspecified the female saint on the left was identified in earlier editions of the National Gallery catalogue as S. Barbara, while the one in front of her was called the Magdalen. The identity of the former with S. Lucy can hardly be doubted but the other figure has no attribute and may merely be a portrait of the donatrix (presumably mother of the boy on the right) to whom a nimbus has been added.

PROVENANCE: Enrico Andreossi, Milan, from whose heirs purchased (Walker fund), 1886.

REPRODUCTION: *Illustrations, Italian Schools*, 1937, p. 83.

REFERENCES: (1) Earlier still in the possession of Sir Charles Eastlake and exchanged by him for a Tura (now no. 772 of this Gallery). The story of the exchange is given by Gustavo Frizzoni: *Arte Italiana del Rinascimento*, 1891, p. 281, and by Morelli: *Munich and Dresden*, English edition (1893), p. 23. It should be noted that the exchange affected Eastlake's private collection and not, as far as he was concerned, the National Gallery. (2) The amount of repaint present makes it difficult to pronounce with absolute confidence on this point, though it seems probable to the present writer. It might also account for some of the peculiarities of the costume—e.g. the very inorganic appearance of the clothes worn by the kneeling female saint in the centre.

## Ascribed to CARIANI

### 41  DEATH OF S. PETER MARTYR

$40\frac{1}{4} \times 57$ ($1.015 \times 1.448$).

Much worn, and retouched in many parts—particularly in the clouds (including the *putti*). The following passages in fair condition: centre soldier's pink breeches and hose (*pentimenti* in his legs), most of the lower part of the saint's white robe, the tree (right centre) and figures on either side of its trunk.

As Giorgione in the collection of Queen Christina and in the National Gallery catalogues up to and including the edition of 1887. Attributed to Cariani since 1888. Called by Crowe and Cavalcaselle 'a Titianesque composition adapted by a Venetian or Ferrarese artist of a modern time'.[1] The pinkish tone of no. 41 is a feature common in authentic works of Cariani, but a considerable element of doubt concerning his authorship must remain, owing to the lack of other parallels of this kind. The costume accords best with a dating in the 1540's, but the arrangement and the format is traditional, and harks back less to Titian's great altarpiece of this subject than to an earlier type, represented by no. 812 of this Gallery.[2]

PROVENANCE: No. 267 in the 1689 inventory of Queen Christina's collection and no. 162 in the 1721 inventory.[3] Thence Orléans—pp. 168–9 in the 1727 catalogue. Presumably no. 44 in the sale (Bryan's, 14th February, 1800) of the remaining part of the Orléans collection (consistently as Giorgione).[4] Bequeathed by the Rev. Holwell Carr, 1831.

REPRODUCTION: *Illustrations, Italian Schools*, 1937, p. 82.

REFERENCES: (1) *North Italian Painters*, III, p. 54. (2) Baldass (Vienna *Jahrbuch* 1929, pp. 97–8) suggests a derivation from an altarpiece of the same subject at Alzano Maggiore, attr. Lotto. The connection is not apparent to the present writer. (3) Both printed (pp. LXXXVI and CIII) in Olof Granberg: *La Galerie de Tableaux de la Reine Christine de Suède*, 1897. (4) For the intermediary history of the Orléans collection see entries for nos. 270 or 1326.

### 2495  MADONNA AND CHILD (*LA VIERGE AUX LAURIERS*)

Canvas, transferred from panel,[1] $35\frac{1}{2} \times 28\frac{1}{2}$ ($0.9 \times 0.72$).

A great deal of local repaint. The important areas most affected are the Madonna's eyes and the whole of the outline of her face on the far side, together with the dark inside of the veil adjoining it. Also most of her left hand. Repaint also in the Child's body, particularly in the lower part of His right leg; but His head, in spite of some disturbance in the outline of the forehead, is better preserved than the Madonna's.

Catalogued as Cariani since its entry into the Gallery except in the editions of 1925 and 1929, when it appears as Bonifazio. In the Leuchtenberg gallery as Giorgione. Attributed by Crowe and Cavalcaselle to Moretto.[2] The Cariani attribution—the least improbable of those suggested—was first made by Herbert Cook[3] and was supported by Borenius[4] and by Berenson.[5] Attributed to Palma Vecchio by Suida.[6]

The case, put in the greatest detail by Berenson, for attributing no. 2495 to Cariani as an early work turns on its resemblance to a *Madonna and Child with SS. Elizabeth and the Infant Baptist* in the Galleria Nazionale, Rome. This is not a documented Cariani but is acceptable to the present writer as his work. It is more evolved in style than no. 2495. Considerable reserve should be entertained in view of the fact that the most primitive in style of the Cariani's acceptable to the present writer—*Madonna and Child with Saints*, no. 156 of the Venice Accademia—has little in common with no. 2495.

The date (1514) on the present frame appears to be modern and is presumably a guess at the date of origin of the picture.

PROVENANCE: In 1828 already in the Leuchtenberg gallery, Munich.[7] Bought by Salting, by whom lent, 1903. Salting Bequest, 1910.

REPRODUCTION: *Illustrations, Italian Schools*, 1937, p. 46.

REFERENCES: (1) 'in three pieces' (1929 catalogue). (2) *Painting in North Italy*, III (1912 ed.), p. 305. (3) *Burlington Magazine*, II (1903), p. 78. (4) In Crowe and Cavalcaselle, *loc. cit.* (5) Notably in *Arte Veneta*, 1954, p. 150; reprinted in *Essays in Appreciation*, 1958, pp. 111–15. (6) In *Belvedere*, XII (1934–7), p. 87. (7) No. 56 in the Leuchtenberg catalogue of that year. No. 7 (with line engraving) in Passavant's catalogue of 1851. Before 1871, when Crowe and Cavalcaselle's *History of Painting in North Italy* was first published, the Leuchtenberg collection had been moved to St Petersburg.

# VINCENZO CATENA
## Active 1506, died 1531

The earliest dated reference to him is of 1st June, 1506 in an inscription on the back of Giorgione's *Laura* portrait (Vienna). This refers to Giorgione as being a partner of Catena's. With the exception of a possible visit to Rome in the year of his death there is no documentary evidence of his presence outside Venice, and Crowe and Cavalcaselle, in particular, have long ago been shown wrong in identifying him with a certain Trevisan painter called Vincenzo dalle Destre.

Some half dozen religious pictures are signed by Catena, but none of them is dated. They are in an idiom ultimately dependent on

Giovanni Bellini before his final period and thus are entirely *quattrocento* in style. The key picture for Catena's later development is a signed portrait of a man (Vienna) which shows a more evolved style, mid-way between the *quattrocento* and the High Renaissance. Round this painting and an altarpiece of the Martyrdom of St Christina at S. Maria Mater Domini, Venice (dated 1520 on the frame and vouched for as Catena's by an early, though not contemporary, source) may be grouped a number of others, including nos. 234 and 694 of this Gallery, once attributed to Palma, but more probably late works of Catena.

In his monograph (1954) Giles Robertson points to the text of Catena's wills as constituting evidence that painting was not his only source of income and to contemporary correspondence as proving that he moved in the same Humanist circles as Marc Antonio Michiel, Bembo and others. In consequence he would have appeared something of a mandarin among the professional painters, and Giorgione may well have chosen to associate himself with him for that reason.

## 234  A WARRIOR ADORING THE INFANT CHRIST AND THE VIRGIN

Canvas,[1] $61\frac{1}{8} \times 103\frac{3}{4}$ ($1 \cdot 55 \times 2 \cdot 63$).
Much worn and extensively retouched. In particular the face of the page, together with the cloud behind, seems largely modern.[2] General appearance of other areas probably less altered by retouching.

First catalogued (in 1854) after entering the Gallery as 'attributed to Giorgione' but altered in Wornum's catalogue of the same year to 'School of Giovanni Bellini' as which it remained until the edition of 1898 when it appeared under the Catena attribution originally put forward by Crowe and Cavalcaselle (1871),[3] and supported by Morelli and Berenson among others. As Catena in subsequent editions except those of 1925 and 1929 when it underwent its Palma Vecchio phase. The case for Catena's authorship, with which the present writer is in agreement, is best put by Giles Robertson.[4] The fact that no. 234 is appreciably more evolved in style than Catena's *Martyrdom of St Christina* which is dated (on the frame) 1520 necessitates a dating between then and Catena's death in 1531.

The iconographic problems in this picture arise from the fact that the warrior's armour and doublet are European, but the enamelled trappings of his horse, his belt and curved dagger hanging underneath, as well as the silk of his head-gear, appear to be of Islamic design.[5] His features, too, seem non-European, though some of this effect may be due to retouching. The question therefore arises whether the warrior is a European affecting some measure of Eastern accoutrement or whether he is a Saracen convert wearing European armour. On the whole the present writer inclines to the latter hypothesis, from which it would follow that no. 234 might well have been painted to commemorate a conversion—probably one that had caused considerable stir. A case of this kind occurred after the capture by the Turks of the Venetian colony of Modone in the Peloponnese in 1500. On this occasion a certain Bernardino Mocenigo was captured with two of his sisters who subsequently married two Turkish officers. All five eventually returned to Venice where the two Turks were baptised in 1515 by the Patriarch, Antonio Contarini, receiving the christian names Pier Giovanni and Giovanni Piero respectively. On the 13th May, 1522, the Doge Antonio Grimani made provision for the two converts in Cephalonia. The fact that no. 234 probably dates, as already indicated, from some time after the year 1520 and that the Turks in the Mocenigo story are specified as being warriors would provide a possible link, though not a sufficiently strong one to be classed as more than conjecture.[6]

A similar quail to those on the left also occurs in no. 694 (Catena) of this Gallery in the entry for which picture the subject is discussed.

PROVENANCE: From the Standish collection. Subsequently, in 1841, with Italian dealers in Florence and Rome. Sold by Baldeschi to Woodburn,[7] at whose sale in 1853 purchased for the National Gallery.[8]

REPRODUCTION: *Illustrations, Italian Schools*, 1937, p. 236.

REFERENCES: (1) Certain parts of the craquelure suggest that the picture may originally have been painted on panel and transferred to canvas at an early date. It is not, however, possible to pronounce with certainty on this point. (2) Crowe and Cavalcaselle (*Painting in North Italy*, 1871, vol. 1, p. 255, note 2) mention the page as 'blackened and spoiled'. (3) *Loc. cit.* (4) *Catena*, 1954, p. 68 and elsewhere. (5) Notes in the Gallery archives from various authorities on these subjects. See also O. M. Dalton in *Proceedings of the Society of Antiquaries*, 2nd series, vol. XXI, pp. 376–80 and 383, and Sir James Mann in *Archaeologia*, vol. LXXXIII, 1930, p. 301. The silk of the warrior's cap, which is not a proper turban, is said to be North African. (6) The sources for this anecdote are Litta: *Famiglie Celebri*, XII, Mocenigo di Venezia, Tavola XIX and Sanudo's diary (entries for 7th January and 22nd February, 1515) (the present writer's attention was kindly drawn to the Sanudo reference by Stella Mary Pearce). According to Sanudo, provision was already made for the converts at Cephalonia or Zante at the time of baptism in 1515. The Doge's letter of 13th May, 1522 to this effect is mentioned by Litta but not by Sanudo. (7) All this information in a record dating from 1853 in the Gallery archives. (8) Lot 80, 1st day (24th June) as Giorgione.

## 694 S. JEROME IN HIS STUDY

$29\frac{7}{8} \times 38\frac{3}{4}$ (0·75 × 0·98)[1]
The paint has worn thin and a great deal of retouching is apparent. But it is mostly local and though widespread does not involve any whole feature.

Purchased as Giovanni Bellini, but attributed to Catena as early as 1871 (Crowe and Cavalcaselle).[2] The alternative attribution to Palma[3] (under whose name no. 694 appears in the National Gallery catalogues of 1925 and 1929) is now generally discredited.[4]

The iconography of this picture is unusual in several respects. The colours of S. Jerome's robes—bright pink and blue—are abnormal and the blue cardinal's hat particularly so. If this is not merely a whim of the painter or of whoever commissioned the picture it may be meant as an indication of S. Jerome's penitence.⁵ Alternatively, Moroni mentions a tradition that newly elected cardinals, on their way to receive their red hats, wore for the occasion hats of the same '*pontificale*' shape which were green if they were bishops and blueish or lilac ('*pavonazzo*') if they were not.⁶ S. Jerome, though normally depicted as a cardinal, was not a bishop.

A similar bird to that on the left of no. 694 also occurs in Catena's *Holy Family* at Dresden and in no. 234 ('*Warrior adoring Christ and the Virgin*') of this Gallery. Also, *inter alia*, in no. 1418 (Antonello) of this Gallery. The fantastic building in the background of no. 694 recurs in the same position in the Dresden *Holy Family*.

In his will of 1518 Catena bequeathed to Giovanni Battista Egnazio '*unum aliud telarium sancti Hieronymi ab heremo*', but this in itself hardly constitutes sufficient evidence to presuppose a connection with no. 694.⁷

VERSION: Frankfurt-am-Main, Staedel Institute. Replica adapted to smaller format, thereby cutting out the floor in the foreground and some of the area to the left of the desk, including the stool and the lion. S. Jerome's hat apparently red.

PROVENANCE: Manfrin collection, Venice (no. 406, as Giovanni Bellini, in the 1856 catalogue), from which (with nos. 695 and 696) purchased, 1862.⁸

REPRODUCTION: *Illustrations, Italian Schools*, 1937, p. 265.

REFERENCES: (1) A strip about ½″ wide running along the bottom of the original canvas has been painted over at some later date with dark paint. (2) *Painting in North Italy*, vol. 1, p. 256. (3) Holmes and Collins Baker in *Burlington Magazine*, vol. 42, pp. 230 and 239. (4) Giles Robertson: *Catena* (1954), pp. 61–3, gives the best summary of the Catena/Palma problem and demonstrates the impossibility of the Palma attribution in the present instance. (5) A blue cardinal's robe (but not a blue hat) occurs in no. 4759 (Sassetta) of this Gallery, in connection with which Martin Davies (*The Earlier Italian Schools*, catalogue, 1951, p. 395, note 6) pointed out that cardinals wear violet for mourning or penitence. Giles Robertson, *loc. cit.*, suggested that the sitter in Catena's portrait of a man at Vienna might also be the patron of no. 694 as he wears the same combination of colours. In a miniature in the British Museum (MS. Add. 38126, f. 227ᵛ) S. Jerome is shown with a blue hat and also a blue gown. (6) Moroni: *Dizionario Storico-Ecclesiastica*, 1859, vol. IX, p. 183, and vol. XCVI, p. 230. In the latter reference he says '*cappelli pontificali verdi se vescovi o paonazzi se semplici prelati*'. Elsewhere (vol. LV, p. 142) Moroni quotes the definition of a '*prelato*' given at the Council of Toul (859) as '*chiunque presiede ad una comunità religiosa*'. Notes by Stella Mary Pearce on the subject, and on the exact colour indicated by the word '*pavonazzo*', are in the Gallery archives. (7) See Robertson, *op. cit.*, p. 7. (8) Seen in the Manfrin collection by Mündler in 1858 and attributed by him to Lotto (MS. in the Gallery archives).

## 1121 PORTRAIT OF A YOUNG MAN

Panel, painted area 12 × 9¼ (0·3 × 0·23).¹

Some obvious small retouchings, mostly in the face and in the clouds, but in general well preserved. *Pentimento* in the spectator's left side of the face.

In the Hamilton Palace collection as Leonardo da Vinci. Catalogued after entering the National Gallery as 'Venetian School, 15th century'. Other suggestions have been Cima,[2] Basaiti[3] and Bissolo.[4] The attribution to Catena, first made in 1897 by Berenson,[5] has been pretty generally accepted since and seems justifiable. Giles Robertson[6] pointed out that it depends primarily on the resemblance of type between no. 1121 and the donor portraits in the signed pictures by Catena of the *Sacra Conversazione* type at Liverpool and in the Pospisil (ex-Melchett) collection, though both of these are profiles.

VERSION: The 1929 catalogue mentions a picture at Isola Bella (a photograph is Alinari, no. 14,492). Berenson (*Lists*, 1957) as perhaps Pietro degli Ingannati. Any resemblance this picture may bear to no. 1121 is likely to be fortuitious.

PROVENANCE: Hamilton Palace (lot 344, as Leonardo, in sale of 24th June, 1882, where purchased).[7]

REPRODUCTION: *Illustrations, Italian Schools*, 1937, p. 93.

REFERENCES: (1) The panel has been cut at the top but not on the other three sides. (2) Collins Baker (with reserve) in the *Burlington Magazine*, vol. 42 (1923), pp. 239 ff. (3) *Notes on the National Gallery* (reprinted from *The Guardian*) by Sir Walter Armstrong, 1887, p. 24. (4) Jacobsen (with reserve) in *Repertorium für Kunstwissenschaft*, 1901, p. 372. (5) *Venetian Painters* (3rd edition). (6) Giles Robertson: *Catena* (1954), p. 46. (7) Robertson (*op. cit.*) suggests tentatively an identification with an entry in an inventory of 1643 of the Duke of Hamilton's pictures. He is, however, mistaken in assuming that no. 1121 might have been cut at the bottom. Despite the present cradling it is still possible to see that the priming ends short of the present edge and therefore that there has been no cutting along it. Robertson points out that, contrary to what is stated in the National Gallery catalogue of 1924 and 1929, no. 1121 is not identical with the picture described by Waagen at Hamilton Palace as Girolamo da Santa Croce (Waagen—*Treasures of Art* . . ., III, p. 300—says that the latter picture had a landscape background). There seems no warrant for the statement in the 1929 catalogue that no. 1121 was 'purchased as by Giovanni Bellini'. It appeared as Leonardo in the Hamilton sale catalogue and as 'Venetian School, 15th century' in the next edition of the National Gallery catalogue (1883).

5751  PORTRAIT OF THE DOGE, ANDREA GRITTI

$38\frac{1}{4} \times 31\frac{1}{4}$ (0·97 × 0·79).

The face, neck and beard much abraded and extensively repainted. The hands rather less so. Parts of the robe and nearly all the cap well preserved. *Pentimenti* in the outline of the latter. The identity of the sitter can be vouched for by comparison with contemporary inscribed medals—e.g. Hill, *Corpus* 456.

A votive-picture by Titian of the Doge Andrea Gritti kneeling before the Madonna and Child was painted in 1531 and destroyed in the Doge's Palace fire of 1574. Hadeln[1] demonstrated convincingly that it is reproduced in a surviving wood-cut except that in the latter the Doge Francesco Donato is substituted for Andrea Gritti. The substitution (presumably in honour of the then reigning Doge) would have involved no more than the head, since a drawing by Titian on the back of a study for S. Bernardino in the same picture shows the same pose as in the wood-cut—kneeling in profile.[2] This wood-cut was evidently the source used by Tintoretto when painting the existing replacement to the Gritti votive-picture (in the Sala del Collegio of the Doge's Palace) which follows the general arrangement of Titian's picture as shown in the wood-cut. Since the Doge's features in the wood-cut were not those of Gritti, however, he would have had to take another model, and in fact his model was almost certainly no. 5751, with which his representation corresponds exactly, even to the handkerchief in the clenched left hand and the unusual gesture (for a votive-picture) of the right.[3]

No. 5751 was generally attributed to Titian (even being cited as a perfect example of Titian's 'finish' by Burne-Jones in the libel action brought against Ruskin by Whistler in 1878)[4] until identified as Catena by Wilde in 1931.[5] The Catena attribution was subsequently upheld by Robertson.[6] Inasmuch as Andrea Gritti (1455–1538) did not become Doge until 1523 the Titian attribution is impossible, since by that time Titian was painting more broadly (cf., for example, no. 1944 of this Gallery which is certainly earlier than the year 1523 but already more evolved in style than no. 5751). Despite the bad condition of the face and hands, the type of pose, system of folds in the draperies and the handling of the embroidery (cf. the warrior's cap in no. 234 of this Gallery) seem to the present writer fully to justify the Catena attribution.[7] The picture must therefore be a late work—between Gritti's election in 1523 and Catena's death in 1531.

The linen head-cloth ('rensa') just visible projecting from under the cap should have a string hanging down in order to tie under the chin. Presumably it had one once, but the area where it would be is now largely repaint.[8]

The device on the ring worn by the sitter apparently represents the Doge kneeling (on the right) to St Mark (left) whose banner is vertical in the centre. This device was normal on contemporary Venetian coins.[9]

VERSIONS: 1. Tintoretto, Doge's Palace, Sala del Collegio (see above). 2. Cambridge, Fitzwilliam Museum (ex-Holford). Inferior old replica.

PROVENANCE: Said to have come from the Palazzo Contarini, Venice.[10] Collection of Dr Gilbert Elliott, Dean of Bristol, who exhibited it, as Titian, B.I., 1863 (53). Bought from him by Ruskin, shortly before 2nd September, 1864.[11] Lent by Ruskin (as Titian) to R.A., 1870 (57). Hung for many years in Ruskin's house, Brantwood, Coniston.[12] Passed with the house to Ruskin's cousin, Mrs Arthur Severn. Bought by Langton Douglas by whom sold to Otto Gutekunst, 1917.[13] Exh. Olympia, 1928 (X57) (as Titian, lent Mrs Gutekunst). Presented by Mrs Gutekunst in memory of her husband, 1947.

REPRODUCTION: Photographs available from National Gallery negatives. Also reproduced by Giles Robertson: *Catena* (1954), pl. 45.

REFERENCES: (1) Prussian *Jahrbuch*, vol. XXXIV (1913), pp. 234–8. (2) For this reason alone Hadeln's subsequent attempt (*Pantheon*, 1930, p. 489) to identify no. 5751 as an actual fragment of Titian's votive-picture is untenable. Ruskin had already advanced the same view (*Works*, Library Edition, vol.

XXIV, p. 184). (3) Of the other three Tintoretto votive-pictures in the Sala del Collegio only one (that of Francesco Donato) shows the Doge in the old-fashioned praying attitude. In the other two (Alvise Mocenigo and Nicolo da Ponte) the Doge is shown with arms outstretched. This is a conventional gesture of wonderment, essentially different from the gesture in the Gritti votive-picture. (4) Some of Burne-Jones' evidence in this connection is printed in Whistler's *The Gentle Art of Making Enemies*, 1890, p. 16. (5) J. Wilde in the Prussian *Jahrbuch*, vol. LII (1931), p. 96. (6) Giles Robertson: *Catena* (1954), p. 69. (7) Robertson, *op. cit.*, convincingly relates no. 5751 stylistically to other late works of Catena. Tietze (*Tizian*, 1936, Textband, p. 135) mentions an oral attribution (by Fiocco, subsequently published in his monograph, 1939, pp. 135–6) to Pordenone which he wisely ignores. His own suggestion that no. 5751 is after Tintoretto's picture rather than the source of it is best treated in the same fashion. Berenson (*Lists*, 1957) assumes that in no. 5751 Titian was copying Catena. (8) This contention is supported by the fact that such a string occurs in Tintoretto's version already mentioned. (9) This is made clear by comparing a macro-photograph of the ring with representations of the same device on coins of Andrea Gritti or Giovanni Dandolo (reproduced on pp. 46 and 47 of the *Guida Illustrata del Museo Civico Correr*, 1909). (10) In the B.I. catalogue of 1863. A portrait 'by Titian' of 'Duke Grettie' was in Charles I's collection, but was larger than no. 5751 (4′ 4″ × 3′ 4″) and showed him 'with his right-hand holding his robes' (Bathoe's catalogue, 1757, p. 105, no. 5). (11) Letter of that date to Rawdon Brown published in Ruskin's *Works*, Library Edition, vol. XXIV, p. 184. (12) Where seen by Sydney Cockerell as Ruskin's guest (letter in the Gallery archives). (13) Information supplied by Messrs P. and D. Colnaghi from Gutekunst's records.

## Ascribed to CATENA

### 3540 MADONNA AND CHILD WITH THE INFANT S. JOHN THE BAPTIST

Panel, $28\frac{1}{2} \times 22\frac{1}{2}$ (0·72 × 0·57).

Much damaged, particularly down the centre, where repeated flaking and worm holes have led to extensive repainting. A good deal of repainting in other areas. The only parts in reasonably good condition are the area of the Madonna's mantle (which is painted over a red underpaint) on the spectator's right and S. John's green tunic.

In the 1929 catalogue as Catena. Its status was affected by the publication, in 1957, by Cornelius Müller Hofstede of an X-ray photograph of the Giorgione self-portrait at Brunswick.[1] This revealed part of a composition of a Madonna and Child underneath the self-portrait. It was truncated like the portrait, but showed clearly the most unusual and original feature of the design of no. 3540 and the other versions, namely the attitude of the Child, who supports Himself by holding on to the Madonna's neck with His left hand while turning His head in the opposite direction. Müller Hofstede argued convincingly that the Brunswick portrait was the work of Giorgione and not a copy as had been alleged, and went on to claim that the Madonna underneath was in essentials of Giorgione's invention, that it was the model for the various versions including no. 3540 painted by Catena and his followers and that it could be dated around the year 1506 when Giorgione and Catena were in partnership. The fact of this partnership—which is documented by the inscription on the back of the Giorgione portrait called 'Laura' at Vienna—would admit of the possibility that Giorgione painted the Brunswick portrait over a Madonna not by himself but by Catena. Though Müller Hofstede may well be correct in arguing that the essential novelty in the design of no. 3540 and the other variants— the motive of the Child's left arm—is probably due to Giorgione, the germ of the other elements in the Madonna and Child group is already present in an earlier work undoubtedly by Catena—Virgin and Child with Saints and a Donor (Liverpool). Some collaboration between Giorgione and Catena in the evolution of the design of no. 3540 is therefore in every way likely, as Müller Hofstede admits (*op. cit.*, p. 25).

As regards the execution, a version at Posen, including in addition S. Zacharias and a female saint, is generally considered superior to no. 3540 and attributed to Catena himself. A somewhat inferior variant, with an adult S. John the Baptist, a female saint and two donors, is in the Galleria Estense at Modena, attributed to a follower of Catena. Of the several versions without flanking saints no. 3540 is the best and the possibility is not to be excluded that the execution may be Catena's own, but the bad condition of most of it, together with the evident popularity of the design, precludes a dogmatic judgement.[2]

VERSIONS (see also above): Basel, Museum (Bachofen-Burckhardt Stiftung) (attributed Bissolo) and Florence, Museo Bardini.[3]

DRAWING: Vienna, Albertina. Red chalk drawing closely corresponding with no. 3540. Robertson (*op. cit.*) calls it a student's copy.

PROVENANCE: Acquired from Colnaghi by Alfred de Pass, by whom presented, 1920.

REPRODUCTION: *Illustrations, Italian Schools*, 1937, p. 92.

REFERENCES: (1) Cornelius Müller Hofstede: *Untersuchungen über Giorgiones Selbstbildnis in Braunschweig* in *Mitteilungen des kunsthistorischen Institutes in Florenz*, October, 1957, pp. 13–34. (2) Berenson (*Three Essays in Method*, p. 122) suggested that the design may have originated in Giovanni Bellini, but Müller Hofstede's arguments (*loc. cit.*) render this unlikely. In Berenson's *Lists* (1957), no. 3540 appears as Catena. Giles Robertson (*Vincenzo Catena*, 1954, p. 79) opposes the attribution of no. 3540 to Catena himself on the grounds that the warm flesh tones and the quality of the modelling are not quite Catena's. It could be answered that much of the pink tone of the Child's body may be due to retouching and for the same reason it is difficult to judge what the quality of the modelling originally was. (3) The Mansueti at Venice (mentioned by Berenson, *loc. cit.*) is only indirectly connected and contains other figures. Other variants with flanking saints are too numerous to specify.

## GIORGIO DA CASTELFRANCO, called GIORGIONE
### Active 1506, died 1510

The form 'Giorgione', instead of the Venetian 'Zorzi', or 'Zorzo', for 'Giorgio', seems first to be used in print by Paolo Pini (1548). It was adopted by Vasari and has been universal since.

He is referred to as 'maistro Zorzi da Castelfranco' in an inscription of 1st June, 1506 on the back of a portrait of a lady at Vienna.[1] Also, under the same name, in two documents, of August, 1507 and January, 1508, in connection with a painting for the audience chamber of the Doge's Palace at Venice, and finally (still by the same style) in two more documents, of 1508, connected with paintings on the exterior of the Fondaco dei Tedeschi, Venice. No other document certainly dating from his life time and mentioning him has survived,[2] but an exchange of letters in October and November, 1510, between Isabella d'Este (who was anxious to secure a painting by Giorgione) and Taddeo Albano, shows that he was then recently dead (of the plague). There is no reliable evidence for the date of his birth,[3] and the theory that he belonged to the noble family of Barbarella is probably no more than wishful thinking of the seventeenth century.[4] Nevertheless, it cannot be doubted that he was still a young man at the time of his death.[5] It can also be deduced with confidence that he enjoyed a considerable reputation as a painter during his life time[6] and that less than a genera-tion after his death he was already considered one of the greatest Venetian artists.[7]

The extreme scarcity of facts concerning Giorgione's life and work, combined with the rapid growth of his legend, the degree to which he was imitated and the high market value of pictures attributable to him, has created the utmost confusion in identifying them. In fact no sur-viving painting can be ascribed to him with complete certainty.[8] How-ever it cannot reasonably be doubted that the following four pictures (whose attribution has in each case a certain degree of documentary or other external support) are his work: *Portrait of a Lady* (Vienna),[9] *The Three Philosophers* (Vienna), *The Tempest* (Venice),[10] the *Castelfranco altar*.[11] Round this nucleus can be grouped a few others—pre-eminently the *Judith* (Leningrad), and the *Portrait of a Young Man* (Berlin)—which, though lacking documentary support, are yet generally accepted as Giorgione's at the present time. The major problem still in dispute centres round five pictures of high quality and more evolved style than those so far mentioned—*Venus* (Dresden),[12] *Madonna and Child with Saints* (Prado), *Judgement of Solomon* (Bankes collection, Kingston Lacy),[13] *Christ and the Adulteress* (Glasgow), *Fête Champêtre* (Louvre). These, in one view, constitute 'late Giorgione' which would then blend imperceptibly into early Titian, to whom, with the exception of the Kingston Lacy picture (for which Sebastiano is the favourite alternative candidate), the other view attributes them. Even without considering this group, however, and judging only from the other paintings already specified, it is clear that Giorgione, emerging from the orbit of Giovanni Bellini, introduced a new note, at once lyrical and fantastic, into Venetian painting which for a time had wide influence.

REFERENCES: (1) First correctly published, and discussed, by J. Wilde in the Prussian *Jahrbuch*, 1931, p. 91: *Ein unbeachtetes Werk Giorgiones*. (2) A con-tract of 13th February, 1508, between Giorgione and Alvise de Sesti in respect of four pictures illustrating the story of Daniel was published in 1878 and reprinted by G. M. Richter (*Giorgio da Castelfranco*, 1937, p. 303). This document has now disappeared and doubts have been cast on its authenticity. Recently (*Arte Veneta*, 1954) Philip Hendy attempted to bring the Glasgow so-called *Adulteress* into connection with this document. The fragmentary inscription on the back of the San Diego portrait (see reference no. 9) may be a further contemporary reference to Giorgione, but its incompleteness precludes any certainty. (**3**) It is Vasari who first gives a date for Giorgione's birth—1477 in his first edition (1550), 1478 in his second (1568). In addition to this discrepancy he gives the date of his death as 1511 which is demonstrably a year too late. For these reasons it would clearly be unwise to accept his literal word without confirmation, though the general sense of his information on this subject is no doubt reliable. In view of the number of people who would have remembered Giorgione and who were still alive when Vasari wrote, the latter's statement may be accepted as constituting good evidence at least that the former died young. (**4**) This legend was published by Ridolfi (*Maraviglie*, 1648). (**5**) See reference 3. (**6**) The contracts both for the Doge's Palace and for the Fondaco dei Tedeschi were of some importance and would only have been given to a painter whose work was well thought of. Moreover, Isabella d'Este's letter, already referred to, shows that by the time of his death Giorgione's fame had spread to Mantua and that Isabella thought him worthy of her attention. It is also significant in this connection that not even her influence could persuade the owner of the picture by Giorgione which she had asked for to part with it. (**7**) Baldassare Castiglione (*Il Cortegiano*, 1524) mentions Giorgione with Leonardo, Mantegna, Raphael and Michelangelo as most excellent painters. Furthermore the *Anonimo Morelliano* (see reference 10) pays particular attention to Giorgione's pictures. (**8**) I.e. in the sense of a painting (such as Titian's Frari *Assunta*, for example) whose history can be traced back with certainty to an unquestionably authentic document. In Giorgione's case the fragment of a fresco from the Fondaco dei Tedeschi would in fact answer to this definition. But its condition is so ruinous that it can no longer qualify as a work of art. (**9**) The attribution of this work depends on an inscription on the back published by J. Wilde (*loc. cit.*). This states that the picture is by Giorgione and gives a precise date and precise details. As it cannot be *proved* that the inscription is authentic and contemporary the attribution of the picture to Giorgione must stop just this side of complete certainty. Nevertheless Wilde demonstrated the overwhelming probability that the inscription is genuine and in consequence the picture must be considered the best authenticated of any still surviving. The portrait of a man (San Diego, California) known as the 'Terris Portrait' may be in a similar category to the Vienna portrait, since it is attributed to Giorgione on the strength of an inscription on the back. But this inscription—to judge from the photograph published by Richter (*op. cit.*, p. 227)—is so damaged and so fragmentary as to afford less evidence for its being contemporary than is the case with the Vienna portrait. (**10**) The attribution of these two pictures to Giorgione depends on identifying them with two described in a MS. in the Marciana, Venice. The author is referred to as the 'Anonimo Morelliano' and is generally identified with Marc Antonio Michiel, a Venetian aristocrat. He gives short descriptions of pictures he had seen. His entries in respect of paintings by Giorgione range in date from 1525 to 1532. Only one of them—the *Christ* of S. Rocco—is still in the place where he described it, but in this case his wording is ambiguous and not certainly to be interpreted as meaning he thought the picture by Giorgione. The subsequent fate of all the other pictures he mentions as by Giorgione cannot be traced with certainty beyond the seventeenth century, and as most of his descriptions are very short it is usually hazardous to identify existing pictures with them. But the subjects of the *Three Philosophers* and of the *Tempest* are so very unusual that in spite of gaps in their pedigrees (and, in the case of the *Tempest*, also of a certain oddity in the *Anonimo's* wording) it is universally assumed that they are the ones he means. Even then, naturally, the date of the *Anonimo's* notes does not render his statements first-rate documentation. Recently (*Arte Veneta*, 1954, p. 165)

W. Suida has published a portrait of an armed man (Vienna) which corresponds with a description by the *Anonimo* of a picture sufficiently unusual in subject to render identification very tempting. (11) From a documentary point of view the attribution of this work to Giorgione is the least supported of the four, since it goes back no farther than the mid-seventeenth century (Ridolfi). Apart from Ridolfi's testimony (of little value in itself) the attribution rests on two main factors. First, the altarpiece has always been in the town from which it is known that Giorgione came. Secondly, it is both a major masterpiece and utterly different in style from that of the very few other artists of the requisite stature to have painted it. (12) Often (but not universally) identified with the *Anonimo's* '*Venere nuda, che dorme in uno paese cun Cupidine, fo de mano de Zorzo da Castelfranco, ma lo paese et Cupidine forono finiti da Titiano.*' The identification in this case is clearly more hypothetical and more hazardous than with the *Three Philosophers* or the *Tempest* owing to the greater commonness of the subject. (13) This, as a large picture of a judicial scene, would have been suitable as the subject of Giorgione's Doge's Palace contract of 1507. If he had delivered such a picture it would doubtless have been burnt in the fire of 1574. The Kingston Lacy picture is unfinished and therefore could not have been delivered. Assuming for this reason that the Kingston Lacy picture was intended for the Doge's Palace and that it is by Giorgione, Philip Hendy (*Arte Veneta*, 1954, pp. 170–1) also points out that Vasari, in his life of Titian, says that Giorgione changed his manner of painting around the year 1507. These points must all be borne in mind, but are inconclusive in themselves that the picture is by Giorgione.

## 1160  ADORATION OF THE MAGI

Panel, painted area (irregular) *c.* $11\frac{3}{4} \times c.$ 32 (0·29 × 0·81).

There have been innumerable small losses of paint, caused by flaking, over most of the area, but no substantial portion is entirely lacking in original paint. Much of the original surface quality seems still present in small areas, particularly in the well-preserved doublet and belt of the youth on the right, leaning on a staff. Cleaned, 1947.

Perhaps originally part of the predella of an altarpiece.[1] Purchased as by Giovanni Bellini. Catalogued, from the edition of 1889 on, as Giorgione, with the exception of the editions of 1925 and 1929, when it appeared as Bonifazio.[2] Other attributions have been Catena,[3] Cariani[4] and Palma.[5] The most recent cleaning (1947) has shown the virtual impossibility of any of the four last-named masters. Meanwhile there has been increasing agreement in favour of a return to the former attribution to Giorgione himself.[6] This seems to the present writer to be justified.

The costumes shown would accord most easily with a date around 1506 or 1507.[7] This is a factor in the attribution, since Catena is the only serious alternative, and even his advocates in this matter (e.g. L. Venturi: *Giorgione e il Giorgionismo*, 1913, p. 229) point out that if it were his it must be late—after 1520.

PROVENANCE: No. 23 (as Giovanni Bellini) in the printed catalogue (1822) of pictures at Leigh Court, near Bristol, in the collection of Philip John Miles. In the introduction to this catalogue it is stated that most of the Miles pictures had originally been collected by Richard Hart Davis and purchased from him privately.[8] In the Miles collection (where noted, as Giovanni Bellini, by Waagen in 1835 and 1850)[9] until 1884. Exh. R.A., 1870 (63) (as Giovanni Bellini, lent by Sir William Miles). Sir Philip Miles sale, Christie's, 28th June, 1884 (5) (as Giovanni Bellini) where purchased by Waters for the National Gallery (Clarke Bequest).

REPRODUCTION: *Illustrations, Italian Schools*, 1937, p. 45.

REFERENCES: (1) Suggested by G. M. Richter: *Giorgio da Castelfranco*, 1937, pp. 223–4. (2) First suggested by Sir Charles Holmes: *Burlington Magazine*, vol. 42 (1923), pp. 237–8. (3) By Morelli (*Munich and Dresden*, 1893, p. 205), followed by Berenson (*Lists*, 1897), and, with a query, in editions of 1932 and 1936, and by Lionello Venturi (*Giorgione e il Giorgionismo*, 1913, pp. 299–30). (4) Tancred Borenius in his edition of Crowe and Cavalcaselle: *History of Painting in North Italy*, vol. III, p. 11, note. (5) By Gamba: *Giovanni Bellini*, p. 35. More recently also by Fiocco (*Giorgione*, 1941, p. 45, no. 97). (6) The attribution to Giorgione was made by Crowe and Cavalcaselle, *op. cit.*, vol. III, pp. 10–11, and was supported by H. Cook (*Giorgione*, 1907, p. 53) and by L. Justi (*Giorgione*, 1926, vol. 1, *Anhang* no. 25), also by Roberto Longhi (in *Vita Artistica*, 1927, pp. 218–19 and in *Viatico per Cinque Secoli di Pittura Veneziana*, 1946, p. 19), by Antonio Morassi (*Giorgione*, 1942, pp. 70 and 164) and by Berenson in the latest edition (1957) of his Venetian lists. The so-called 'Allendale Group' consists of the ex-Allendale *Nativity*, the ex-Benson *Holy Family* (both Washington) and no. 1160. According to Cook (*op. cit.*, p. 21) these three pictures were first assigned to an independent 'Beaumont Master' in a letter to the *Daily Telegraph* of 29th December, 1899. Cook (*op. cit.*, p. 22) admits that the three pictures were even then 'universally admitted to be by the same hand'. A dissenter from this generally held view was Berenson in *Venetian Painting in America*, 1916, p. 256, where he called no. 1160 and the ex-Benson picture Catena and the ex-Allendale *Nativity* the work of 'another artist'. All three as Giorgione in his 1957 *Lists*. (7) Notes in the Gallery archives by Stella Mary Pearce. As early as 1927 Longhi (*Vita Artistica*, pp. 218–19) had associated no. 1160 with the Vienna portrait and had suggested a date around 1505. This was before the publication of the date (1506) on the back of the Vienna portrait. (8) Redford (*Art Sales*, vol. II, 1888, p. 232) lists a Giorgione 'Offering of Magi' as bought by Woodford for £38 17s. from 'N.N' in 1803. At the Hon. C. F. Greville's sale (31st March, 1810) lot 86 was catalogued as 'Giorgione: The Adoration of the Magi, in a finely illumined landscape' and sold for £89 5s. There is no reason why these should be identical with each other, or either with no. 1160, though a possibility would remain. (9) *Works of Art and Artists in England*, vol. III (1838), p. 144, and *Treasures of Art in Great Britain*, vol. III (1854), p. 185.

## Imitators of GIORGIONE

Taddeo Albano's letter of November, 1510 to Isabella d'Este included the information that the picture by Giorgione which she had wished to acquire was not to be had at any price. Fourteen years later Castiglione listed Giorgione among the most eminent Italian painters and the only representative of Venice, and during the rest of the sixteenth century and throughout the seventeenth there was no diminution of Giorgione's fame. In view of this situation and of the limited quantity of genuine works by Giorgione resulting from the shortness of his career, it is clear that the demand for them not only exceeded the supply at the time of his death but also that it would not have been likely to diminish with the passage of years. There would thus have been every inducement for painters to imitate his work, and the essential fantasy of much of it would have rendered the task incomparably simpler than in the case of the other short-lived giant of the sixteenth century, namely Raphael.

The imitations of Giorgione may be divided into three groups. For some years after his death his followers who were his contemporaries continued to work in a Giorgionesque vein. Some time later there were various revivals and partial revivals in which painters, probably with no fraudulent intent, attempted to reconcile forms *alla Giorgionesca* with some version of the then current idiom. A considerable body of evidence exists in respect of this activity. Niccolò Frangipane, active in the second half of the sixteenth century, put his name to at least one picture which was little more than a pastiche of Giorgione,[1] and Caravaggio himself was accused in his lifetime of reverting to Giorgionesque features. The case of Pietro della Vecchia (1605–78) whose fame rested on the skilfulness of his Giorgionesque imitations links this category with the third—that of the deliberate forgers. Whether or not Pietro's own motives were entirely dishonest there is no doubt that his pictures were mistaken for Giorgione's on occasion, as we know from Boschini[2] and Sandrart.[3] It is likely that deliberate forging of Giorgione had started long before Pietro's time—probably soon after the extinction of the living tradition before the middle of the sixteenth century—but documentation of this activity is lacking, for obvious reasons. Though the three pictures catalogued in the following section seem to the present writer to belong to this last category and to date variously from the mid-sixteenth century to some time in the seventeenth such a view of them cannot be regarded as more than hypothetical.

REFERENCES: (1) See editorial, *Burlington Magazine*, October, 1945. (2) *Le Ricche Minere della Pittura Veneziana* (1674), pp. 14–15 of *Breve Instruzione*. (3) *Teutsche Academie . . .*, ed. Peltzer (1925), p. 373.

## 269   A MAN IN ARMOUR

Panel, painted area $15\frac{5}{8} \times 10\frac{5}{8}$ (0·39 × 0·26).

X-rays reveal losses extending over most of the sitter's left arm and also his features. But the most conspicuous parts of the armour seem to be well preserved.

A variant of the figure on the left in Giorgione's *Madonna and Saints* in the Duomo at Castelfranco.

In the 1929 catalogue as 'Giorgione'. Despite the claim made by Crowe and Cavalcaselle[1] (put forward again, more recently, by Antonio Morassi)[2] that no. 269 is an original study by Giorgione for the Castelfranco altar its technique seems to the present writer to be appreciably later, very possibly of the seventeenth century. It differs from the corresponding figure at Castelfranco in not wearing a helmet and in details of the armour—e.g. the breast-plate is unornamented and in one piece and the rosette at the shoulder comprises seven sections instead of six. Of these features, the bare head and plain breast-plate recur in a fresco of a single saint by Pellegrino da S. Daniele at the church of S. Antonio at S. Daniele (Friuli)[3] and to that extent no. 269 is closer to it than to the figure in the Castelfranco altar which was doubtless the origin of both. Though the present writer is inclined to regard no. 269 as an imitation of Giorgione, the alternative possibility, that it is a copy of a lost picture by Giorgione (cf. Berenson: *Lists*, 1957) should be recorded.

The large copy, apparently of no. 269, made by Philippe de Champaigne for Cardinal Richelieu was engraved as representing Gaston de Foix, and this title has at times been applied to no. 269 also, but without justification.

VERSIONS: A large version corresponding with no. 269 rather than with the figure on the Castelfranco altar was painted by Philippe de Champaigne for Cardinal Richelieu's *Galerie des Hommes Illustres* in the Palais Cardinal (Palais Royal) and is now at Versailles. A 'Gaston de Foix by Giorgione' from the Orléans Gallery was included in the sale of Orléans pictures at Bryan's, 26th December ff, 1798 (lot 76—marked in the National Gallery copy of the catalogue as reserved for the Earl of Carlisle) and was lent later to the B.I. in 1818 (38) and 1844 (33). This was another composition, showing the figure only at half length and with a page—engraved by Besson (in *Galerie du Palais Royal*, 1808, vol. II) and described (in *Description des Tableaux du Palais Royal*, 1737, p. 167) as '*haut de sept pouces, large de six pouces*'. This picture was lent by George Howard to the Giorgione exhibition, Venice, 1955 (53). A late copy of no. 269 is in the Czartoryski Museum, Cracow. Another was lot 165, anonymous sale, Christie's, 2nd April, 1954. A picture described as 'Knight in Armour, believed to be a study for the figure of San Liberale in Altarpiece at Castel Franco' was lent by Sir H. M. Vavasour to the Fine Art and Industrial Exhibition, York, 1879 (517).

ENGRAVINGS: By M. Lasne (as Raphael: background and halo added). A further engraving, unsigned and undated, has a border consisting of small scenes from the life of Gaston de Foix with sub-titles in French.

PROVENANCE: In the possession of Benjamin West by the year 1816, when he exhibited it at the B.I. (56). An inscription in French still existing on the back[4] makes it probable that before that it was in the Prince de Conti sale (1777, no. 89—'*Le Giorgion. Le Portrait de Gaston de Foix. Bois. 14 pouces sur 10. On en connaît l'estampe par Lasne. 500 liv.*')[5] and, before that again, in the Pierre Vigné de Vigny sale, 1st April, 1773 (no. 1—'*Georges Barbarelli dit le Giorgion.—Un homme en cuirasse qui se trouve dans le tableau qui est à Castel Franco, dans le Trevisan, représentant une Sainte Vierge assise sur des nuées entre St François et la figure peinte dans ce tableau; on prétend que c'est Gaston de Foix . . . 15 pouces de haut; sur 10 pouces de large; on en trouve l'estampe gravée par l'Asne avec la marque de Raphael d'Urbin . . . 499 liv. 19*').[6] Earlier still perhaps in the collection of the first Duc de St Simon ('*le portrait de Gaston de Foix, attribué longtemps à Raphael, et probablement du Giorgione*').[7] Benjamin West sale, 2nd day (24th June, 1820), lot 62, bought Samuel Rogers,[8] by whom bequeathed, 1855.

REPRODUCTION: *Illustrations, Italian Schools*, 1937, p. 156.

REFERENCES: (1) *History of Painting in North Italy*, vol. III (1912), p. 13. (2) *Giorgione* (1942), p. 79. (3) Reproduced in Venturi: *Storia*, IX, 3, fig. 401

(p. 611). (4) '*figure tiré d'un tableau de Giorgione, d'une Ste. Vierge assise sur des . . . St François et la presente figure qu'on pretend être Gaston de foix. Le Tableau est a Castel franco dans le Trevisan. Cette note est de Monsieur Mariette*'. (5) Catalogue in *Le Trésor de la Curiosité*, vol. 1, p. 375. (6) *Réunion des Sociétés des Beaux-Arts des Départements*, 1894, p. 634. (7) Bonnaffé: *Dictionnaire des Amateurs français au XVII siècle*, 1884, p. 282. If this French provenance during the eighteenth century is justified for no. 269 it can hardly be identical with lot 70 in an anonymous sale, 125, Pall Mall, London, 10th December ff., 1789 ('Giorgione . . . full length portrait of Gaston de Foix') since it is there said to have come from the collection 'of the late Sig. Guarienti at Venice'. (8) Priced copy of sale catalogue in the National Gallery library.

## 1173 HOMAGE TO A POET

Panel, $23\frac{1}{2} \times 19\frac{1}{4}$ (0·59 × 0·48).

The main area of damage is vertical, slightly to the spectator's left of the centre, where splits in the wood have brought about extensive stopping and repainting. Repaint also in the clouds and in different parts of the figures.

Hitherto catalogued as 'Studio of Giorgione'.

The subject is obscure.[1] 'The Golden Age', proposed by H. Cook[2] and incorporated in the National Gallery catalogues from 1913 to 1929, is a vague title. The wreath worn by the enthroned figure presumably indicates a poet.

A certain naïvety in the execution, particularly of the figures,[3] must preclude an attribution to Giorgione himself.[4] Clearly the work of a painter trying to emulate Giorgione, but not necessarily a member of his studio, while if the analysis of the costumes is taken into consideration—which accord best with a dating as late as about 1540[5]—the picture would emerge as a very early imitation or forgery, which is what the present writer inclines to consider it.

PROVENANCE: Probably no. 15 ('Giorgione—King David instructing a pious man in his devotions'—'from the Aldobrandini Villa') in the catalogue printed by Buchanan[6] of pictures exhibited for sale by Alexander Day in 1800–1. No. 9—'*Solomon instructing Youth* by Giorgione'—in the exhibition of pictures belonging to Alexander Day, Egyptian Hall, London, before 1833, where stated to be from the 'Aldobrandini Cabinet at Rome'.[7] No. 21 (under the same description) in the Day sale, Christie's, 21st June, 1833, where bought White.[8] No. 301 (as Raphael) in Edward White sale, Christie's, 6th April, 1872, where bought H. B(ohn).[9] No. 113, H. Bohn sale, Christie's, 19th March, 1885, where bought Lesser for the Gallery.

REPRODUCTION: *Illustrations, Italian Schools*, 1937, p. 156.

REFERENCES: (1) Andrew Pigler (*Burlington Magazine*, vol. 92, 1950, p. 135) suggested a derivation from a fifteenth-century Florentine engraving representing the 'children' of Jupiter. The arrangement is indeed similar, but this does not seem a satisfactory explanation of no. 1173, since it leaves out of account the crucial factor of the enthroned figure's wearing the poetic wreath. This latter element would in fact have been taken into account in an alternative suggestion by R. Eisler (cf. G. M. Richter: *Giorgio da Castelfranco*, 1937, p. 224) that no. 1173 represents 'the boy Plutus calling on the poet laureate with his brother, Philomelus (with the lute), and his father, Jasion (with the bowl)'. Unfortunately, Eisler's work seems never to have been published, and the bare statement quoted by Richter is insufficient to assess its validity. (2) *Giorgione*, 1907, pp. 92–3. (3) Cf., in particular, the disproportion of scale between the seated figure and the others. Furthermore, the perspective of the steps is wrong, and the child and the kneeling man are shown at right angles, not to them (as would be logical), but to the spectator, thereby revealing their profiles, rather than the more difficult *profil perdu* pose. (4) As made, among others, by H. Cook (*op. cit.*, pp. 91–3). (5) Notes by Stella Mary Pearce in the Gallery archives. (6) *Memoirs*, II, p. 6. In this catalogue a distinction is normally drawn between pictures 'from the Aldobrandini Cabinet' and 'from the Aldobrandini Villa'. Since the picture shown later by Day (which is certainly identical with no. 1173) is described as from the 'Aldobrandini Cabinet' a possibility would remain that the one shown in 1800–1 ('from the Aldobrandini Villa') was a different one. (7) Undated catalogue. The copy belonging to E. K. Waterhouse is inscribed at the top 'Day's Colln'. (8) Marked copy of catalogue in the Gallery library. (9) Redford, II, p. 248.

## 1695 NYMPHS AND CHILDREN IN A LANDSCAPE WITH SHEPHERDS

Panel, painted area $18\frac{1}{3} \times 34\frac{1}{2}$ (0·465 × 0·875).

Damaged as a result of flaking in a horizontal strip across the middle and in many other places near the right hand edge. Cleaned 1957.

As 'Venetian School, 15th–16th Century' in the 1929 catalogue. Attributions have included Campagnola, Battista Dossi,[1] Cariani,[2] 'early Bordone'[3] and 'copy of early Titian'.[4] All these suggestions seem wide of the mark to the present writer who sees in no. 1695 either a copy of a lost Giorgione (cf. Berenson: *Lists*, 1957), or, more probably, a deliberate forgery of Giorgione dating from a relatively early period. It seems to be, in fact, a pastiche of Giorgionesque elements. The oval face of the recumbent nymph as well as her jewelled head-dress can be paralleled in the Hermitage *Judith*, the type of her right hand and of that of the standing nymph (with the index finger crooked) occurs in the naked woman in the *Tempest* (Venice, Accademia), which picture also offers a close prototype for the dark wispy foliage to the spectator's left of the head of the recumbent nymph in no. 1695 and above it. The head of the standing nymph in no. 1695 exactly echoes the ex-Melchett *Courtesan* and also that of the Adulteress in the Glasgow picture. Finally, the foliage in no. 1695 is too close in type (though not in quality) to that of the *Tempest* and many other Giorgionesque pictures to need stressing. These factors go beyond mere 'influence' and suggest deliberate imitation. Certain coarsely painted details in no. 1695— notably the two children—together with the other elements already indicated, suggest a date late in the sixteenth century or some time in the seventeenth.

REPRODUCTION: *Illustrations, Italian Schools*, 1937, p. 374.

PROVENANCE: Bequeathed (Mitchell Bequest), 1878, to the Victoria and Albert Museum (341–78), by whom lent, 1900.

REFERENCES: (1) Referred to in the 1929 catalogue. (2) W. Schmidt in *Repertorium für Kunstwissenschaft*, 1908, p. 117. (3) A. Morassi (orally) in 1938. (4) Berenson, *Lists*, 1932 and 1936.

## GIROLAMO DA TREVISO
### Active 1524, died 1544

He is referred to in the contract for the decoration of the Saraceni chapel in S. Petronio, Bologna as 'magister Hieronimus quondam Thome de Trivisio pictor ac sculptor'.[1] One of the frescoes in the chapel in question is signed, like no. 623 of this Gallery, 'Hieronimus Trivisius'.[2] If, as seems justifiable, the wording of the S. Petronio contract be interpreted as meaning that his father's name was Tommaso it would preclude the identification of him, first proposed by Federici,[3] with a member of the family of Pennacchi, since the crucial document for that thesis, a baptismal entry of 2nd February, 1499, gives the name as 'Hieronimus Joannes filius ser petri marie de penachis'.[4] It would also eliminate any more reliable date for his birth than Vasari's statements, which in fact are contradictory. Forty-six is given as his age at death in Vasari's first edition and thirty-six in his second.

According to Vasari Girolamo worked in Treviso, Venice, Bologna, Trento and Genoa.[5] The S. Petronio frescoes, already mentioned, are documented as of 1525–6. Some sculptural work by Girolamo in the same church is documented as of 1524–5.[6] Some frescoes at Faenza are signed and dated 1533. By 1538 he was in England in the service of Henry VIII.[7] Killed at the siege of Boulogne (1544) when acting as military engineer to Henry.[8] Vasari mentions his attempt to emulate Raphael—presumably mainly by study of the *S. Cecilia* at Bologna. His art also shows elements derived from Parmigianino, the Venetians and the Ferrarese.

REFERENCES: (1) Document printed in I. B. Supino: *Sculture delle Porte di S. Petronio*, 1914, p. 104, no. 78. (2) Crowe and Cavalcaselle: *North Italian Painters*, vol. III (1912), p. 128, note 2. (3) *Memorie Trevigiane* . . ., 1813, vol. i, pp. 117, 118, 238, vol. II, pp. 9, 25. (4) Document printed by G. Biscaro in *Archivio Storico dell' Arte*, 2nd series, 1895, p. 364, note 1. (5) Vasari/Milanesi, V, pp. 135–9. For the work at Genoa p. 614 of the same volume (life of Perino del Vaga). (6) Documents published by Corrado Ricci in *Arte Nostra* (Treviso), 1910, pp. 5–7. Supino (*Nozze Treves-Artom*, 7th April, 1927) proposed a dating of 1523 for an altarpiece at Dresden, there attributed to Bagnacavallo. (7) Letter, dated 30th August, 1538 from Pietro Aretino to Andrea Odoni (Aretino's *Letters*, vol. II, Paris, 1609, p. 50). Philip Pouncey (*Girolamo da Treviso in the Service of Henry VIII* in *Burlington Magazine*, vol. 95 (1953), pp. 208–11) suggests a connection between Girolamo's visit to England and an earlier commission for an altar in S. Salvatore, Bologna, which according to Malvasia was used by English students. (8) Letter of 1545 from Aretino to Sansovino (Aretino's *Letters*, vol. III, Paris, 1609, p. 158V).

623 ALTARPIECE. MADONNA AND CHILD WITH ANGELS, SAINTS AND A DONOR

Panel, painted area 88¾ × 58 (2·254 × 1·473).
Splits in the wood have led to repeated flaking. Where this has not occurred the paint is in good condition.
Signed (on the plinth): IEROИIMVS. TREVISIVS. P̄.

The saint on the right is identifiable as S. James the Greater by his pilgrim's staff.[1]

Despite gaps in the pedigree there can be little or no doubt of the identity of no. 623 with the altarpiece mentioned by Vasari and other early writers as in the church of S. Domenico at Bologna. Vasari calls it Girolamo's best work.[2] Masini (1666)[3] specifies the chapel from which it came as that of the Boccaferri family[4] and adds that the chapel also contained representations in fresco of the four patron saints of Bologna. Malvasia/Zanotti (1706) mentions only SS. Petronius and Domenico as lateral frescoes by Girolamo.[5] No. 623 would have been removed when the church was remodelled by Carlo Francesco Dotti in 1728–32.[6]

WOOD-CUT: Chiaroscuro by Alessandro Gandini, dated 1610 (Bartsch, XII, p. 65), with variations, particularly in the background.

PROVENANCE: Boccaferri chapel of S. Domenico, Bologna until shortly before 1732 (see above). Said to have passed thence to a private collection at Imola and then to have been sold abroad.[7] In England in the Solly collection by 1835.[8] Lot 40, Solly sale, 8th May, 1847, bought Lord Northwick,[9] by whom exh. B.I., 1847 (52).[10] Northwick sale, 3rd August, 1859 (565), where purchased.

REPRODUCTION: *Illustrations, Italian Schools*, 1937, p. 160.

REFERENCES: (1) No attributes are shown for the other two saints. The National Gallery Report of 1860 and I. B. Supino (*L'Arte nelle Chiese di Bologna*, 1938, p. 237) identify them as SS. Joseph and Paul but take the opposite view as to which is which. (2) Vasari/Milanesi, V, p. 137. See also P. Lamo, *Graticola di Bologna*, 1560 (ed. of 1844, p. 21) and Scanelli, *Microcosmo*, 1657, pp. 258 f—both descriptions more detailed than Vasari's. (3) *Bologna Perlustrata*, I, p. 114. (4) I. B. Supino, *loc. cit.*, identifies the donor in no. 623 with 'Lodovico Boccadiferro'. (5) *Le Pitture . . .*, p. 241. (6) Dates from Thieme-Becker's article on C. F. Dotti. Malvasia/Zanotti's edition of 1732 no longer mentions no. 623. (7) Schorn and Förster's edition of Vasari, vol. III, 2nd part (1845), repeated in Milanesi's note in his edition (vol. V, p. 137, note 3). Search in Giovanni Villa's *Guida Pittorica d'Imola* (1794, ed. Gambetti 1925) failed to find any trace of no. 623. (8) Seen by Waagen on his first visit which took place in that year (*Works of Art and Artists in England*, II (1838), p. 191) as from S. Domenico, Bologna. Solly catalogue, n.d., no. 15. (9) Marked copy of sale catalogue in the Gallery library. (10) No. 270 in *Hours in Lord Northwick's Picture Galleries*, 1858, where the provenance is wrongly given as 'the church of St Salvatore'.

## Ascribed to GIROLAMO DA TREVISO

218 THE ADORATION OF THE KINGS (AFTER BALDASSARE PERUZZI)

Panel, $56\frac{3}{4} \times 49\frac{1}{2}$ (1·442 × 1·257).

Movement in the panels has led to flaking at different times, and the present discoloured varnish makes it difficult to assess the state of the paint. It seems probable, however, that this is basically good for a picture of its age.

A painted version of the cartoon by Peruzzi which is no. 167 of this Gallery. The latter is neither punched nor squared but the individual figures are of approximately the same size in both. The larger over-all size of no. 218 is due to the greater space above the heavenly host and between the latter and the top of the arch; also to the inclusion of extra figures at the sides. As no. 167 has certainly been reduced in size at the top and at the sides (and the figures at the edges made up in places) it is possible that it originally included the latter figures. In that case, however, they could hardly have been in exactly the same relative positions. Of the two dogs, lower right in no. 218, who do not figure in no. 167, the foremost one conceals the legs of the man looking over the top of the chest, which are clearly visible in no. 167 and not appreciably retouched. Similarly, on the left of no. 167, above the horse's head on the extreme left, there is no sign of a further horse's head and of a pointing hand which occupy this area in no. 218. It should be pointed out, moreover, that Agostino Carracci's engraving of 1579 after no. 167 (see below) shows it with the sides in their present state, without the extra figures.

Vasari says that Girolamo da Treviso made a painted version of Peruzzi's cartoon of the Adoration of the Magi for Conte Giambattista Bentivoglio, who also possessed the original cartoon.[1] Both the cartoon and the painted version were recorded by Pietro Lamo in the possession of Conte Andalò Bentivoglio.[2]

Though it is stated in the Higginson catalogue that no. 218 came from the Bentivoglio family this information was clearly derived from a note in the Lapeyrière sale catalogue of 1825 of which the wording leaves no doubt that this provenance was not a continuous tradition but depended merely on the inscription on Agostino Carracci's engraving after no. 167 which gives Conte Costanzo Bentivoglio as the owner of the original.[3] Nevertheless, stylistic factors, though slight, do seem to the present writer to point to Girolamo da Treviso (to whom no. 218 is attributed by Berenson—*Lists*, 1936). Though no. 218 is a fairly accurate copy of no. 167 it is immeasurably coarser in draughtsmanship and in physiognomical differentiation, and certain details, such as the angels supporting the Almighty, whose faces are of different types from Peruzzi's, seem to show an approximation to Girolamo da Treviso's idiom. When no. 218, moreover, is placed next no. 623 of this Gallery (a signed work of Girolamo da Treviso) a marked similarity of colouring is also noticeable. It may also be pointed out, without being unduly stressed, that no. 218 is clearly a sixteenth-century work and that as no. 167 was in private possession at that time the number of copies taken from it might be expected to be relatively small; also that since the owner possessed in addition one painted version he would have less inducement to commission another, whether or not he permitted copies to be made for other people. In fact, only one other copy is recorded as having been made in the sixteenth century, and this was probably done in connection with Agostino Carracci's engraving. The latter is dated 1579, the former, which was on canvas and has since disappeared but which belonged in the nineteenth century to Michelangelo Gualandi, 1576. Both depart from no. 167 and no. 218

alike in that additional angels and some heads of cherubs are included in the heavenly host.[4]

VERSION: A picture formerly in the Northwick collection (no. 511 in 'Hours in Lord Northwick's Picture Galleries', 1858, no. 141 in the Northwick sale catalogue, 27th July, 1859) is referred to in editions of the National Gallery catalogue from 1915 on as a 'repetition' of no. 218. The present writer, however, has not been able to check if it was of the same design.

PROVENANCE: Probably exported from Italy at the time of the Napoleonic upheavals, since Buchanan, who was much concerned in that traffic, noted that it had once belonged to him,[5] and the preface of the 1825 Lapeyrière sale catalogue mentions it among the pictures which had become available as a result of the Revolution. Conceivably, but improbably, identical with a picture in the Truchsessian Gallery—1804 exhibition catalogue, no. 537 'The Adoration of the Magi, 1486, B. Peruzzi' and no. 222 in the sale, 29th March (3rd day), 1806 ('B. Peruzzi . . . The Adoration of the Magi, a curious specimen of that early period'). No. 41 in the Lapeyrière sale, Paris, 19th April, 1825.[6] Probably no. 112 in the Delahante sale, London (Phillips), 8–9th July, 1828.[7] Pages 220–4 of the 1841 catalogue (by Henry Artaria) of the Edmund Higginson Gallery and no. 227 in the latter's sale (where bought in), Christie's, 6th June, 1846, in both cases as from Bentivoglio, Lapeyrière and 'Mr Gray's' collections. Presented by Edmund Higginson, 1849.

REPRODUCTION: *Illustrations, Italian Schools*, 1937, p. 274.

REFERENCES: (1) Vasari/Milanesi, IV, 597 f, and V, 137. (2) *Graticola di Bologna*, 1560. Ed. of 1844, p. 35. (3) 'Ce tableau, qu'Augustin Carrache trouve digne d'exercer son burin, se voyait du temps de cet artiste dans le palais du Comte Constantin Bentivoglio, à Bologne.' (4) See publication of 1853 by Gualandi—'L'Adorazione dei Magi, Pittura del XVI Secolo'. The copy in question is there attributed to Bartolomeo Cesi, or to Cesi and Agostino Carracci in conjunction. Gualandi points out, among other things, Rosini's error in assuming that Agostino Carracci's engraving was made after the painting formerly in the Rinuccini collection, which, as can be seen from the engraving (pl. XXXVI of the *Etruria Pittrice*) was quite different. (5) MS. note in copy of the 1851 National Gallery catalogue in the Gallery library. (6) Date corrected in MS. in the National Gallery copy from 14th March. Not in the 1817 Lapeyrière sale, as stated in earlier editions of the National Gallery catalogue. (7) The sale catalogue specifies that the picture is on panel and is from 'the Palace of Constantine Bentivoglio at Bologne' (therefore following the 1825 Lapeyrière catalogue). No immediate provenance is given, but these particular Delahante pictures are specified as having been collected 'during the last ten years'. The long catalogue entry makes hypothetical identifications of some of the figures in no. 218, e.g. Michelangelo and Sebastiano del Piombo 'in the centre' and 'on the right . . . the Artist . . . with his dogs by his side, and next him Pope Leo X'. The man with the dogs in no. 218 does indeed look like a self-portrait, whether of Peruzzi or Girolamo da Treviso.

## BERNARDINO LICINIO
### Born not later than 1491, still alive 1549

One of a family of artists. Ridolfi,[1] following Vasari, confused the issue by stating that the name Licinio was also borne by the painter Pordenone and that the family as a whole came from the Friuli. This mistake was still current in the nineteenth century, but it has since been established[2] that Pordenone's name was not Licinio and that the latter family came, not from the Friuli, but from the village of Poscante (Bergamo). The Licinio family was well established at Murano and at Venice by the end of the fifteenth century, and it is at the latter city that Bernardino is first recorded, in 1511, in a contemporary document as a painter. He is referred to, still at Venice, in subsequent documents, the last being dated 1549. He presumably died some time between then and 1565 since he is not referred to in his brother Zuan Baptista's will of that date.[3] The latter died in 1568, aged 77. This gives the date of his birth as 1491 and, since he was apparently younger than Bernardino, also the *terminus ad quem* for the birth of the latter.[4]

A sufficient number of pictures signed by Bernardino Licinio survives to permit of an estimate of his work which emerges as that of a minor Giorgionesque, following the Giorgione/early Titian tradition in portraiture, and in religious painting predominantly that of Palma Vecchio.

REFERENCES: (1) *Maraviglie*, ed. Hadeln, vol. 1 (1914), pp. 112 ff. (2) By Vincenzo Joppi (*Contributo Terzo alla Storia dell' Arte nel Friuli . . .*, 1892, p. 29) and by G. Ludwig in the Prussian *Jahrbuch*, 1903, *Beiheft*, pp. 44 ff. (3) See Ludwig, *op. cit.*, p. 55. (4) Ludwig, *loc. cit.*

### 1309 PORTRAIT OF STEFANO NANI

$36 \times 30\frac{1}{3}$ (0·91 × 0·77).
The present discoloured varnish makes a reliable estimate of the condition difficult. Nevertheless it seems in good state.

Inscribed and signed: STEPHANVS | NANI.ABAVRO | XVII. MDXXVIII | .LYCINIVS.P.
The figure XVII in the inscription presumably refers to the sitter's age. According to Frizzoni no member of the Venetian patrician family of Nani bore the christian name Stefano and he suggested in consequence that the inscription meant that the sitter came from the village of Auro in the province of Brescia or alternatively that it was a case of a derivation from the old Venetian name of Orio.[1] Gustav Ludwig found documents showing that Stefano Nani held the post of *Scrivan delle Rason vecchie* in the year 1542 and that he was also *Scrivan* of the *Scuola della Trinità*.[2]

VERSION: Rome, Accademia dei Lincei (from Palazzo Corsini).[3]

PROVENANCE: This or an identical copy was in the Algarotti collection in the eighteenth century.[4] Otherwise first recorded in the Manchester exhibition of 1857 (no. 171, 'Pordenone', lent F. Perkins). George Perkins sale, 14th June, 1890 (43), as Pordenone, where bought for the Gallery.

REPRODUCTION: *Illustrations, Italian Schools*, 1937, p. 185.

REFERENCES: (1) Frizzoni in *Archivio Storico dell' Arte*, 1895, p. 98. Berenson (*Lists*, 1936) gives the sitter's name as Stefano Nani Doria. (2) G. Ludwig in Prussian *Jahrbuch*, 1903, *Beiheft*, p. 56. (3) Berenson, *loc. cit.*, lists this as autograph. (4) *Catalogue des Tableaux . . . de la Galerie du feu Comte Algarotti à Venise*, n.d. The collection was formed by Count Francesco Algarotti and continued by his brother, Bonomo. The latter died in 1776. On page XIX of the catalogue, under the heading 'REGILIO *Jean Antoine* dit *Licinius* & plus communement le *Pordenon*' is a description of a picture exactly corresponding with no. 1309 down to the inscription and the dimensions. It is possible that this may have belonged to Algarotti as early as 1743, since he mentions a 'Pordenone' in a letter of 17th June of that year (published by Posse in the Prussian *Jahrbuch*, 1931, *Beiheft*, p. 42), and this picture does not seem to have been bought by the Saxon king, unlike others discussed in the same context.

### 3075 MADONNA AND CHILD WITH ST JOSEPH AND A FEMALE MARTYR

*C*. 27 wide (0·68). Original panel 19⅛ high (0·48) to which narrow strips of later wood have been added, top and bottom.

Extensively retouched, particularly in the flesh areas. Nevertheless, the statement in earlier editions of the National Gallery catalogue that it is 'completely repainted' is a great exaggeration.

As 'Venetian School' in the editions of 1920 onwards. Attributed to Licinio when in Layard's possession and by Crowe and Cavalcaselle.[1] Closely related in style to other pictures of the same type, such as those in the Uffizi,[2] the Piccinelli collection, Bergamo and (formerly) in the Crespi collection, Milan (Madonna and Child with SS. Joseph, infant John the Baptist and Anthony of Padua—A. Venturi's catalogue p. 156). None of these pictures is signed but all are acceptable as Licinio's.

PROVENANCE: Tanara collection, Verona, from which purchased before 1869 by Sir A. H. Layard.[3] Exh. South Kensington Museum, 1869 (52) (lent Layard). Layard Bequest, 1916.

REPRODUCTION: *Illustrations, Italian Schools*, 1937, p. 374.

REFERENCES: **(1)** *Painting in North Italy*, 1912 ed., vol. III, p. 190, note (as 'Venice, Lady Layard'). An ephemeral attribution to Girolamo da Santa Croce is referred to in earlier editions of the National Gallery catalogue. **(2)** Reproduced by Venturi, *Storia*, IX, III, p. 479. **(3)** Layard MSS. in the Gallery archives.

## Lorenzo LOTTO

### Born *c*. 1480, still alive September, 1556

The approximate date of his birth is deduced from his will of 1546, in which he describes himself as 'circha' 66 years old. He was apparently from Venice, but led a nomadic life and was active also at Treviso and Bergamo and in various cities of the Marches, particularly Recanati, Jesi, Ancona and Loreto. In 1509 he was in Rome. In 1554 he became an oblate of the Santa Casa at Loreto.

Lotto was influenced at the beginning by Giovanni Bellini, among others, but evolved an individual style at an early stage. There are many signed and dated works.

4—v.s.c.

699 THE PHYSICIAN, GIOVANNI AGOSTINO DELLA TORRE, AND HIS SON, NICCOLÒ

$33\frac{1}{4} \times 26\frac{3}{4}$ (0·844 × 0·68).

Rather worn in a number of places, and retouched.[1]

Signed (on the arm of the chair, bottom right):

*L.LOTVS.P.* | 1515

The scroll held by the foreground figure in his right hand is inscribed:

*Medicorum Esculapio | Joanni Augustino Ber | gomatj*

The letter on the table behind is inscribed:

*Dno Nicolao de la tur | re nobili bergom . . . | . . . amicosingmo |Bg.mj*

Morelli, to whom the picture belonged at one time, first suggested that the figure on the right (Niccolò) was added later.[2] He deduced, on the flimsiest evidence, that Lotto was in Venice in the year (1515) when no. 699 was painted, and by reiterating the statement made by Zancon (*op. cit.*) to the effect that Giovanni Agostino della Torre was a professor in the university of Padua, he concluded that Lotto called at Padua on his return from Venice to Bergamo in 1515, painted the portrait of Giovanni Agostino there and then took the picture to Bergamo where he added the figure of Niccolò. This theory was supported by Berenson.[3] There is, however, no justification for assuming Lotto's presence in Venice in 1515,[4] and it is certain that Giovanni Agostino della Torre was not then at the university of Padua.[5] In point of fact there can be little doubt that the artist and both sitters were all at Bergamo in the year 1515. Nevertheless this need not refute Morelli's theory that the figure of Niccolò was added later. The placing of the figures in relation to the surround forcibly suggests this, while the occurrence of an after-thought need not also presuppose a lengthy time-lag.[6] Niccolò della Torre was the son of Giovanni Agostino.[7] The latter died in 1535 at the age of 81.[8]

DRAWINGS: Tietze and Tietze-Conrat[9] connect a head of a bearded man in the Uffizi (no. 1876F) with no. 699. Though there seems some similarity of features there is no need to assume either that the Uffizi drawing represents Niccolò della Torre or that it is a study for no. 699. Berenson, indeed (*op. cit.*, 1955, p. 221) dates the drawing some ten years after the painting.

ENGRAVING: Zancon (*loc. cit.*), 1812.

PROVENANCE: In 1812 in the possession of General Teodoro Lechi of Brescia (Zancon, *op. cit.*). According to Morelli[10] Lechi had bought it in that year from the della Torre family at Bergamo. No. 31 in the Lechi catalogue of 1824. No. 44 in the Lechi catalogue of 1837. Sold by Lechi, 31st May, 1847,[11] to Count Festetits, Vienna. No. 142 in the sale of the latter's collection, Vienna, 11th April, 1859, where bought by Morelli,[12] from whom purchased, 1862.

REPRODUCTION: *Illustrations, Italian Schools*, 1937, p. 200.

REFERENCES: (1) In the engraving published by Zancon (*Galleria Inedita*, 1812, tavola XIV) the hat of the figure on the right is circular. Morelli suggested (MS. quoted by Frizzoni in *Archivio Storico dell' Arte*, 1896, p. 24) that this was due to a seventeenth-century restoration. The circular form of the hat in the nineteenth century is confirmed by a statement in the Lechi catalogue of 1824. Nevertheless it is worthy of note (a) that no sign of the circular hat is visible in X-ray photographs, and (b) that the existing hat (which must be, at least in part, nineteenth-century restoration) accords well with the fashions of the early sixteenth century. (**2**) *Munich and Dresden*, 1893, p. 51, note 1. (**3**) Monograph of 1895, p. 138. Italian edition of 1955, p. 53. (**4**) Berenson (*op. cit.*, 1955, p. 52) admitted that Morelli's evidence for Lotto's stay in Venice in 1515 was inadmissible. (**5**) Frizzoni (*Archivio Storico dell' Arte*, 1896, p. 23, note 2) stated that no Giovanni Agostino da Bergamo figured in the registers of the university of Padua. Furthermore, the university was closed in 1509 as a result of the war and no professor of medicine was nominated until 1518. (**6**) Banti (*Lotto*, 1953, p. 71) rejects the theory of Niccolò's being an after-thought *consentendo all'unità di tempo per tutto il dipinto.* (**7**) Frizzoni, *loc. cit.* Zancon, *loc. cit.*, had referred to them as brothers. (**8**) Frizzoni, *loc. cit.* (**9**) *Drawings of the Venetian Painters*, 1944, p. 185. (**10**) MS. quoted by Frizzoni, *loc. cit.* (**11**) Information supplied by Conte Fausto Lechi, 1950. (**12**) *Loc. cit.*

1047 FAMILY GROUP

45$\frac{1}{4}$ × 55 (1·149 × 1·397).

On the whole in reliable condition. A certain amount of local retouching. Signed: .L.Lotto. This signature does not appear in the (nineteenth century) engravings of the picture (see ENGRAVINGS below), but it gives no indication of being a forgery.

No. 1047 has been associated with the following entry in Lotto's account book: *A dì 23 settembre del 47 die dar el sopradito misser Zuane de la Volta mio patron di casa per un quadro de picture, con el suo retrato de naturale et la dona con doi fioli tuti insema cioè n. 4—qual quadro era indicato e per bontà e per colori finissimi con el coperto suo sul timpano duc. 50.*[1]

The specification merely of a man and his wife and two children would not of itself be sufficient to link document and picture. But the inclusion in the document of the date—1547—constitutes a further indication, since the costumes in no. 1047 certainly date from about then (cf., for example, closely comparable female costumes in the frescoes of music-making ladies and gentlemen painted by Niccolò dell' Abate between 1547 and 1552 in the university at Bologna).[2] These considerations, combined with the fact that no other portrait group by Lotto of a married couple and two children is known, would render the identification of the subject of no. 1047 with the family of Giovanni Della Volta a plausible possibility.

ENGRAVINGS: 1. By Ricciani. No. 112 in *Choix de Gravures à l'Eau Forte . . . de la Galerie de Lucien Bonaparte*, 1812 (does not reproduce the signature on the painting). 2. By Cristofani, in Rosini: *Storia della Pittura Italiana*, epoca terza (1845), pl. CXXXVI (there stated to be in England). As in no. 1 the signature is omitted.

PROVENANCE: No. 170 ('Carlo Lotto—His Own Family') in the original catalogue (1812) of the Lucien Bonaparte collection.[3] No. 171 (again under this heading), Lucien Bonaparte sale, 6th February *et seq.*, 1815. Lot 160, Lucien Bonaparte sale, 14th May *et seq.*, 1816. Lot 31 ('Portrait of the Artist with his Wife and Children') in the sale of 'Edward Solly, esq., Deceased', 8th May, 1847, as from Lucien Bonaparte's collection.[4] Presumably bought in. Bequeathed by Miss Sarah Solly, 1879.

REPRODUCTION: *Illustrations, Italian Schools*, 1937, p. 201.

REFERENCES: (1) Extracts from Lotto's account book were published in *Le Gallerie Nazionali Italiane*, I (1894), pp. 115–224. Part of the entry quoted here is given on p. 126 of that publication, but it is given in fuller detail in Berenson's monograph on Lotto, 1955, p. 165 (Italian edition). (2) Reproduced in Venturi: *Storia* . . . IX, vi, pp. 600–1. Berenson (*loc. cit.*) specifically says that it was the costumes in no. 1047 which caused him to revise his earlier dating of the picture to 1523 (1895 edition of his monograph, p. 194). (3) Printed in W. Buchanan's *Memoirs of Painting*, vol. II (1824), pp. 288–94. (4) The signature— 'L. Lotto'—is mentioned on this occasion as also in an undated 'Descriptive catalogue of the Collection of Italian Pictures of the Raffaelle Period of the late Edward Solly, Esq.' in which no. 1047 figures as no. XIII.

## 1105 THE PROTHONOTARY APOSTOLIC, GIOVANNI GIULIANO

$37 \times 28\frac{1}{8}$ (0·94 × 0·714).[1]

Good condition in general. Some retouching, notably round the sitter's right eye.

The two letters in front of the sitter are both inscribed:

*Al Rdo monsig Juliano proton . . . aptico | dgmo S. . . . | a Padua | al borgo dogni santj* [2]

G. F. Hill[3] drew attention to a portrait medal in the Museo Civico at Brescia inscribed IOANNES. IVLIANVS. PROTONOTARIVS. APOSTOLICVS which clearly represents the same sitter. He also quoted passages in Sanudo's diary relative to the sitter, viz.:

1504. Zuan Zulian, son of Ser Marco, mentioned as *cubicolario del Papa.*

1517. The prothonotary Zuan Zulian benefited under the will of Pietro Grimani.

1518. He entertained Antonio Pucci on his way to Rome.[4]

No. 1105 has been generally attributed to Lotto[5] except by Longhi, who proposed Moretto as author instead.[6] This attribution has found little support[7] and is unacceptable on stylistic grounds—no. 1105, although differing in conception from the run of Lotto's portraits, shows many features of handling closely comparable with signed works.[8]

The *Catholic Encyclopaedia* (1911) gives the following definition of a Prothonotary Apostolic: 'member of the highest college of prelates in the Roman Curia, . . . also . . . the honorary prelates on whom the pope has conferred this title and its special privileges'.

PROVENANCE: Purchased from M. Guggenheim, Venice, 1881.

REPRODUCTION: *Illustrations, Italian Schools*, 1937, p. 200.

REFERENCES: (1) Dimensions of outside of stretcher. The original canvas turn-over still exists and is roughly painted. (2) The elaborate abbreviations cannot be printed, but the three words mainly affected are clearly 'protonotario', 'apostolico' and 'degnissimo'. It has been suggested that the illegible words are 'se ascriva' (for 'si indirizzi'). This would make good sense, though at the cost of twisting the letters somewhat. (3) *Burlington Magazine*, vol. 29 (1916), p. 245. (4) Hill quoted two more entries from Sanudo—one of 1519 referring to a Zuan Zulian, canonico Cenedese, and one of 1528, mentioning a 'prelate Zulian'—but pointed out that it could not be established that they referred to the prothonotary. (5) E.g. by Berenson (monographs of 1895 and 1955), Borenius (edition of Crowe and Cavalcaselle's *Painting in North Italy*, vol. iii (1912), p. 428) and A. Venturi (*Storia* IX, iv, p. 43). (6) In *Pinacotheca*, 1928–9, p. 270. Reasserted in *Viatico . . .*, p. 62. (7) The attribution is supported, unsurprisingly, in Banti and Boschetto: *Lotto*, 1953, p. 107. (8) Cf., for example, the landscape with that in no. 1047 of this Gallery. It may be added that if no. 1105 were by Moretto it would have to be an early work, as Longhi admitted. The (very slight) indications afforded by the costume, however (notes by Stella Mary Pearce in the Gallery archives), would tend to favour a date not before the 1530's. Berenson (*Lotto*, 1955) dates no. 1105 *c.* 1519/20.

2281 VIRGIN AND CHILD, WITH SS. JEROME AND ANTHONY OF PADUA

Canvas,[1] $35\frac{1}{4} \times 29\frac{1}{4}$ (0·895 × 0·743).
Much worn and restored.

The signature has clearly been tampered with. In its present state it reads: ( ?)*Lo* (or *u*)*renti*– (the letter after the *i* may be *u* and *s* run together) *Lotto* | *1521*. It seems probable that *some* signature was always on the picture—perhaps of the form *Laurentius Lotus*, which is that used on the other version (Costa di Mezzate, see below)—but in their present state both signature and date are unreliable.

The present inferior appearance of no. 2281 seems due to its bad condition. There is no reason to doubt that it is the remains of an autograph work.

A picture dated 1522 (Contesse Giuseppina and Maria Edvige Camozzi, Costa di Mezzate)[2] of slightly smaller dimensions (0·74 × 0·68) repeats the Virgin and Child group of no. 2281, but substitutes SS. John the Baptist and Catherine of Alexandria and also omits the landscape background.

VERSION: Costa di Mezzate (see above). A copy of no. 2281 was lot 160, Professor R. M. Dawkins sale, Sotheby's, 2nd November, 1955.

PROVENANCE: Catalogued by Berenson (*Lotto*, 1895, p. 187) as in the possession of Mrs Martin Colnaghi. Exh. R.A., 1908 (28), lent Martin Colnaghi, by whom bequeathed, 1908.

REPRODUCTION: *Illustrations, Italian Schools*, 1937, p. 202.

REFERENCES: (1) Catalogued since entering the Gallery as on panel, but it is on canvas now and there is no record of its having been transferred. Before entering the Gallery it was catalogued as on canvas in the R.A. winter exhibition, 1908. The vertical crack through the Child's body suggests at first that the picture had originally been on panel, but other factors indicate the opposite. (2) No. 47 in the Lotto exhibition, Venice, 1953 in the catalogue of which reproduced.

4256  A LADY AS LUCRETIA

$37\frac{3}{4} \times 43\frac{1}{2}$ (0·959 × 1·105).

The flesh areas, particularly neck and bosom, extensively rubbed and retouched; also, to a lesser extent, the orange parts of the dress and the background.

Inscribed on the paper: NEC VLLA IMPVDICA LV | CRETIÆ EXEMPLO VIVET.[1] Attributed in the nineteenth century to Giorgione. The Lotto attribution, which cannot be doubted, was first made by Crowe and Cavalcaselle.[2] Entitled 'Lucretia' in the 1929 catalogue and elsewhere.[3] The practice of allegorical or 'fancy' portraiture was more common in the seventeenth and eighteenth centuries than in the sixteenth. In one sixteenth-century prototype—Bronzino's *Andrea Doria as Neptune* (Milan, Brera)—the sitter assumed the dress, or undress, of the mythological character in question. In another—no. 24 of this Gallery—a lady in her ordinary clothes is shown with the attributes of S. Agatha. In no. 4256 the lady, for the moment, is identifying herself with Lucretia (represented in the drawing in her left hand) in order to assert her virtue, and points to the inscription on the table to emphasise her sentiment.[4] The costume in no. 4256 unequivocally indicates a date around the year 1530.[5] The picture as a whole is pre-eminently of the type which has been claimed, and justifiably, as an influence on the young Caravaggio.[6]

VERSION: Old copy mentioned by Crowe and Cavalcaselle in the Liechtenstein collection (Crowe and Cavalcaselle, *loc. cit.*).

DRAWINGS: Venturi[7] drew attention to a female head formerly in the Oppenheimer collection. Facially it resembles the sitter of no. 4256 but the costume is different and no support seems to have been found for the attribution of it to Lotto. The same applies to a drawing published by Suida.[8]

PROVENANCE: Lent (as Giorgione) to B.I., 1854 (46) by Sir James Carnegie (Lord Southesk) of Kinnaird Castle, Brechin, from whom bought, 1855, by R. S. Holford.[9] Exh. R.A., 1887 (124) as Lotto (lent R. S. Holford), Grafton Galleries ('Fair Women'), 1894 (9) (lent Captain G. L. Holford), New Gallery (Venetian Art), 1894–5 (218) (lent Captain G. L. Holford), Grosvenor Gallery, 1913–14 (48) (lent Sir G. L. Holford). Lot 68, Sir G. L. Holford sale, Christie's, 15th July, 1927, where purchased with the aid of gifts from the Benson family and from the N.A.-C.F. Exh. National Gallery (N.A.-C.F. exhibition), 1945–6 (17).

REPRODUCTION: *Illustrations, Italian Schools*, 1937, p. 201.

REFERENCES: (1) The *o* of *exemplo* seems originally to have been an *m*. (2) *North Italy*, vol. II (1871), pp. 159–60 and 532 '. . . displays the well-known smorphia and affectation of Lotto'. Banti and Boschetto (*Lotto*, 1953, p. 83) are wrong in ascribing a Cariani attribution to Crowe and Cavalcaselle. (3) E.g. in the catalogue by R. F. Benson of the Holford collection. (4) 'The lady doth protest too much, methinks' as Hamlet's mother remarked. Though there can be no evidence (since the lady is unidentified) that no. 4256 was painted to counteract the impugning of her virtue attention may be drawn to a comparable allegorical portrait of the seventeenth century—Van Dyck's *Lady Venetia Digby as Prudence* (Windsor). Lady Venetia was notoriously imprudent. (5) Berenson (*Lotto*, 1955, p. 133): 'non è anteriore al 1529/30'. A detailed analysis of the costume by

Stella Mary Pearce is in the Gallery archives. (6) See W. Friedländer: *Caravaggio Studies*, 1955, pp. 44 ff. (7) *Storia* IX, iv, pp. 87–8. (8) *Pantheon*, 1928, p. 531. (9) Date of purchase from Christie's sale catalogue, 15th July, 1927 (68).

# Damiano MAZZA
## Active 1573

Mentioned by Ridolfi[1] as a follower of Titian and as a native of Padua. A document quoted by Hadeln[2] records payment to him in 1573 for an altarpiece in the church at Noale (Veneto). This picture is still in position and is in a markedly Titianesque style. Pictures mentioned by Ridolfi as Mazza's which are still identifiable are a *Coronation of the Virgin* in the church of the Ospedale di SS. Giovanni e Paolo in Venice and, perhaps, no. 32 below.

REFERENCES: (1) Ridolfi/Hadeln, I, pp. 223–4. (2) Article in *Zeitschrift fur bildende Kunst*, 1913, pp. 249–54.

## Ascribed to Damiano MAZZA

### 32 THE RAPE OF GANYMEDE

Octagon enlarged to rectangle.[1] The eight sides of the original octagon are each about 28" (0·71) long. The rectangle measures 69¾ × 73½ (1·77 × 1·866). Cleaned 1955.

Good condition in general. There has been a vertical tear running down from half way along the under side of the eagle's left wing. In the 1929 catalogue as 'School of Titian'. The attribution to Damiano Mazza, first made, tentatively, by Crowe and Cavalcaselle,[2] and later, more emphatically, by Hadeln,[3] depends on identifying no. 32 with a ceiling painting mentioned by Ridolfi[4] as having been in a pavilion at Casa Assonica, Padua, and as the work of Damiano Mazza. Ridolfi describes it as representing Ganymede carried off by the eagle and as of such high quality as to be mistaken for a Titian. No. 32 was in Palazzo Colonna in Rome during the eighteenth century and may therefore be identified with a *Rape of Ganymede* specified by Mariette[5] as the work of Titian, as having been engraved by G. Audran and as having entered the Colonna possession through the marriage of the 'connétable . . . avec l'héritière de la maison Salviati'. The Audran engraving in question is after no. 32. The marriage was evidently that between Fabrizio Colonna and Caterina Salviati which took place, according to Litta, in 1717. Even if Ridolfi's information is correct (and the date of his work—1648—is far from constituting first-rate documentation in regard to Mazza) it would be necessary to find a connection between the Ganymede ceiling at Padua in the seventeenth century which was by Damiano Mazza but could be mistaken for a Titian and the first certain mention of no. 32—at Rome as 'Titian' in the eighteenth century. The fact that no. 32, though strongly Titianesque (comparable in design with the Salute ceiling decorations from S. Spirito and in format with the *Historia* of the Biblioteca Marciana) was clearly not painted by him, that it was evidently intended for a ceiling and that Ridolfi's use of the past tense ('vedevasi') suggests that the Assonica picture was no longer *in situ* at the time when he wrote, renders an assumption of identity very tempting but provides no positive evidence in favour of it. Even Mariette's story of a Salviati marriage is no help in bridging the gap since the Salviati were not a Paduan family but a Florentine one. Nevertheless some link, though an imperfect one, exists in a remark in Mündler's note-book [6] that a picture seen by him at Padua in 1856 was a replica of no. 32 and that the owner attributed it to Damiano Mazza. While it is possible that the owner's attribution was due not to a genuine local tradition but to speculative identification with Ridolfi's account the present writer is led to conclude that the attribution of no. 32 to Mazza, though not demonstrated, is yet a plausible possibility. Whether or not the design is due in some or any degree to Titian cannot be determined.

The Ganymede legend is given in different forms by different classical writers, but one of the chief variables—whether or not the eagle was Jupiter himself in disguise—is irrelevant to no. 32 or to other well-known *cinquecento* representations of the subject, such as Correggio's or Michelangelo's.

ENGRAVINGS: By G. Audran (octagonal) and Dom. Cunego (1770) (rectangular).

PROVENANCE: Mentioned by Mariette as in Palazzo Colonna, Rome (see above). No. 120 ('opera celebre di Titiano') in the Colonna catalogue of 1783. A MS. note (? early nineteenth century) against this entry in a copy of the latter catalogue in the possession of E. K. Waterhouse reads 'venduto a Gio.' de Rossi' who may therefore have been an intermediary for Alexander Day who exhibited the picture, with others, in London in 1800–1.[7] Bought by Angerstein, May, 1801.[8] Purchased with the Angerstein collection, 1824.

REPRODUCTION: *Illustrations, Italian Schools*, 1937, p. 358.

REFERENCES: (1) Ramdohr (*Ueber Mahlerei . . . in Rom*, II, 1787, p. 72) accuses Carlo Maratti of having made the sky too blue during a restoration, but there is no evidence that the enlargement was also due to him. (2) *Titian*, vol. II (1877), p. 459. An attribution to Tintoretto is made in J. B. S. Holborn: *Tintoretto*, 1903, pp. 34–5. (3) *Zeitschrift für bildende Kunst*, 1913, p. 252. (4) Rifolfi/Hadeln, I, p. 224. Francesco Assonica was a friend of Titian's and possessed pictures by him. See Vasari/Milanesi, VII, 456, and Cicogna: *Inscrizioni . . .*, iii, 152. (5) *Abecedario*, V, p. 321. (6) In the Gallery archives. (7) W. Buchanan: *Memoirs*, II (1824), p. 4. (8) Farington Diary, 7th May, 1801 (vol. 1, p. 308).

# PALMA GIOVANE
## 1544–1628

His name was Iacopo Palma, the son of Antonio Palma and the great-nephew of Palma Vecchio.[1] The date of his birth is from Ridolfi whose accuracy does not seem to have been questioned in this instance.

Patronised in youth, according to Borghini, by Guidobaldo, Duke of Urbino, who sent him to study in Rome. He may still have been in Rome in 1568.[2] Boschini, in his notes on Titian in the introduction to the *Ricche Minere* (1674), says Palma told him he had had some instruction from Titian, whose last *Pietà* he completed.

Active for nearly all his long life in Venice, engaged on a multitude of commissions, mainly religious and historical, including work on the redecoration of the Doge's Palace following the fires of 1574 and 1577. His important series of paintings at the Oratorio dei Crociferi, Venice, is documented as of 1583–96. His vast practice included commissions for pictures to be sent to widely different parts of Italy and also abroad (e.g. to the Emperor Rudolph II and King Sigismund III of Poland).[3]

Palma Giovane was left the dominant personality in Venetian painting on the death of Tintoretto in 1594.

REFERENCES: (1) Borghini, *Il Riposo*, 1584, p. 559. For the relationships in the Palma family see G. Ludwig in the Prussian *Jahrbuch*, 1901, pp. 184–9. (2) Drawing inscribed 'Mateo da leze pitor in Roma nel 1568 quale (?) morto poi nel . . . compagno di giacomo palma', repr. in *A Selection from the Collection of Drawings formed by C. Fairfax Murray*, n.d., pl. 74. (3) Ridolfi/Hadeln, II, pp. 189–95.

## 1866 MARS AND VENUS

$51\frac{1}{2} \times 65\frac{1}{4}$ (1·309 × 1·656).

Thick engrained varnish at present. The canvas has been torn in several places; otherwise the paint seems fairly well preserved.

In the 1929 catalogue as 'Ascribed to Palma Giovane'. The attribution to Palma Giovane dates, in all probability, from as early as the mid-seventeenth century (see PROVENANCE below). No reasonable doubt concerning its correctness need be entertained, particularly in view of the obvious resemblance between no. 1866 and a *Venus and Cupid* at Cassel which is a signed work of Palma Giovane.

Mythological pictures by Palma Giovane are rare. Ridolfi mentions in his catalogue of this painter's works only one representation of *Mars and Venus*—which he says was painted for Cavaliere Marino, the poet.[1] It is, however, doubtful for two reasons whether no. 1866 can be identical with the Marino picture. First, because the poet himself describes the picture as 'Venere in atto di disuelarsi a Marte',[2] which is not an accurate description of no. 1866, since the action in question is there shown as already complete. Secondly, Venus' hair-dressing, which is fashionable, would accord best with a dating probably in the late 1580's,[3] which is somewhat early if the picture was painted for Marino (born 1569). Alternately, Ridolfi mentions 'alcune Veneri di giocondissimo colorito' among the pictures painted by Palma Giovane for the Emperor Rudolph II.[4] But though no. 1866 would have accorded admirably with that monarch's taste there is no positive evidence for assuming his implication.[5]

PROVENANCE: Almost certainly the picture seen by Richard Symonds in the possession of the Earl of Northumberland in 1652: 'Palma Giovene. A Venus whole body on a bed, and Mars a fat red knave which she pulls down and Cupid pulls off his buskins.'[6] The latter picture was clearly the one recorded in Symon Stone's (unpublished) list of pictures at Petworth (1671) ('a large piece done by young Palmer of Mars Venus and Cupid'). No. 1866 was presented (as by Tintoretto) in 1838 by the Duke of Northumberland, together with no. 1868 (*Leda*, after Michelangelo). As the donor stated at the time that the pictures were not suitable for public exhibition[7] they hung for many years in the Director's office[8] and no. 1866 was not catalogued until 1929.

REPRODUCTION: *Illustrations, Italian Schools*, 1937, p. 263.

REFERENCES: (1) Ridolfi/Hadeln, II, p. 202. (2) *La Galeria del Cavalier Marino*, 1620, p. 13. It appears that Marino later presented his picture to Giovan Carlo Doria and then tried to persuade Palma to do him a replica on a small scale (see Hadeln, *op. cit.*, p. 202, note 2). (3) Notes by Stella Mary Pearce in the Gallery archives. (4) Ridolfi/Hadeln, II, p. 194. (5) There is no record of a *Mars and Venus* by the younger Palma in the 1621 inventory of Rudolph's pictures (published by Olof Granberg; *Kejsar Rudolf II's Konstkammare* . . ., 1902, Bilaga 1). (6) C. H. Collins Baker in *Burlington Magazine*, vol. 21, 1912, p. 235. (7) Letter in the Gallery archives. (8) Collins Baker, *loc. cit.*

# PALMA VECCHIO
## Active 1510, died 1528

He was from Serinalta (Bergamo) but already domiciled in Venice (where he lived for most of the rest of his life and where he died) when first mentioned in documents (1510).[1] The date usually given for his birth (1480) rests on no other evidence than Vasari's statement that he was 48 years old at his death. His name was originally Iacomo Negreti. He had adopted the name Palma as early as 1513.[2]

There is no reliable information on Palma's apprenticeship and the documentation of works attributable to him is extremely unsatisfactory. Three surviving pictures (Chantilly, Knoedler (New York) and Berlin) bear Palma signatures but the authenticity of the signatures has been questioned in all three cases and the Berlin picture, in particular, is merely a copy of one by Carpaccio. Of documented works, what is probably part of a *Sposalizio* which was reported to be finished in 1522 was in the Giovanelli collection (Venice), but it is only a small fragment and is much restored. An *Adoration of the Kings* (Milan, Brera) is certainly identical with one commissioned of Palma in 1525 but its appearance suggests that it was largely executed by Palma's pupils after his death three years later. A portrait of Francesco Querini (Venice, Querini Stampalia collection) is beyond reasonable doubt identical with one specified in an inventory of Palma's goods, but it is unfinished.[3] Of eight pictures attributed to Palma by the *Anonimo Morelliano* (Marc Antonio Michiel) four have been plausibly identified with existing pictures (at Dresden,[4] Alnwick,[5] Brunswick[6] and Leningrad[7]) but the identification is in no case beyond dispute. Finally, Vasari speaks, among other pictures, of the important altarpiece of S. Barbara at S. Maria Formosa, Venice, but the date of his work and his general vagueness on Palma does not render this good authority. Nevertheless, the S. Barbara (which is also mentioned as Palma's by Sansovino) shows a highly individual style which is certainly not that of any other known painter and which can be easily recognised in a number of other pictures—mainly religious scenes and portraits of voluptuous blonde women. The attribution of pictures of this kind to Palma is thus precarious in an academic sense only, and in fact is never doubted. His *œuvre*, though resting on foundations as apparently insecure as those of the city of Venice itself, is yet in the main equally firm. But the extreme scarcity of reliable information precludes any rigid chronology, and thus the definition of the early and of the latest work of Palma is of the greatest difficulty. His putative early works have frequently been confused with Catena's putative late ones and his own putative late ones with Bonifazio's putative early ones.

REFERENCES: (1) The date 1500 occurring with a 'Palma' signature on the Chantilly picture (see below) is not usually accepted as genuine. (2) It could be questioned whether 'Iacomo de Antonio de Negreti depentor' and 'Jacomo Palma depentor' were really the same person. However a comparison of the family connections of 'Jacobus pictor quondam ser Antonii Nigreti' (document of 1523, reproduced by Ludwig in the Prussian *Jahrbuch*, 1903, *Beiheft*, pp. 66–7) and of 'Iacobus Palma pictor qm. ser Antonij' (Palma's will, reproduced by Ludwig, *op. cit.*, pp. 70–1) leaves no doubt on this matter. Furthermore, Molmenti (in *Emporium*, June, 1903, quoted by Venturi, *Storia*, IX, iii, pp. 387–8) states that the 'Jacomo de Antonio de Negreti' and 'Jacomo Palma' signatures are written in identical handwriting (fascimiles in further article by Ludwig, Prussian *Jahrbuch*, vol. 22 (1901), p. 185). (3) A companion portrait of Francesco's wife, little more than a lay-in, is not specified in the inventory. The attempts made by Ludwig (*loc. cit.*) to identify other pictures mentioned in the inventory can hardly be upheld. (4) 'Three Sisters' (repr. Gombosi, *Klassiker der Kunst, Palma*, p. 63). (5) Portrait of a Lady (repr. Gombosi, p. 84). (6) Adam and Eve (repr. Gombosi, p. 31). (7) Christ and the Adulteress (repr. Gombosi, p. 2).

## 636 PORTRAIT OF A POET, PROBABLY ARIOSTO

33 × 25 (0·83 × 0·63).

Transferred from panel to canvas by Paul Kiewert, Paris, 1857.[1] Remounted on panel, 1916.

Much repainted. The best preserved passages are the white shirt and the red silk of the sleeves.

The identification of the sitter with Lodovico Ariosto (1474–1533), made in the early editions of the National Gallery catalogue but long abandoned, may well be correct for the following reasons[2]:

1. The costume of no. 636 accords most easily with a date around 1515–16.[3] Ariosto would then have been 41 or 42 years old which is not inconsistent with the appearance of the sitter.

2. The most authentic likeness of Ariosto—the wood-cut by Titian in the edition of 1532 of the *Orlando Furioso*—is in profile and certainly dates from some years after no. 636. Nevertheless, it shows some basic similarity of feature—the high forehead with hair receding at the top, very long nose with high bridge, short upper lip and straggling beard.

3. What appears to be the original of numerous painted portraits of Ariosto—a portrait attributed to Titian (Casa Oriani, Ferrara)[4]—though less well authenticated than Titian's engraving, yet probably represents him. Being only in semi-profile a comparison with no. 636 is easier and some degree of resemblance seems undeniable. In particular, it shows, like no. 636, a slight squint.[5]

4. The sitter of no. 636, with a book in his hand and laurels behind, seems intended not merely as a poet but to some extent also as the type of poet. Owing to Ariosto's pre-eminent fame it is questionable whether any other poet would have been painted in this guise at this time— precisely the period, if the indications afforded by the costume are correctly interpreted, of the initial publication of the *Orlando Furioso* (1516), the success of which was 'instantaneous and universal'.[6]

A near-contemporary description of Ariosto's features refers to his hair as black and wavy ('i capelli neri e crespi'),[7] whereas the hair in no. 636 is brown. Some or all of this effect, however, may be due to the repaint, and this should also be borne in mind when considering Ariosto's description of himself as bald for some time before the year 1517.[8] In any case, baldness is a relative term: Ariosto is not shown as entirely bald in Titian's wood-cut published in 1532. Consideration of these various factors leads to a conclusion that the identification of no. 636 with Ariosto is a plausible possibility though it cannot be demonstrated with certainty.

No. 636 appears in the National Gallery catalogues from 1861 to 1888 as 'Portrait of Ariosto, by Titian'. From 1889 to 1901 it figures as 'Portrait of a Poet, by Palma'. In the 1906 edition it makes a fleeting appearance as 'Portrait of a Poet, by Titian' and from 1911 to 1929 again as 'Portrait of a Poet, by Palma'. The attribution to Palma, now general and unquestionable, seems first to have been published by Reiset.[9]

PROVENANCE: In the Tomline collection[10] before or after 1850 (the year of Waagen's visit: he does not mention the picture).[11] In Paris by 1857 (when it was transferred to canvas). Purchased with the Beaucousin collection, 1860. Earlier provenance obscure. The assumption, made in the 1929 catalogue and elsewhere, that it was successively in the Renieri and Vianoli collections at Venice[12] rests on identifying it with each of two pictures recorded respectively by Ridolfi (1648) and Fontanini (1736) but which are not necessarily even identical with each other. Ridolfi says that Titian *fece il di lui* (Ariosto) *ritratto in maestosa maniera con veste di velluto nero foderato di pelle di lupi ceruieri apparendogli nel seno con gentil sprezzatura le crespe della camiscia. Hor trouasi in Venetia appresso del Signor Nicolò Renieri degno Pittore, ornato di molte riguardeuoli conditioni.*[13] It will be seen that the specification of a black velvet robe lined with lynx fur is not an adequate description of the gorgeous colours of the dress in no. 636—regardless of whether or not the basic material of the robe in the picture could justly be called black velvet or the fur lynx. Fontanini says simply *già molti anni io vidi l'Ariosto dipinto da Tiziano presso i signori Vianoli in Venezia a San Canciano*.[14] It is thus apparent that the Vianoli picture is not necessarily identical with the Renieri—in which collection, incidentally, there seems to be no other mention of it.[15]

REPRODUCTION: *Illustrations, Italian Schools*, 1937, p. 264.

REFERENCES: (1) Tracing from inscription made at the time. (2) No. 636 has not figured as Ariosto in the National Gallery catalogues since the edition of 1888. The purchase in 1904 of the Darnley Titian (no. 1944) as 'Ariosto'—an impossible identification—confused the issue and may have had something to do with no. 636 being catalogued again as Titian in the 1906 edition only (the first in which no. 1944 appeared). Cook (*Giorgione*, p. 82) refers to an article in the *Magazine of Art*, 1893, in which no. 636 is considered to be 'the portrait of Prospero Colonna, Liberator of Italy, painted by Giorgione in the year 1500'. (3) Notes in the Galley archives by Stella Mary Pearce. (4) Published by Georg Gronau (*Burlington Magazine*, LXIII, 1933, pp. 194–203). Gronau dismisses the identification of no. 636 with Ariosto, partly because earlier champions of it had based their case on an assumption of identity with a picture mentioned by Ridolfi as by Titian. This latter hypothesis is in fact improbable owing to the lack of close correspondence in the dress (see below under PROVENANCE). (5) Pointed out by Giuseppe Agnelli: *I Ritratti dell' Ariosto* (*Rassegna d'Arte*, 1922, pp. 82–98). The author accepts the identification of no. 636 with Ariosto. (6) J. Shield Nicholson: *Life and Genius of Ariosto* (1914), p. 58. Regarding the dating of no. 636, Gombosi (*Klassiker der Kunst, Palma Vecchio*, 1937, p. 65) suggests 'about 1515'. (7) From the biography attached to one of the editions of the *Orlando Furioso* of 1558. The status of this biography is discussed by Agnelli, *loc. cit*. (8) *Satira*, II, lines 217 ff . . . *il capo calvo da un tempo*. . . . (9) *Une Visite aux Musées de Londres en 1876* in *Gazette des Beaux-Arts*, 1877, vol. XV, p. 452. Reprinted 1887, p. 126. Crowe and Cavalcaselle (*Titian*, vol. 1, 1877, pp. 200–1) had suggested Pellegrino da San Daniele or Dosso Dossi. (10) Tomline provenance from a note in the Gallery archives. (11) Waagen on the Tomline collection is pp. 439–43 of vol. III of *Treasures of Art in Great Britain* (1854). (12) Not Vianoti as the 1929 catalogue would have it. (13) Ridolfi/Hadeln, I, p. 162. (14) Quoted by Agnelli, *loc. cit*. (15) Hadeln, *loc. cit*., note 2. Sir Charles Eastlake (MS. note-book in the Gallery's archives, entry for 1858, the fifth book for that year) refers to it in the Beaucousin collection: 'it is said that the portrait has always been in the family from which it was purchased (at a high price)'.

### 3939  A BLONDE WOMAN

Wood. Original panel $30\frac{1}{2} \times 25\frac{1}{4}$ (0·77 × 0·64). To this a strip 1″ high has been added along the top. On the right the priming extends to the edge of the wood. On the left and at the bottom it stops short of it, but paint (whether original or later) extends beyond it in these places to the edges.

Very fair condition. The repaint, most extensive in the shadow side of the face and adjoining hair, is for the most part easily recognisable. Called 'Flora' in earlier editions of the National Gallery catalogue, partly, no doubt, because of the flowers held in her right hand, and probably also because of the resemblance, often pointed out, to Titian's famous picture called by this name (Uffizi). Though not capable of proof, in default of contemporary written references to the picture, it is likely enough that some such intention existed, since the summary treatment of the features in no. 3939 precludes an assumption of precise portraiture.

In type and handling alike pre-eminently characteristic of Palma. Despite the extremely unsatisfactory state of the documentation in general (see the biographical notice of him) the attribution to him cannot be questioned.

Comparison of the hair style shown here with similar features in contemporary Venetian painting—particularly dated works of Lotto— suggests a date around 1520.[1]

VERSIONS: 1. Formerly Duke of Northumberland, Syon (sold Sotheby's, 26th March, 1952 (109)).[2] 2. Anonymous sale, Sotheby's, 12th December, 1934 (62). 3. Spahn (*Palma Vecchio*, 1932, p. 126) mentions another (with a pearl necklace) sold at Cologne, 1904.

PROVENANCE: William Delafield sale, Christie's, 30th April, 1870 (53) (as Paris Bordone) where bought Becci.[3] Bought Mond, 1889,[4] by whom lent to R.A., 1892 (119), Grafton Galleries ('Fair Women'), 1894, no. 8 and 'Venetian Art', New Gallery, 1894–5, no. 210. Mond Bequest, 1924.

REPRODUCTION: *Illustrations, Italian Schools*, 1937, p. 264.

REFERENCES: (1) Notes by S. M. Pearce in the Gallery archives. (2) Presumably the picture referred to by J. P. Richter (Mond catalogue, 1910, vol. 1, p. 136) as being labelled 'Sir Peter Lely, after Titian', from which (and on no other evidence) Richter deduced that the original (i.e. no. 3939) had belonged to Charles I. A picture in the inventory of Charles II (no. 318) is not no. 3939 but the 'Sibyl' at Hampton Court which repeats the design of a picture (ex-Queen Christina and Orléans, engraved in the 1786 catalogue of the latter) erroneously identified by Gronau (*Gazette des Beaux-Arts*, 1895, p. 435) with no. 3939. (3) Richter, *op. cit.*, p. x. In the National Gallery copy of the Delafield sale catalogue the buyer's name is spelt 'Beggie'. (4) Richter, *loc. cit.*

### Ascribed to PALMA VECCHIO

#### 3079 S. GEORGE AND A FEMALE SAINT

Canvas (transferred from panel),[1] $40\frac{1}{2} \times 28\frac{3}{4}$ ($1\cdot02 \times 0\cdot73$).
Much damaged and heavily repainted.[2]

The wingless soldier is identifiable as S. George by the remains of the dragon on the ground beside him. But there is no reason to suppose, as has been done hitherto, that the lady is his Princess. No. 3079 is in all probability the fragment of a *Sacra Conversazione*. The Madonna and Child would have been farther to the left and the female figure would have been intended as another saint. There is a complete picture precisely of this type by Palma in the Munich Gallery (no. 1108 in the 1911 catalogue of the Alte Pinakothek). The attribution to Palma does not seem to have been questioned, but the condition of the picture is too bad to permit of certainty.[3]

PROVENANCE: Layard's MS. states 'from the Grimani family at Venice, purchased from the dealer, Richetti'. Lent by Sir Austen Layard to South Kensington, 1869 (no. 6). Layard Bequest, 1916.

REPRODUCTION: *Illustrations, Italian Schools*, 1937, p. 265.

REFERENCES: (1) In 1880, by Professor Botti, according to Layard (no. 7 in his MS. catalogue in the Gallery archives). The transfer was done very unevenly. If the picture is held up to a strong light some areas are seen to be translucent, others opaque. Evidently the support and priming were entirely removed in some places but not in others. X-ray photographs also show this effect. (2) An old Alinari photograph (no. 13,604) shows differences in the picture's appearance and was probably taken before the restoration by Cavenaghi which took place soon after September, 1896 (letter from Lady Layard in the Gallery archives). (3) Ludwig's statement (Prussian *Jahrbuch*, XXIV, 1903, *Beiheft*, p. 78) that no. 3079 is identical with one which figures in Palma's inventory is ruled out by the fact that the latter picture was specified as on canvas whereas no. 3079 was originally on panel.

## Giovanni Antonio PORDENONE
### Married 1504, died 1539

In a fresco at Valeriano of 1506 (his earliest surviving dated work) he signs Zuane Antonius de Sacchis, subsequently generally known as Giovanni Antonio da Pordenone, from his home town in the Friuli. His father, Angelo de Lodesanis, was from the neighbourhood of Brescia (Corticelle). The old date given as that of his birth (1484) depended merely on Vasari's statement that he died in 1540 at the age of 56.[1] When it was found that he died in fact in 1539 the birth date was accordingly shifted to 1483. In any case there is no more reliable evidence for it. Vasari, and following him Ridolfi, is likewise responsible for the mistake, long prevailing, that Pordenone's surname was Licinio.[2]

Active as a painter of religious frescoes and altarpieces over a wide area of northern Italy. A journey to Rome—of which Vasari makes no mention—is usually assumed, and may have occurred. But the evidence for it is confined to the existence of a fresco reasonably attributed to Pordenone at Alviano in Umbria (some fifty miles north of Rome). Reminiscences of the Roman work of Raphael and of Michelangelo are adduced as supporting evidence. The journey has been hypothetically dated 'around 1515'[3] and 1516.[4]

Pordenone died at Ferrara. Vasari emphasises his attempt to set up as a rival to Titian.

REFERENCES: (1) Milanesi ed., vol. V, pp. 118 and 121. (2) This myth was exploded by Vincenzo Joppi (*Contributo Terzo alla Storia dell' Arte nel Friuli . . .*, 1892, p. 29). Hadeln (Ridolfi/Hadeln, I, p. 113, note 3) suggests a misreading of an inscription on an engraving after Pordenone by Fabio Licinio as source of the error. (3) W. Arslan, article on Pordenone in Thieme-Becker. (4) Fiocco, *Pordenone*, 1939, p. 46.

### 4038 S. BONAVENTURE

Panel, octagonal, each side *c.* $11\frac{3}{4}$ (0·299) (variable), overall measurements of painted area $28\frac{3}{4} \times 27\frac{7}{8}$ (0·721 × 0·708).

The red of his mantle in reasonably good state. His lawn sleeves, hood, face and hands heavily retouched, also the shadow of his Cardinal's hat. The tail of his mitre on the spectator's right seems originally to have extended in front of (or behind) his hood. For commentary and provenance see under no. 4039.

## 4039    S. LOUIS OF TOULOUSE

Panel, octagonal, each side *c*. $11\frac{3}{4}$ (0·299) (variable). Overall measurements of painted area $28\frac{1}{4} \times 27\frac{7}{8}$ (0·718 × 0·708).

Similar state to no. 4038, but less retouched. The area behind his head (with the crudely painted and architecturally meaningless mouldings) is suspect.

This and no. 4038 are stated in the catalogue of the Francis Capel-Cure sale (1905) to have come from a ceiling in the Scuola di S. Francesco ai Frari at Venice, on the strength of which they were connected by C. Jocelyn Ffoulkes[1] with part of a series of nine pictures by Pordenone described by Boschini (1664) as in that building[2] (the four Evangelists and SS. Bonaventure, Louis, Bernardino and Anthony of Padua in separate compartments round a central full length, apparently on a smaller scale, of S. Francis receiving the stigmata). The central panel is still missing. The four Evangelists and SS. Bernardino and Anthony were subsequently located at Budapest[3] and since they are clearly part of the same series as nos. 4038 and 4039 no doubt can be entertained of the provenance of all from the Scuola di S. Francesco, despite gaps in the pedigree. The perspective of the background in the four Evangelist pictures (which are square) indicates that they would have been in the corners of the ceiling, the four Franciscan saints (which are octagonal) at the sides.[4]

A. M. Zanetti, in his *Descrizione* (1733)[5] says that the paintings had decorated the ceiling of a ground floor room at the Scuola but that at the time of writing they were in an upper room. In the same writer's *Della Pittura Veneziana* (1771)[6] the reason is given for the removal— the pictures were deteriorating in their original site. Nos. 4038 and 4039 are characteristic works of Pordenone's late style and closely comparable with the Beato Lorenzo Giustiniani altarpiece (Venice, Accademia), commissioned in 1532. It is therefore reasonable to assume a similar date of origin, and Ridolfi in fact mentions the two works in the same sentence (Ridolfi/Hadeln, I, p. 125).

PROVENANCE: With no. 4038, from the Scuola di S. Francesco ai Frari, Venice (see above). The Scuola was suppressed probably at the end of the eighteenth century. In 1778 nos. 4038 and 4039 and the other seven pictures of the series were handed over to 'Giuseppe Rocchi Vicario per il Signor Francesco Nardi Guardian Grande'.[7] Said to have been bought in Venice probably around the middle of the nineteenth century by Edward Cheney,[8] from whom they passed to Francis Capel-Cure.[9] His sale, Christie's, 6th May, 1905 (58).[10] Sir Claude Phillips Bequest, 1924.

REPRODUCTION: *Illustrations, Italian Schools*, 1937, p. 288.

REFERENCES: (1) In *L'Arte*, VIII (1905), pp. 284–5. (2) *Le Minere* . . ., S. Polo, p. 305, also in *Le Ricche Minere* (1674), S. Polo 47. Ridolfi (Ridolfi/

Hadeln, I, 125) when referring to what is clearly the same series, speaks in error of the Doctors of the Church in addition to the four Evangelists. (3) See A. Pigler in the Budapest *Jahrbuch*, 1931, pp. 118–30. (4) Earlier descriptions of the shapes of the panels are sometimes contradictory. Zanetti (*Descrizione*, p. 300) speaks of them as 'parte ottagoni e parte rotondi' and in the Capel-Cure catalogue (and by Ffoulkes) the National Gallery pictures are referred to as 'hexagonal'. As regards the disposition on the ceiling, the four Evangelists are shown with transverse beams behind their heads, thus forming corners which would have been intended to blend with the corners of the room. SS. Anthony, Bernardino and Bonaventure are shown merely with flat mouldings behind them. S. Louis of Toulouse was probably originally shown likewise, the attempt at a transverse beam behind his head being probably later repaint. (5) p. 300. (6) p. 219. (7) Ffoulkes, *loc. cit.* (8) Ffoulkes, *loc. cit.* The Budapest pictures were bought in Venice in the '20's of the nineteenth century (Pigler, *loc. cit.*). (9) The sale catalogue is headed 'Collection . . . formed by Edward Cheney, Esq . . . the property of Francis Capel-Cure, Esq'. (10) In the National Gallery copy of the sale catalogue the purchaser is stated to be Carfax; apparently Phillips bought them soon after.

## Ascribed to PORDENONE

### 2146   PORTRAIT OF A LADY

Panel, painted area $20\frac{1}{4} \times 16\frac{3}{8}$ ($0·514 \times 0·416$).
Many small retouchings on face and hands. Bosom, bodice and the pink bow in better condition.

Purchased with the Galvagna collection as 'the Painter's Daughter, by Palma Vecchio'. Lent to Dublin in 1857 and still there when mentioned in the 1925 catalogue. First catalogued, 1929, as 'Italo-Flemish School, *c.* 1540'. The date is inadmissible on account of the costume which is closely comparable with that shown in various Italian works of around 1515.[1] The attribution to Pordenone was made by Berenson.[2] No. 2146 seems indeed to show some general affinities of type (at least in respect of the treatment of the hands and of the draperies) with the female saints in Pordenone's early *Madonna and Saints* (Venice, Accademia, from Collalto), which is dated 1511; also with the Madonna della Misericordia (Pordenone, Duomo) which was commissioned in 1515, and, perhaps, with certain figures in the vault frescoes in the church of S. Odorico, Villanova (commissioned 1514). The attribution therefore seems a plausible possibility to the present writer, though in default of an authentic early Pordenone portrait the evidence is too vague to permit of certainty.[3]

PROVENANCE: Bought, 1855, with the Galvagna collection, Venice.

REPRODUCTION: *Illustrations, Italian Schools*, 1937, p. 179.

REFERENCES: (1) Notes by Stella Mary Pearce in the Gallery archives. (2) *Lists*, 1936. (3) An attribution, apparently oral, by R. Longhi to 'Lotto in a Palmesque phase' (note in the Gallery archives) seems much less probable to the present writer.

5—V.S.C.

# Ludovico POZZOSERRATO
## Active 1581 or earlier, died between 16th August, 1603 and 9th November, 1605

Ridolfi[1] gives a short biography to Pozzoserrato in which he says he was of Flemish birth, long domiciled in Italy and settled at Treviso. He adds that he was a landscape painter and that he was active at the same time as Paolo Fiammingo (who died in 1596). Van Mander says that at the time of writing (edition of 1604) there were still two Netherlandish painters active in the Venice area, one of whom was a certain Lodewijck Toeput, who was then living outside Venice, at 'Derviso' (Treviso). As Van Mander specifies that he was a good landscape painter ('cloeck in Landtschap') there would be a *prima facie* case for equating him with Pozzoserrato. When, in addition, it is borne in mind that 'Toeput' and 'Pozzoserrato' have the same meaning ('closed well') there can be no reasonable doubt concerning the equation, despite the absence of documentation asserting it.

Documents published by Luigi Menegazzi indicate that Pozzoserrato came from Antwerp[2] and had settled at Treviso by 1582, but the date of his arrival in Italy is not known. Ridolfi mentions frescoes done 'in gratia del Signor Daniel Barbaro' in 'un palagio vicino à Castelfranco'.[3] As Daniel Barbaro died in 1570 Pozzoserrato would thus have arrived in Italy (if Ridolfi is correct, which cannot be checked, and has been doubted) some time before that. The first certain date, however, is a drawing signed with the L.T.O.E. monogram (see below) and the date 1581.[4] As the drawing may represent part of the Colosseum it might also constitute evidence for a Rome visit. A visit to Florence is also implicit in one of Ridolfi's statements.[5]

Of surviving pictures, a large *Tower of Babel* (Kirchheim, Schwaben —see entry for nos. 5466–7) is dated 1583 or 1587 and a *Fall of Phaeton* (Hanover, Kestner Museum) 1599. Both these pictures also display a monogram compounded of the letters L.T.O. and E.—which are common to 'L. Toeput' and 'L. Pozzoserrato'.[6] Of specific works mentioned by Ridolfi, six pictures for the Monte di Pietà at Treviso are still in position there. Ridolfi adds that Pozzoserrato painted the landscape in Jacopo Bassano's picture of SS. Fabian, Roch and Sebastian.[7] A number of attributed paintings and drawings are reproduced and discussed by Menegazzi (*loc. cit.*).

REFERENCES: (1) Ridolfi/Hadeln, II, pp. 93–4. (2) *Ludovico Toeput (il Pozzoserrato)* in *Saggi e Memorie*, I, Cini Foundation, Venice, 1957, pp. 167–223. This is an important and fundamental work. For the artist's birth-place Van Mander had seemed to indicate Malines. His words (1604 ed., fol. 296r) are 'eenen Lodewijck Toeput (ick meen) van Mecchel'. Whether the reservation phrase, 'I think' ('ick meen'), implies doubt as to the form of the name or as to whether it really was Malines that he came from would be an arguable point. (3) The building in question can hardly be other than the Villa Barbaro at Maser. For the question of Pozzoserrato's participation in these frescoes see Luigi Coletti in *Dedalo*, anno VI, 1925–6, vol. II, pp. 377–410, Charles Sterling in *Old Master Drawings*, December, 1931, pp. 44–8, R. A.

Peltzer in *Münchner Jahrbuch*, 1933, pp. 270 ff, and Menegazzi, *loc. cit*. Ridolfi also mentions a picture by Pozzoserrato of 'l'incendio del Palazzo Ducale di Venetia', but there were fires both in 1574 and 1577 and in any case the artist need not himself have been an eye witness. Menegazzi (*op. cit.*, p. 175) reproduces an engraving of the 1577 fire said to be after Pozzoserrato. (4) Vienna, Albertina, repr. Peltzer, *loc. cit*. (5) 'Un quadro co' spettacoli di alcuni fuochi fatti in Firenze per occasione di nozze'. (6) A landscape in the Brera (no. 647, 16 × 22 cm) is stated in the catalogue to have a monogram C.T. This has been claimed as a corrupt reading or damaged version of Pozzoserrato's initials. (7) Ridolfi/Hadeln, I, p. 397. The picture was no. 263 in the catalogue of the Kunsthistorisches Museum, Vienna, of 1907, where illustrated. Reproduced by Menegazzi (*op. cit.*, fig. 44) as being in the Museo Civico, Treviso.

## Ascribed to Ludovico POZZOSERRATO

### 5466 LANDSCAPE WITH MYTHOLOGICAL FIGURES

$72\frac{3}{4} \times 81\frac{1}{4}$ (1·847 × 2·06).[1]

Worn thin in many places, and damaged in particular along the horizontal join of the canvas in the centre, but in general in fairly good condition. Cleaned 1955.

For commentary and provenance see the entry for no. 5467.

REFERENCE: (1) At some time in the past notches have been cut in the canvas and stretcher at both sides, *c*. 8–9″ from the top and bottom.

### 5467 THE SONS OF BOREAS PURSUING THE HARPIES

$72\frac{3}{4} \times 80\frac{3}{4}$ (1·847 × 2·05).[1]

Thin in places, but in general well preserved. Cleaned 1955.

Nos. 5466–7 are unpublished, except for a short statement in *Arte Veneta*, 1947 (p. 148).

In the possession of their former owner as Tintoretto, but clearly belonging to the genre known as Veneto-Flemish landscape and in particular to the type practised by Paolo Fiammingo and Ludovico Pozzoserrato.[2]

The principal surviving landscape paintings whose attribution to Fiammingo has some external support are the following:

1. A set of four *Continents* at Kirchheim (Schwaben). These are apparently to be identified with some mentioned in contemporary correspondence with Fiammingo.[3]

2. A *Rape of Proserpine* (Rome, Doria gallery) together with its pendant, *Orpheus*.[4] The *Rape of Proserpine* connects with a drawing in the Rijksmuseum, Amsterdam, which is inscribed 'Paolo Fiamengho' on the back.

The principal surviving landscapes justifiably attributable to Pozzoserrato are the following:

1. A *Tower of Babel* at Kirchheim. Bears monogram.[5]

2. A *Fall of Phaeton* at Hanover (Kestner Museum). Bears monogram.[6]

3. Six pictures at the *Monte di Pietà* at Treviso. Attribution due to Ridolfi.[7]

Nos. 5466–7 are extremely similar in design to a landscape engraving of Aesop's fable of the raven and the scorpion, which is inscribed as by Raphael Sadeler after 'Lodovico Pozzo',[8] and in colour (particularly in respect of the greyish tone of the foliage) to the Kirchheim *Babel* and the Treviso pictures.[9] The presence, in addition, of numerous similarities in the treatment of figures and foliage alike between nos. 5466–7 and the Pozzoserrato's listed above seems to the present writer to constitute sufficient evidence for at least a provisional attribution to that painter. The chief difficulty comes from the existence of comparable features in the Kirchheim series—which includes three further sets of four landscapes with figures[10]—in which both Fiammingo and Pozzoserrato participated, but which display considerable homogeneity of landscape style. Starting with the four *Continents*, documented as Fiammingo, all seventeen pictures of this kind at Kirchheim would seem attributable to Fiammingo and studio. Starting with the *Babel*, which has Pozzoserrato's monogram, the reverse is the case. It is clear from this that the styles of Fiammingo and Pozzoserrato were very close, at least at one period, and at Kirchheim some collaboration between the two seems *prima facie* a probability. Ridolfi's distinction between their work, however—that Fiammingo excelled in foreground landscape and Pozzoserrato in distant landscape[11]—would seem to support the other evidence in favour of associating nos. 5466–7 with the fairly well defined personality of the latter painter rather than with the somewhat nebulous one of the former. A picture clearly by the same hand as nos. 5466–7 is the *Diane chasseresse* at Nancy (no. 128 in the 1909 catalogue, attributed to Tintoretto).

Regarding the subject of the pictures, the air-borne monsters in no. 5467 are readily recognisable as harpies, and the bearded man on the ground, right, with upraised left hand who seems to derive from the figure of Homer in Raphael's *Parnassus* is clearly intended to be blind. He is therefore identifiable with Phineus who had been smitten by Zeus with blindness and a lingering old age and to have his food defiled by the harpies. The story is given in book II of the *Argonautica* of Apollonius Rhodius (which would have been well known in sixteenth-century Venice after the Aldine edition of 1521), where Zetes and Calais, the sons of Boreas, who were winged, chased the harpies away from Phineus and would have killed them but for the intervention of Iris. If this account is in fact the source for no. 5467 it has been followed with some licence. The depiction of the same figure (in this case the two sons of Boreas) more than once within the same picture is not unusual in Mannerist works, but whereas in the *Argonautica* Iris plays a restraining rôle here she seems rather to be encouraging the harpy hunt. A further unexplained peculiarity is the monster at the top, centre, who seems to have a combination of wings and human arms and legs (as the sons of Boreas did) but also a head like a bird's and the tail of a harpy. If no. 5467 were regarded as no more than a fantasy on the Phineus theme it might be legitimate to consider its pendant, no. 5466, as a fantasy on the Circe story, a version of which also figures in the *Argonautica* (book IV). The exact theme of no. 5466 would be difficult to define, but the most striking element is that three, at least, of the main figures are monsters—the woman, centre, whose body tails into the head half of a serpent, and the creatures, of unspecific sex, upper left and lower left, who have the heads respectively of an indeterminate monster and of a pig. The figures in Circe's train in the *Argonautica* are described as not resembling wild beasts or men but with a medley of limbs, compounded of various ones. This would be a fair description of the figures shown in no. 5466. Nevertheless the main feature of the Circe episode in the *Argonautica*—the purification by Circe of Jason and Medea—is certainly not the theme of no. 5466, while the erotic nature of the activity shown in the picture, together with the presence of the recumbent man on the right and other details, do not figure in Apollonius Rhodius' account. Either, therefore, no. 5466 is an illustration of a different story, as yet unidentified, or it is a fantasy loosely based on the Circe story.

PROVENANCE: Bought, together with no. 5466 (as Tintoretto) by Frederick Cavendish Bentinck in October, 1892 from A. Marcato of Venice who said he had purchased them 'a good many years before . . . they had originally been part of the decoration of one of the rooms in the Palazzo Vendramin & were removed from the Palazzo many years before when certain alterations were carried out'.[12] Bought from F. C. Bentinck, 1944.

REPRODUCTION: Negatives in the possession of the Gallery.

REFERENCES: (1) At some time in the past notches have been cut in canvas and stretcher at both sides, *c.* 8–9″ from the top and bottom. (2) An attribution in *Arte Veneta* (*loc. cit.*) to Rottenhammer need not be considered seriously. For Fiammingo see Ridolfi/Hadeln, II, pp. 81–3. Ridolfi refers to him as 'Paolo Franceschi' or 'Paolo Fiamingo' and confirms that he was Flemish. Not identical, as formerly supposed, with a painter called Paolo de' Freschi, but very possibly identical with one Pauwels Franck who was a master in the Antwerp guild of St Luke in 1561. The death certificate (20th December, 1596) of 'Paolo Fiamengo pittor' gives his age as 50. As this would make him a master at the early age of 15 either the Franck-Fiammingo identification or, more probably, the statement of age at death, is likely to be wrong (Ridolfi gives the date of his birth as 1540). Surviving documented works include a painting in the *Sala del Gran Consiglio* of the Doge's Palace and a signed *Pietà* at Munich (no. 1159 in the 1904 edition of the catalogue of the Alte Pinakothek). Also four pictures at Kirchheim discussed in this entry. (3) The documentation is given in detail in G. Lill: *Hans Fugger und die Kunst*, 1908, pp. 140–4, where also one of the *Continents* is reproduced (fig. 26, pl. XIX). (4) Nos. 174 and 175 in the catalogue by E. Sestieri (1942). The *Proserpine* and its drawing reproduced in the *Münchner Jahrbuch*, 1924, pp. 136–7. (5) Reproduced by R. A. Peltzer in the *Münchner Jahrbuch*, 1924, p. 146. (6) Reproduced by Peltzer, *op. cit.*, p. 150. (7) Ridolfi/Hadeln, II, 94. A detail of one of them reproduced by Coletti in *Dedalo*, anno VI, 1925–6, vol. II, p. 406. (8) Reproduced C. Sterling in *Old Master Drawings*, December, 1931, pp. 44–8. (9) The present writer was able to study the Kirchheim and Treviso pictures *in situ* but knows the Hanover one only in reproduction. (10) Three pictures of one series are reproduced by Peltzer, *op. cit.*, pp. 133, 134 and 135, where they are attributed to Fiammingo. Two of another series on pp. 130–1, likewise as Fiammingo. The last series, the four seasons, not reproduced. (11) Ridolfi/Hadeln, II, p. 93: 'Paolo fiamingo nelle cose vicine. Ludouico però più dilettaua nelle lontane.' Ridolfi's further description of the type of landscape favoured by Pozzoserrato, an evidently romantic genre, with extensive views, mountains, ruins and water, fits nos.

5466–7 well. **(12)** Memorandum by F. C. Bentinck in the Gallery archives. Various *palazzi* in Venice have borne the title 'Palazzo Vendramin'. Of these the most famous—Palazzo Vendramin-Calergi, which was the scene of Wagner's death in 1883—had been bought by the Duchesse de Berry in 1844. The sale of her pictures (Hôtel Drouot, Paris, 19th April, *et seq.* 1865) did not include nos. 5466–7.

## Andrea PREVITALI
### Active 1502, died 1528

For biographical notes and details of the other pictures in the National Gallery by or ascribed to him see 'The Earlier Italian Schools' by Martin Davies (1951). At the time when the latter work was written the following picture was still attributed to Giorgione.

### Ascribed to PREVITALI

4884    SCENES FROM AN ECLOGUE OF TEBALDEO

1. Damon broods on his unrequited love.
2. Thyrsis asks Damon the cause of his sorrow.
3. Damon takes his life.
4. Thyrsis finds the body of Damon.

Painted area of each of the four $7\frac{3}{4} \times 7\frac{1}{4}$ ($0\cdot2 \times 0\cdot185$). On two strips of wood, each *c.* $17\frac{3}{4} \times c.$ $7\frac{3}{4}$ ($0\cdot453 \times 0\cdot2$).

Good condition in general. A little worn in places.

Perhaps intended as part of a piece of furniture.

The attribution to Previtali, suggested by Pouncey, was first published by G. M. Richter,[1] who demonstrated that many features in no. 4884 were almost identical with comparable elements in authentic works by Previtali.[2] These resemblances are indeed so striking as to leave little doubt that Previtali was the author of no. 4884. Nevertheless, some caution must be observed in view of the fact that no works of humanist subject definitely by Previtali are known, nor any in which he approaches quite so close to Giorgione, Richter's analogies being drawn, with one exception, from the backgrounds of Previtali's religious pictures. The identification of the subject is due to Dr Ernst Gombrich.[3] The Arcadian story of the suicide of Damon the shepherd on account of his unrequited love for Amaryllis occurs in the second eclogue of the Ferrarese poet, Antonio Tebaldeo, printed in the Venetian edition of his works (1502).

PROVENANCE: Until 1936 in the collection of Count da Porto, at Schio, near Vicenza, who alleged that it had been in the Manfrin collection, Venice. Subsequently with Podio at Venice.[4] Purchased, 1937 (Grant-in-Aid and Temple-West Fund, with a contribution from the N.A.-C.F.).

REPRODUCTION: *Burlington Magazine*, vol. LXXI (1937), p. 201.

REFERENCES: **(1)** Letter to the *Burlington Magazine*, vol. LXXII (1938), p. 33. This had followed an article by Kenneth Clark (*Burlington Magazine*, vol. LXXI (1937), p. 199) attributing the scenes, with reserve, to Giorgione himself, and a letter from Tancred Borenius (*Burlington Magazine*, vol. LXXI (1937), p. 286) favouring an attribution to Palma Vecchio which the same writer also suggested in a letter to *The Times* newspaper of 21st October, 1937. Immediately Richter suggested Previtali, however, Borenius veered and supported it (same issue of the *Burlington Magazine*). In the course of the lengthy correspondence conducted chiefly in *The Times* and *Daily Telegraph* Georg Gronau supported the attribution to Giorgione (*The Times*, 23rd November, 1937) as did Ludwig Justi (in a statement in the Gallery archives). The attribution to Previtali was supported by A. Morassi (*Giorgione*, 1942, pl. 180) and by R. Longhi (*Viatico per Cinque Secoli . . .*, 1946, p. 64). Berenson (*Lists*, 1957) calls no. 4884 a 'Giorgionesque furniture painting'. (2) There would be no point in recapitulating Richter's analysis here, but one element which he himself did not stress may be indicated. The curious and naive form of the sheep in no. 4884 recurs in an almost identical form in the background of the *Madonna and Child* at Detroit, which is a signed work of Previtali. (3) Gombrich's results were published by Clark (*loc. cit.*). There can be no reasonable doubt that the identification is correct—cf., in particular, Tebaldeo's mention of Damon's breaking his lyre before killing himself (*E tu, mia cetra, sopra questo sasso | spezata rimarai, poi chel tuo sono | mai non mosse colei per cui sol lasso*). In the third scene of no. 4884 the broken instrument is shown on the ground. See also the entry in the Supplement (1939) to the National Gallery catalogue of 1929. (4) Letter from G. M. Richter to the *Daily Telegraph*, 26th January, 1938. This provenance renders dubious a rumour current at the time of purchase that no. 4884 had come from Malta. There is, however, no confirmation of the Manfrin provenance.

## Giuseppe SALVIATI

### Active 1535, still alive 1573

His name was Giuseppe Porta. He took the name Salviati from his master, Francesco Salviati, who himself had adopted it from his patron, Cardinal Salviati. According to Vasari, he came from Castelnuovo della Garfagnana[1] (east of Carrara) and was taken in 1535, 'giovanetto', to Rome, where he became Francesco Salviati's pupil. Accompanying the latter on his visit to Venice, in 1539,[2] he was encouraged by his reception there and decided to settle. He returned to Rome in 1565[3] for a short time to finish, according to Vasari, a painting started by Francesco Salviati in the Sala Regia of the Vatican. The last evidence of his existence is in a letter of 27th November, 1573.[4] His book on the Ionic capital was published in 1552.

Ridolfi records that Salviati lived so long in Venice that he was considered Venetian,[5] and it is significant in this context that no. 3942 of this Gallery should have been attributed formerly to Zelotti. The frescoes on the exterior of Venetian buildings, on which Salviati's fame primarily rested during his life time, have not survived. The key works for reconstructing his *œuvre* are the three *tondi* in the *Libreria* at Venice, which are documented as of 1556–6,[6] together with a number of pictures mentioned by Vasari[7] as in Venetian churches and still identifiable. Though the precise chronology of these is difficult to establish, the general tendency, as was to be expected, is of a Central

Italian art gradually becoming more Venetian. In certain works Giuseppe Salviati approaches fairly close in style, at least superficially, to Paolo Veronese.

REFERENCES: (1) Vasari/Milanesi, VII, pp. 45–7. Ridolfi (Ridolfi/Hadeln, I, p. 241) also records a signature in the form 'Ioseph Garfagninus'. (2) The date is deduced from Vasari's statement (VII, 17–18) that Francesco Salviati went to Venice shortly before the marriage of Duke Cosimo, which occurred in June, 1539. (3) Date from payment published by R. Lanciani: *Storia degli Scavi di Roma*, III, p. 228. (4) Cf. B. Gonzati: *La Basilica di S. Antonio di Padova*, 1852–3, vol. I, p. CI, Doc. XCIII. (5) *Op. cit.*, p. 240. (6) Cf. Laura Pittoni: *La Libreria di S. Marco*, 1903, pp. 111 ff, and *Archivalische Beiträge aus dem Nachlass G. Ludwigs*, 1911, pp. 142–5. (7) *Loc. cit.*

### 3942  JUSTICE

Original canvas *c.* $34\frac{1}{4} \times 41\frac{1}{4}$ (0·87 × 1·048). Canvas subsequently added round the curved part brings the over-all measurements to $35\frac{1}{2} \times 49\frac{1}{4}$ (0·902 × 1·251). This later canvas includes the horns of the crescent moon and most of the left hand lion. As the crescent moon is not normally associated with Justice it may have been added for merely decorative reasons—to blend with the semi-circular shape of the painting. The additions seem to be crudely painted but at what date cannot be determined.

The paint on most of the original canvas is thin and there are numerous retouchings, particularly on the left.

In the Cavendish Bentinck sale, in 1891, as by Zelotti, but subsequently convincingly identified by J. P. Richter[1] with a picture from the *Zecca* (Mint) at Venice which had been sent to Milan in 1808— 'Porta, Giuseppe. La Giustizia sedente fra due Leoni . . . mezza figura in tela, e mezzo tondo, altezza 2–8. pied. venez. larghezza 3–7. pied. venez.'[2] (i.e. $36\frac{1}{4} \times 49''$).[3] Evidently the picture was among those looted at the time of the Napoleonic régime which were never restored to their place of origin. Various paintings 'in mezza luna' are specified by Boschini (1664) as in the *Zecca*, but not this one.[4] The coat of arms shown is that of a branch of the Contarini family.[5] The *Zecca* was rebuilt for the most part between 1537 and 1545.[6] The officials known as *Provveditori in Zecca* held office at this time for one year. A Tommaso Contarini was elected *Provveditore* in October, 1542 and a Paolo Contarini in October, 1558. These are presumably identical with the Tommaso and Paolo Contarini whose dates were 1506–60 and 1532–87 respectively, both of whom bore the form of the Contarini arms shown in no. 3942.[7] The latter could have been commissioned, therefore, either in 1542–3 or in 1558–9. Stylistically the attribution to Giuseppe Salviati is unexceptionable. The figure is comparable with the *Libreria* decorations of 1556–7 and with the S. Francesco della Vigna altarpiece of the Madonna and Child with SS. Bernard and Anthony Abbot (the latter vouched for as Giuseppe Salviati's by Vasari in effect, though his description of it is vague).

PROVENANCE: Almost certainly painted for the *Zecca* at Venice and sent to Milan with other Napoleonic loot in 1808 (see above). No. 759 in the G. A. F. Cavendish Bentinck sale, Christie's, 13th July, 1891,[8] where bought Richter for Mond. Ludwig Mond Bequest, 1924.

REPRODUCTION: *Illustrations, Italian Schools*, 1937, p. 289.

REFERENCES: (1) Mond catalogue, vol. 1 (1910), pp. 178–85. Berenson (*Lists*, 1957) maintains the Zelotti attribution. (2) Richter, *loc. cit.*, quotes the documents *in extenso*. The extract given here is from two of them. (3) Richter's calculation. (4) *Le Minere . . .*, pp. 84–6. (5) Rietstap (*Armorial Général*, vol. 1, 1884, p. 456) lists it as no. 4 of the various forms of the Contarini arms, of which the basic one was the diagonal blue and gold strips as shown in the second and third quarterings here. (6) G. Lorenzetti: *Venezia e il suo Estuario*, 1956, p. 155. (7) This information kindly supplied by Dr Ferruccio Zago of the Archivio di Stato, Venice. A third Contarini, Federico, held office for three months only in 1543. The pictures mentioned by Boschini (*loc. cit.*) as in the *Zecca* range from Bonifazio to Domenico Tintoretto and would therefore have been put there at different times. (8) 'Zelotti, 759 Justice, with a shield bearing the arms of the Contarini family.'

## ANDREA SCHIAVONE
### Active 1540(?), died 1563

His name was Andrea Meldolla, called 'Schiavone' because he came from Zara on the Dalmatian coast.[1] Vasari says he himself commissioned a picture from him in the year 1540. It is not known where Schiavone was in that year and Vasari does not specify where the incident occurred,[2] but as Vasari was not in Venice until the following year and as Schiavone spent at least the last part of his working career there it has sometimes been assumed that Vasari meant 1541.[3]

Facts concerning Schiavone and documented works by him are alike extremely scanty. His etching of the *Rape of Helen* is dated 1547 and a letter to him from Pietro Aretino dates from the following year, as does a reference in Paolo Pini's *Dialogo di Pittura*.[4] Between 1556 and 1560 he received payment for work at the *Libreria*, Venice[5] (an important commission; the painters involved are said to have been chosen by Titian). In 1563 he died.[6] Lomazzo says (apparently) that he was the pupil of Parmigianino.[7] Vasari's statement that the majority of Schiavone's work was done for private patrons explains the extreme difficulty of identifying it from the early sources. Works in the two Venetian churches specified by Vasari are still in position[8] but are clearly not characteristic. The key paintings are the three *tondi* for the *Libreria*,[9] and starting from them and the signed etchings it is possible to identify a considerable number of extant paintings in a style in which the blending of elements derived from Titian and from Parmigianino occasionally approaches close to Tintoretto.[10]

REFERENCES: (1) This is proved by his will in which he describes himself as 'Io Andrea pittor fiol del condam miser Simon Meldola' (on the back is written 'Ser Andreas Meldola de Hiadra pictor'). The documents in question were published by G. Ludwig in the Prussian *Jahrbuch*, vol. XXIV, 1903, *Beiheft*, p. 88. In a further document of 1563 the painter is described as

'Andreas Sclabonus dictus Medola' (document published by E. Harzen in *Deutsches Kunstblatt*, 1853, pp. 327–9, also (less well) by A. Venturi, *Storia* . . ., IX, IV, I, pp. 691–2). These documents contribute to disproving the theory now abandoned but widely held in the nineteenth century that Andrea Medola or Meldolla, whose signature appears on some etchings, was distinct from Andrea Schiavone (see particularly Harzen, *loc. cit.*). Further confusion came from Ridolfi's statement that Schiavone came from Sebenico, that he was born in 1522 and died at the age of 60. This led Moschini (*Guida per la Città di Venezia*, vol. II, 1815, p. 628) to identify him with a certain Andrea de Nicolò da Curzola, also called Andrea da Sebenico. To conform with Ridolfi, Moschini alleged that the latter artist died in 1582, but in fact he was still alive in 1591 (Hadeln's edition of Ridolfi, I, p. 247, note 1). (2) Contrary to what is stated by L. Fröhlich-Bum—article on Meldolla, Andrea in Thieme–Becker where she alleges that Vasari specified Venice as the locale. The relevant passage in Vasari is vol. VI of the Milanesi edition, pp. 596–7. (3) See W. Kallab: *Vasaristudien*, 1908, p. 69. Against this assumption it should be pointed out that Vasari does not give the date in figures but in words ('L'anno mille cinquecento e quaranta'). (4) April, 1548. Published in vol. IV, p. 222, of the Paris edition (1608) of Aretino's letters. Fröhlich-Bum (*loc. cit.*) refers to this letter as 'nicht datiert'. The reference to the 1548 edition of Pini's *Dialogo* is pp. 18v and 19r. (5) Documents in *Archivalische Beiträge aus dem Nachlass G. Ludwigs*, 1911, pp. 144–5. (6) Ludwig in the Prussian *Jahrbuch, loc. cit.* (7) Index of the 1584 edition of the *Trattato*: 'Andrea Schiauone, copioso pittore, discepolo del Mazzolino'. (8) Viz. S. Sebastiano and the Carmine. The *Presentation in the Temple* at the latter church, attributed to Schiavone by Vasari, has frequently been attributed to Tintoretto. (9) The documents published by Ludwig speak of 'tondi' without specifying which ones. This omission however was made good by Ridolfi—'i tre primi tondi verso il campanile'. (10) The fundamental modern work on Schiavone is an article by L. Fröhlich-Bum in the Vienna *Jahrbuch*, vol. 31, 1913–14, pp. 137 ff.

## Ascribed to ANDREA SCHIAVONE

### 1883 A MYTHOLOGICAL FIGURE

7⅜ (0·187) square.
Worn, and made up in places.

For provenance and commentary see under no. 1884.

ENGRAVING: The design (in a more upright format) engraved by Antonio Belemo as after Parmigianino. An etched version of this, by R. Ford, is dated 1822.

### 1884 TWO MYTHOLOGICAL FIGURES

7⅜ (0·187) square.
Worn, and made up in places.

Nos. 1883 and 1884 are characteristic of a type of mythological picture of which a fair number of examples survive. The attribution of such pictures to Schiavone is general, but cannot be shown to extend back to the sixteenth century. Some similar paintings at Vienna—such as the *Curius Dentatus*, *Scipio Africanus*, *Birth* and *Education of Jupiter*, *Apollo and Daphne* and *Apollo and Cupid*, are catalogued as the work of Schiavone in the Leopold William inventory of 1659 and engraved as his in the *Theatrum Pictorium* of the next year.[1] Some of these pictures are very close in style to nos. 1883 and 1884. Earlier still are some drawings in the Andrea Vendramin sketch-book of 1627 where a number of mythological scenes are marked as 'di Andrea Schiavon'.[2] Finally the female figure in no. 1884 repeats almost exactly the attitude of Psyche in the ex-Chatsworth *Marriage of Cupid and Psyche* which of all the Schiavone mythologies comes closest in style to the documented allegories of the *Libreria* ceiling (see biographical notes on Schiavone). The present writer has therefore no doubt that nos. 1883 and 1884 are either by or after Andrea Schiavone, though their present condition precludes a decision between these alternatives.

No precision seems justified as regards the subject of the two pictures. No. 1883 was tentatively identified in earlier editions of the National Gallery catalogue as 'Apollo killing the Python', and the male figure in no. 1884 characterised as 'old'.

PROVENANCE: With no. 1883 probably in the Algarotti collection in the eighteenth century.[3] In the Baron V. Denon collection, 1826.[4] Later Beaucousin collection, with which purchased, 1860.[5] Lent to Dublin in the same year and not catalogued until 1915.

REPRODUCTION: *Illustrations, Italian Schools*, 1937, p. 326.

REFERENCES: (1) The Hampton Court *Judgment of Midas*, whose pedigree may extend back to the Reynst collection in the seventeenth century, is probably in the same category (see D. Mahon: *Notes on the 'Dutch Gift' to Charles II*, part III, in *Burlington Magazine*, vol. 92, 1950, p. 13). (2) E.g. pages 57–60 of Borenius' edition of the book. See also his article in the *Burlington Magazine*, vol. 60 (1932), p. 140. (3) P. XXII of the catalogue—'Schiavone, André . . ., Apollon dans un bois qui tire de l'arc. Le pendant. Un vieillard qui tient une jeune fille embrassée. Sur bois, hauts 6½ pouc. l. 6½ pouc. (Ce dernier tableau a été mis en estampe par A. M. Zanetti)'. The present writer has not traced Zanetti's print. If the reference is indeed to nos. 1883 and 1884 the catalogue is in error in describing the pictures as on wood as they are not only now on canvas but appear always to have been. (4) Pp. 19–20 of the volume headed 'Tableaux' of the Denon catalogue—'Schiavone (André) . . . des sujets de la Fable . . . largeur des deux autres 7 pouces et demi.—H. 6 pouces et demi'. The fact that a third picture—of Diana and Callisto—is grouped with these two in the Denon catalogue and that a picture of the same subject and size (with a 'pendant' of Solomon and the Queen of Sheba) also figured in the Algarotti catalogue is some confirmation that the Denon pictures had been in the Algarotti collection. (5) As 'formerly in the collection of Baron Denon' (National Gallery Report, 1860).

# SEBASTIANO DEL PIOMBO
## Born *c.* 1485, died 1547

His name was Sebastiano Luciani,[1] called Sebastiano Veneziano in Rome, and Fra Sebastiano del Piombo after his appointment to that office in 1531. The date of his birth is deduced only from Vasari's statement that he died in 1547 at the age of 62, but as Vasari had known Sebastiano personally this is unlikely to be substantially inaccurate. Apprenticed first, according to Vasari, to the aged Giovanni Bellini in Venice, then to Giorgione, on whose style he modelled his own. The *Anonimo Morelliano* says that Sebastiano finished one of Giorgione's pictures.[2]

In 1511 Sebastiano went from Venice to Rome at the invitation of Agostino Chigi, for whom, on arrival, he painted some frescoes at the Villa Farnesina. With the exception of a visit to Venice in 1528–9 he remained in Rome for the rest of his life and gradually abandoned his Venetian style in favour of a Roman one.

Some time after his arrival in Rome Sebastiano made the acquaintance of Michelangelo who made considerable efforts to help him in his art. Vasari[3] implies that this was a deliberate move on Michelangelo's part; that he had resented the denigration of his powers as colourist which had been spread by the Raphael faction and that he sought to discredit the latter, without openly participating, by giving Sebastiano some of his drawings to paint from. Whatever Michelangelo's motives in fact may have been there is no reason to doubt Vasari's statement that he supplied a 'piccolo disegno' for the decoration of the Borgherini chapel in S. Pietro in Montorio,[4] while in the commission for an altarpiece for Cardinal Giulio de' Medici to send to his diocese at Narbonne the rivalry between Michelangelo and Sebastiano on the one hand and Raphael on the other became direct and undoubted. Michelangelo assisted Sebastiano with his altarpiece, while Raphael was engaged on an alternative for the same commission. Sebastiano's contribution is now no. 1 of this Gallery.

After Raphael's death in 1520 Sebastiano was regarded as the leading painter in Rome. But in 1531 he was appointed to the lucrative office of the *Piombo* (keeper of the papal seal) and thereafter painted very little. Vasari stresses that his greatest talent lay in the field of portraiture.

REFERENCES: (1) Cf. G. Ludwig in the Prussian *Jahrbuch*, XXIV (1903), *Beiheft*, p. 110. (2) Usually identified with the *Three Philosophers* at Vienna. (3) Ed. Milanesi, V, pp. 566–71. (4) For the most recent and informed discussion of this subject, cf. Johannes Wilde: *Italian Drawings in the Department of Prints and Drawings in the British Museum, Michelangelo and his Studio*, 1953, pp. 27–31. Cf. also reference no. 14 in the entry for no. 1 of this Gallery.

1  THE RAISING OF LAZARUS

Canvas, transferred from panel, *c.* 150 × 114 (3·81 × 2·89).[1]

Said to have been restored by Benjamin West 'whose hand is especially apparent in the right leg of Lazarus, above and below the knee'.[2] Considerably damaged by flaking and at the time of writing obscured by old varnish.

Signed, lower left: SEBASTIANVS. VENETVS. FACIE | BAT

The account given by S. John (chapter 11) is accurately followed, though with some compression. S. Mary Magdalene is shown in the foreground kneeling to Christ and some Jews in the background murmuring. The first episode took place slightly before the miracle, the second immediately after it. The figure behind Lazarus, being the only other prominent woman, must therefore be Martha. Round Christ are grouped the apostles.

Vasari gives the following account of the circumstances in which the picture was commissioned and executed[3]:

*Dopo, facendo Raffaello per lo cardinale de' Medici, per mandarla in Francia, quella tavola, che dopo la morte sua fu posta all' altare principale di San Piero a Montorio, dentrovi la Trasfigurazione di Cristo; Sebastiano in quel medesimo tempo fece anch' egli in un' altra tavola della medesima grandezza, quasi a concorrenza di Raffaello, un Lazzaro quatriduano, e la sua resurrezione; la quale fu contraffatta e dipinta con diligenza grandissima, sotto ordine e disegno in alcune parti di Michelagnolo. Le quali tavole finite, furono amendue publicamente in concistoro poste in paragone, e l'una e l'altra lodata infinitamente; e benchè le cose di Raffaello per l'estrema grazia e bellezza loro non avessero pari, furono nondimeno anche le fatiche di Sebastiano universalmente lodate da ognuno. L'una di queste mandò Giulio cardinale de' Medici in Francia a Nerbona al suo vescovado, e l'altra fu posta nella Cancelleria, dove stette infino a che fu portata a San Piero a Montorio, con l'ornamento che vi lavorò Giovan Barile. Mediante quest' opera avendo fatto gran servitù col cardinale, meritò Sebastiano d'esserne onoratamente rimunerato nel pontificato di quello* (i.e. Clement VII).

Contemporary documentation—mainly the letters of Leonardo Sellajo to Michelangelo—gives many details of the progress of the work. The chronicle of events is as follows.

The commission would have been given to Sebastiano not later than some time in the year 1516.[4] On 19th January, 1517 Leonardo Sellajo told Michelangelo that Sebastiano had had money to buy the wood, also that Raphael was trying hard to prevent his undertaking the job, not wishing to stand the comparison.[5] By 26th September, 1517 Sebastiano had already started painting and was reported to be making good progress.[6] In January, 1518 Michelangelo returned to Rome on a short visit, during which he saw the picture.[7] On 2nd July, 1518 Sebastiano explained the delay in continuing; he did not wish Raphael to see his work since he had still not started his own. Sebastiano reaffirmed on this occasion his eagerness to continue and said he thought he would bring no discredit on Michelangelo.[8] By 1st May, 1519 the picture is described as finished,[9] on 10th December it is said to be 'vernicato' and on 29th December, 1519 Sebastiano reported that it had been exhibited 'in pallazo' with success.[11] The picture was again exhibited from 12th April, 1520, together with the *Transfiguration* of Raphael, who had died six days before.[12]

Regarding the problem of the collaboration of Michelangelo and Sebastiano, the latter's statement, in his letter of 2nd July, 1518, that he thought he would not bring shame on Michelangelo is significant but not conclusive. Probably it is that to which it refers. But as Sebastiano was known to have been Michelangelo's protégé any work by the former would be liable to be interpreted as reflecting to some extent on the latter. As Vasari had known both Michelangelo and Sebastiano well there is no reason to doubt the substance of his statement that the picture was executed 'sotto ordine e disegno in alcune parti' of Michelangelo himself.[13] The words 'ordine' and 'disegno', however, may be interpreted in varying ways, while 'alcune parti' is an elastic term. The problem therefore concerns the extent and the nature of Michelangelo's participation.

The degree of supervision by him was certainly slight: he would only have seen the picture on one occasion during work on it—in January, 1518, some months after Sebastiano had begun painting. Evidence of his assistance centres round the existence of three preparatory studies (one at Bayonne, two in London—see DRAWINGS below) for the figure of Lazarus and for two of his attendants. These drawings had for some time been generally attributed to Sebastiano until Johannes Wilde reattributed them, with convincing arguments, to Michelangelo, as part of his fundamental reassessment of aspects of the latter's style as draughtsman.[14] He postulated the existence of drawings by Michelangelo, no longer surviving, for the figure of Christ in no. 1 (one of the British Museum drawings, no. 16, contains also sketches of a left foot corresponding with that of Christ in the painting) and pointed out that the Christ in no. 1 is an epitome of the God the Father in the first four scenes on the Sistine ceiling, just as the figure of Lazarus is a second Adam. As Sebastiano also used the Lazarus design in his fresco of the prophet on the left half of the arch above the Borgherini chapel in S. Pietro in Montorio, Rome—a work which dates from the autumn of 1516[15]—the drawings would date from before then. The figure of Lazarus in no. 1, and, to a lesser extent, the attendant behind him, corresponds closely with the later of the two British Museum drawings (no. 17), but the attendant on the spectator's right in the foreground of no. 1 is closer to the earlier one (no. 16). The other subordinate figures in no. 1, as well as the landscape, would have been of Sebastiano's invention, as is shown by the Frankfurt drawing for Martha (see DRAWINGS below).

VERSION: Narbonne, Cathedral (Basilisque Saint-Just), chapel of S. Martin. Copy of *c.* 1750 by Carle Vanloo, replacing the original.[16]

DRAWINGS: *A. Attributable to Sebastiano.*

Frankfurt, Staedel Institute. Study in black chalk for Martha (Berenson, *Florentine Drawings*, 1938, II, p. 320, no. 2479B). Corresponds closely with the painting except for the position of the fingers of both hands, which are less raised in the drawing. Those of her left hand show many *pentimenti* and seem to have caused difficulty to the artist. For this reason and on account of the figures behind Martha in the drawing (apparently some apostles who were later placed farther to the left) Berenson's suggestion that it is after the painting and not a study for it is unacceptable.

*B. Attributable to Michelangelo.*

1. Bayonne, Musée Bonnat, no. 682 (Berenson no. 2474C). Two studies in red chalk representing an early stage, one for Lazarus alone, the other accompanied by one of the attendants.

2. British Museum, London (Wilde no. 16, Berenson no. 2483). Red chalk study for Lazarus and two attendants. Also sketches of a left foot, perhaps Christ's.

3. British Museum, London (Wilde no. 17, Berenson no. 2484). Red chalk study for Lazarus and two attendants.

ENGRAVING: By R. De Launay (in reverse), in vol. 1 of the *Galerie du Palais Royal* (1786–1808).

PROVENANCE: Sent from Rome to Narbonne Cathedral some time after 12th April, 1520. Bought or begged by the Regent Orléans from the Chapter of Narbonne some time before his death in 1723 and perhaps after 1715.[17] Pages 448 ff of the 1727 catalogue (by Du Bois de Saint Gelais) of the Orléans collection in the Palais Royal. No. 241, Orléans sale, Lyceum, London, 26th December ff, 1798 where bought Angerstein.[18] No. 1 in the Angerstein catalogue of 1823. Bought with the Angerstein collection, 1824.

REPRODUCTION: *Illustrations, Italian Schools*, 1937, p. 281.

REFERENCES: (1) In the Orléans catalogue of 1727 stated to be on panel. Said to have been transferred to canvas by Hacquin in 1771 (so the National Gallery Board minutes of 27th June, 1880, though the Orléans catalogue of 1786–1808 speaks of it as still on wood: the initials E.B.H. and date 1771 are recorded as inscribed on the back). Though subsequent examination (at the Gallery in 1929) suggested that the picture may merely have been relined on that occasion and found no confirmation that the support had originally been wood there can be no doubt about this. Not only does the 1727 Orléans catalogue specify it: a contemporary document (19th January, 1517, see below) reports Sebastiano as having money to buy wood for the picture. (2) Note in the MS. catalogue in the Gallery archives. (3) Vasari/Milanesi, V, 570–1. Note 1 on page 571 summarises the events arising from the contemporary dispute concerning the valuation of no. 1. (4) Johannes Wilde: *Italian Drawings in the . . . British Museum, Michelangelo and his Studio*, 1953, p. 30. The deduction rests on the assumption that Michelangelo was sponsoring the undertaking and the fact that he left Rome on the 31st December, 1516 (Frey: *Die Briefe des Michelangelo Buonarroti*, 1907, p. 101). (5) Leonardo Sellajo to Michelangelo (Karl Frey: *Sammlung Ausgewählter Briefe an Michelagniolo Buonarroti*, 1899, pp. 58–9): *. . . vi schrissi, chome Bastiano aveva tolto a fare quella tauola, avuti danari per fare e [el] legname. Ora mi pare, che Rafaello metta sotosopra el mondo, perche lui nonlla faca per non uenire a paraghonj.* (6) Frey: *Sammlung . . .*, p. 79, Leonardo Sellajo to Michelangelo: *Bastiano . . . a chomincata la tavola e fa miracholj, dj modo che ora maj si puo dire, abbia vinto.* (7) For this visit of Michelangelo to Rome, cf. Frey: *Die Briefe . . .*, p. 102. For his having seen the progress of the work cf. Sebastiano's letter to him of 29th December, 1519 (Steinmann and Wittkower: *Michelangelo Bibliographie*, 1927, p. 441 and pl. V): *basta che hauete uisto l'opera principiata.* Though no date is specified for this event it could only have been in January, 1518. (8) Frey: *Briefe an . . .*, p. 104: *Credo, che Leonardo [Sellajo] ui habi dicto el tutto circha le cosse mie come vanno et circha la tardita del opera mia, non sia fornita. L'o intertenuta tanto, che non uoglio, che Rafaello ueda la mia, in sino lui non ha fornita la sua . . . et al presente non atendo ad altro, che ognj modo me la espediro prestissimo, adesso che sun fora de suspecione, et credo non ui faro uergogna. Ancora Rafaelo non ha principiata la sua.* A letter of 20th July, 1518 (Domenico da Terranuova to Michelangelo, Frey, *Briefe an . . .*, p. 106) reports an intrigue of Raphael's to try to get Sebastiano's picture framed not in Rome but in France. (9) Frey, *Briefe an . . .*, p. 143: *Bastiano vi si rachomanda e a finito, di modo che ognuno resta balordo, e fra pochi giorni andra alla chapella.* (10) Frey, *Briefe an . . .*, p. 148. (11) Letter given in Steinmann/Wittkower, *loc. cit.* An extract from the diary of Marcantonio Michiel (given in E. A. Cicogna: *Intorno la Vita e le Opere di Marcantonio Michiel*, 1861, p. 46) says: *Non tacerò questo che la terza domenica dell' Advento* [according to A. Cappelli: *Cronologia, Cronografia e Calendario Perpetuo*, 1930, p. 103, this fell on 11th December that year] *m. Sebastiano pictore messe una sua Tavola, ch'egli havea fatto per la Cattedrale di Narbona, et era la resuretione di Lazaro, la pose in palazo, così rechiedendo il Papa in l'antisala, ove la fu veduta con grande sua laude et di tutti, et del Papa.* (12) Milanesi: *Les*

*Correspondants de Michel-Ange*, I, 1890, p. 6. **(13)** Cf. also Lodovico Dolce: *Dialogo della Pittura* (1557; ed. of 1735, pp. 102 and 104) where he makes Pietro Aretino record Raphael's expressed pleasure in taking on the Michelangelo–Sebastiano partnership. **(14)** Professor Wilde's work is incorporated partly in his catalogue (1953) of the drawings of Michelangelo and his studio in the British Museum and partly in some lectures which he delivered at the University of London in May, 1947. The present writer was present on those occasions. At the time of writing the lectures have not been published, but the text of the portion relevant to no. 1 was most kindly supplied by Professor Wilde and is now in the Gallery archives. **(15)** Leonardo Sellajo to Michelangelo, 22nd November, 1516 (Frey, *Briefe an . . .*, p. 51): *. . . Bastiano a fatto que dua profeti.* **(16)** Pierre Caillard: *Narbonne et Ses Environs*, n.d., pp. 23–4. **(17)** Caillard, *loc. cit.* This says the picture was given to the Regent, but Milanesi (edition of Vasari, V, pp. 570–1, note 2) says 24,000 francs were paid for it. Mariette (*Abecedario*, IV, p. 403) says 'M. le duc d'Orléans, régent, eut fait l'acquisition du tableau . . .'. The second edition of de Piles' *Abrégé de la Vie des Peintres* was published in 1715 and speaks of the picture as still at Narbonne. It is described at Narbonne in the *Voyage de Bachaumont et de Chapelle* (1656) (ed. of 1878, Anger, at the end of a volume opening with the *Mémoire de Grammont*, p. 433). The date of the arrival of no. 1 at Narbonne and of its departure have not so far been revealed, despite some research carried out on behalf of the present writer in the *Archives du Département de l'Aude* by Monsieur V. Chomel, through the kind offices of Monsieur Robert Mesuret. Even the location of the picture within the Cathedral during the two centuries it was there is not entirely clear. Louis Narbonne (*La Cathédrale Saint-Just de Narbonne*, 1901, p. 97) says it was 'placé d'abord' in the absidal chapel of St Michel where it was replaced by a *Fall of the Rebel Angels* by Antoine Rivalz which is still there (the engraving of it, by Barthélemy Rivalz, is dated 1728— see R. Mesuret: *Les Miniaturistes du Capitole*, 1956, p. 77). The copy of no. 1 by Carle Vanloo which arrived at Narbonne some time after its departure was placed in the chapel of St Martin. It is sometimes said (e.g. by R. Mesuret in *Gazette des Beaux-Arts*, 1957, p. 330) that no. 1 was at one time over the high altar. The present writer could find no confirmation of this. According to Louis Narbonne (*op. cit.*, pp. 102–10) a new high altar had been consecrated in 1510, which was ornamented principally with sculpture. This was replaced by another high altar in 1694–5 which still exists. **(18)** Marked copy of the sale catalogue in the Gallery library. Angerstein's purchase also recorded in the Farington Diary, I, pp. 258–9. For the intermediary history of the Orléans collection see the entries for no. 270 Titian or 1326 Veronese. Sir Thomas Lawrence said he was 'instrumental in urging Mr Angerstein to buy' no. 1 (letter printed on pp. 416–18 of vol. II (1831) of D. E. Williams' *Life and Correspondence of . . . Lawrence*).

## 24  A LADY AS S. AGATHA

Painted area $36\frac{3}{8} \times 29\frac{5}{8}$ (0·924 × 0·753).

Flesh areas very worn, and made up in places. Green dress in good state.

Signed, bottom right:

.F. SEBASTIANV(S)
.VEN.
.FACIEBAT
.ROMÆ.

Inventory no. 60 (or perhaps 160) painted, bottom left.

The letter 'F' before the name 'Sebastianus' in the signature shows that the picture was painted in or after the year 1531, when Sebastiano was appointed to the office of the *Piombo* which carried the style 'Frate'. After this time he painted very little. The Hermitage *Christ Bearing the Cross* also has this form of signature, and both pictures would be among Sebastiano's latest works. The martyr's palm, the halo, the pincers and the breasts in the dish identify the character portrayed by the sitter as S. Agatha. This was presumably the lady's christian name (cf. entry for no. 4256, Lotto).

PROVENANCE: No. 56 ('St Appolonia'), B.I., 1828 (lent Holwell Carr), where stated to be 'from the Borghese collection'. The Rev. W. Holwell Carr Bequest, 1831.[1]

REPRODUCTION: *Illustrations, Italian Schools*, 1937, p. 282.

REFERENCES: (1) In a MS. list, in the Gallery archives, of the Holwell Carr pictures called (also as ex-Borghese) 'Giulia Gonzaga'—which was a portrait mentioned by Vasari—under which name it got into the National Gallery catalogues. In view of the attributes of S. Agatha this is most improbable. The Borghese inventories have not, as yet, yielded confirmation of a Borghese provenance.

1450  MADONNA AND CHILD WITH SS. JOSEPH AND JOHN THE BAPTIST AND A DONOR

Panel, $38\frac{1}{2} \times 42$ (0·978 × 1·067).

Some losses of paint, particularly in the Child's forehead, left cheek and right leg, in the donor's robes and in the area of background round S. Joseph's head. Paint in other areas reasonably well preserved. Cleaned 1958.

Berenson,[1] seeing a likeness between the donor in no. 1450 and a study at Chatsworth for one of the apostles in Sebastiano's fresco of the Transfiguration in the Borgherini chapel of S. Pietro in Montorio, Rome, postulated that both represent Pierfrancesco Borgherini. Though some degree of resemblance between the two faces seems admissible to the present writer it is difficult to decide such matters, and in any case no authenticated portrait of Pierfrancesco is known. A further suggestion by Berenson is equally inconclusive. Leonardo Sellajo, in a letter to Michelangelo of 1st March, 1517, quoted Sebastiano as saying that with the help of a cartoon by Michelangelo he would be able to paint a picture which should satisfy Pierfrancesco Borgherini.[2] Berenson connected no. 1450 with this incident. Though this period would be acceptable on stylistic grounds as an approximate date of origin for no. 1450 the episode adumbrated in the letter in question seems too hypothetical for further consideration here.[3] Even the assumption inherent in Berenson's theory—that no. 1450 is based on a cartoon, or at least a design, by Michelangelo—cannot be demonstrated (this hypothesis had been advanced long before—see Reference 10). A quick sketch, attributed to Sebastiano, but possibly by Michelangelo, has

6—V.S.C.

been connected with no. 1450, but with insufficient reason, in the present writer's view (see DRAWING below). Though strong influence of Michelangelo has always, and justifiably, been recognised in no. 1450 there is no precise prototype among his works.[4]

DRAWING: Berenson no. 2489 (successively Heseltine and Koenigs collections). Study in red chalk for a Madonna and Child. Berenson as Sebastiano. Before that as Michelangelo.[5] Connected by D'Achiardi,[6] Fischel[7] and Pallucchini[8] with no. 1450, but the connection seems inconclusive. One of the chief characteristics of no. 1450—the sheltering gesture of the Madonna's right arm—is lacking in the drawing, where her right arm is raised, as in Sebastiano's *Madonna del Velo* (Naples). Though the attitude of the Child in the drawing seems similar to no. 1450 it is not certain whether the former incorporates a notable peculiarity of the latter—the fact that the Child straddles His mother's knee (this motive also occurs, though applied differently, in Michelangelo's *Medici Madonna*). No sign in the drawing of SS. John or Joseph.

PROVENANCE: Probably 'una tavola della B. Vergine col Bambino, ed un Santo, di Fra Sebastiano del Piombo' described by C. G. Ratti (*Instruzione di Quanto può vedersi . . . in Genova*, 1780, p. 265) as in 'Palazzo pur Brignole abitato dal Sig. Carlo Cambiaso'. Purchased, 1807–8, 'du sénateur Cambiaso à Gênes' by J. B. P. Le Brun.[9] In the possession of Sir Thomas Baring, 2nd Bart. (1772–1848), by 1816, when exh. by him, B.I., no. 7, 'from the Collection of the Senateur Cambiaso, at Genoa'.[10] Exh. B.I., 1840, no. 63, lent Baring, by whom sold to William Coningham, 1843.[11] No. 61 in the latter's sale, Christie's, 9th June, 1849, where bought Thomas Baring[12] (grandson of the 2nd baronet: in 1866 he succeeded his father, who had been created Baron Northbrook in the same year, and was himself created Earl of Northbrook in 1876). Exh. Manchester, 1857 (no. 213 in the provisional catalogue, no. 161 in the definitive catalogue, lent T. Baring), R.A., 1870 (130) and 1894 (113) lent by the Earl of Northbrook,[13] from whom purchased, 1895.

REPRODUCTION: *Illustrations, Italian Schools*, 1937, p. 280.

REFERENCES: (1) *Florentine Drawings . . .*, 1938, II, pp. 319–20. (2) Letter printed by Karl Frey: *Sammlung Ausgewählter Briefe an Michelagniolo Buonarroti*, 1899, p. 63. (3) In particular, the wording of the letter of 1st March, 1517, is too vague to presuppose a connection, as postulated by D'Achiardi (*Sebastiano del Piombo*, 1908, pp. 149–50, note 1) with a letter of 22nd April, 1525, in which Sebastiano tells Michelangelo to tell apparently Pierfrancesco that his picture will be ready in two days (Milanesi: *Les Correspondants de Michel-Ange*, 1890, p. 32). (4) The general inspiration is undoubtedly the Sistine ceiling. The attitude of the Child in no. 1450 is reminiscent of that of the *putto* supporting the book for Daniel. The latter's projecting left arm and hand has itself something in common with the Madonna's right in no. 1450. (5) Cf., e.g. *Original Drawings by Old Masters of the Italian School* (Heseltine collection), privately printed, 1913, no. 6. (6) *Sebastiano del Piombo*, 1908, p. 149, note 1. (7) In *Old Master Drawings*, XIV (1939–40), p. 31. The author says Berenson is wrong in giving an Oppenheimer provenance for the drawing. (8) *Sebastian Viniziano*, 1944, p. 52. (9) See his *Recueil de Gravures . . .*, 1809, pp. 37–9. Outline engraving of no. 1450 as his no. 21. (10) The exh. cat. says 'Holy Family with St Francis (sic), composition and drawing, Michael Angelo . . .' W. Buchanan (*Memoirs of Painting . . .*, II, 1824, pp. 251–3) says that the finest of the Le Brun pictures, including no. 1450, were purchased by Baring. (11) *A Descriptive Catalogue of the Collection of . . . the Earl of Northbrook*, 1889, p. 151. (12) Marked copy of the sale catalogue in the Gallery library. (13) In the 1870 exh. cat. the owner's name is given as 'Thomas Baring, Esq., M.P.', but he had been Baron Northbrook since 1866.

2493 THE DAUGHTER OF HERODIAS

Panel, $21\frac{5}{8} \times 17\frac{1}{2}$ (0·55 × 0·445).
Fairly extensive damage, probably due to past flaking. Obvious retouching in the shadows of the chin and neck, also in the arm and hand, and in the sky. The back line of the bodice is suspect. Dated, bottom right; 1510.

One of the key works of Sebastiano's early (Venetian) period. Very close in style to a *Magdalen* of almost the same dimensions (Washington, Kress collection, ex-Cook collection) and to the high altarpiece of the church of S. Giovanni Crisostomo, Venice. The latter work is described by Vasari (1568)[1] as Sebastiano's and is datable 1510–11.[2]

PROVENANCE: In the possession of George Salting by October, 1900,[3] by whom lent 1902–10. Salting Bequest, 1910.

REPRODUCTION: *Illustrations, Italian Schools*, 1937, p. 282.

REFERENCES: (1) In his first edition (1550) Vasari had attributed the picture to Giorgione. The reference to it in the second edition corrects his earlier statement and tries to excuse it. (2) For the documents see Rodolfo Gallo in *Arte Veneta*, 1953, p. 152. (3) MS. list, in the Gallery archives, of that date, of Salting's pictures, in which it figures.

## Jacopo TINTORETTO
## 1518–1594

The date of his birth is deduced from the certificate of his death in May, 1594, which gives his age as 75 years and 8 months.[1] The family name was Robusti. Jacopo took the nickname, Tintoretto, from his father's profession of dyer (*tintore*).

Tintoretto's apprenticeship has been much disputed. Ridolfi speaks of an apprenticeship of ten days under Titian.[2] Bonifazio, Schiavone and Bordon have also been suggested as his master. Tintoretto's contemporary, Raffaello Borghini, does not discuss the question of apprenticeship, but apparently states (his account is a little confused) that he modelled his draughtsmanship principally on Michelangelo's (some of whose sculptures he certainly knew in casts or models) and his colouring on Titian's,[3] and this view seems justified.[4] The only occasion when Tintoretto is recorded as having left Venice was in 1580 when he was at Mantua. There is no documentary evidence either for or against his having visited Rome, and such a visit has often been postulated.[5]

There is great difficulty in identifying Tintoretto's early work. The earliest surviving dated picture indisputably his work is the *Last Supper* of 1547 at S. Marcuola, Venice. A picture of Apollo and Marsyas (Wadsworth Atheneum, Hartford, ex-Bromley-Davenport) is generally identified with one of a pair painted for Pietro Aretino in 1545, and a large *Sacra Conversazione*, signed 'IACHOBUS' and dated 1540 is an acceptable attribution.[6] From 1547 on there are a considerable number of datable works.

Though the greater part of Tintoretto's vast output consisted of religious paintings, many portraits and a number of mythologies, allegories and histories also survive. He was evidently able and willing to modify his style considerably in accordance with the nature of the commission, and Ridolfi and Boschini report instances of deliberate imitation by Tintoretto of the styles of Schiavone[7] and of Veronese.[8] Ridolfi[9] and Boschini[10] also give some details of his technical procedure, particularly in respect of his use of small, draped models. Tintoretto's son, Domenico, assisted him in his later works and carried on the studio after his death. Another son, Marco, and a daughter, Marietta, were also painters.

REFERENCES: (1) F. Galanti: *Il Tintoretto* (discorso letto il 8 agosto, 1875 nella R. Accademia in Venezia), 1876, pp. 76 f. (2) Ridolfi/Hadeln, II, p. 13. (3) Raffaello Borghini: *Il Riposo* . . ., 1584, p. 551. (4) It may have been this statement, together with Paolo Pini's hypothesis (not specifically referring to Tintoretto) of the perfection to be expected from a combination of Michelangelo's draughtsmanship and Titian's colouring (*Dialogo della Pittura*, 1548, p. 24) which was the basis of Ridolfi's famous story of Tintoretto's writing on the wall of his studio 'il disegno di Michel Angelo e'l colorito di Titiano'. (5) For this, see in particular Simon H. Levie: *Daniele da Volterra e Tintoretto* in *Arte Veneta*, 1953, pp, 168–70. (6) Formerly with Leger, London. Reproduced and discussed by R. Pallucchini, *La Giovinezza del Tintoretto*, 1950, p. 74. (7) Marco Boschini, *Le Ricche Minere* . . ., 1674, Sestier di Canareggio, pp. 11–12. (8) Ridolfi, *op. cit.*, p. 38. (9) Ridolfi, *op. cit.*, p. 15. (10) Boschini, *op. cit.*, preface ('Breve Instruzione').

## 16 S. GEORGE AND THE DRAGON

62 × 39½ (1·575 × 1·003).

The lower half of the picture, though somewhat worn and retouched, is in generally good condition. The upper half is more thinly painted and more worn and retouched. Of several *pentimenti* mention may be made of the flap (painted on top of the grass) half way along the upper outline of the princess' fluttering cloak.

Marks at the top (more clearly visible in infra-red photographs than to the naked eye) suggest that the picture was formerly framed with an arched top. That this was the original state is confirmed by the fact that the paint in the spandrels, on a dark ground, is different from, and therefore later than, the remaining paint, which is on a light ground. The canvas in the spandrels is, however, continuous.

The historical S. George suffered martyrdom under the Emperor Diocletian but there is no surviving authority earlier than the twelfth century for his fight with the dragon,[1] which was subsequently popularised by inclusion in the Golden Legend.

Several features of the iconography of no. 16 are unusual. In Renaissance representations of S. George and the dragon the princess is most usually shown either on her knees in prayer or else running away. In the present picture Tintoretto has combined the two actions: the princess has suddenly dropped to her knees during flight. The form of the dragon's victim and the figure in the clouds are still more unusual in representations of this subject. According to the Golden Legend, the dragon ate a daily diet of human victims whose mangled limbs are frequently included, but hardly ever their intact corpses (though another instance is the Signorelli in the Rijksmuseum, Amsterdam). As to the celestial personage, no such feature is normal in Renaissance representations of S. George and the dragon, though an angel is shown in a picture by Sodoma (Washington, Kress collection, ex-Cook collection).[2] The figure in no. 16 has no wings and seems intended as God the Father, while the attitude of the dragon's victim seems intended as an allusion to the crucified Christ. The relatively small scale of the picture, together with its type, would suggest that it was commissioned by a private patron and he, in consequence, may be presumed to have specified some personal interpretation of the S. George legend.[3]

The attribution of no. 16 to Tintoretto cannot be questioned, but the unusualness of its type and scale in his *œuvre* is, again, an obstacle in the way of precise dating. It has been considered an early work,[4] but the type of landscape shown does not bear this out.

In the landscape background of the *Adam and Eve* (Venice, Accademia, from the Scuola della Trinità), which is datable 1550–3,[5] there is an early attempt at the concealed or 'magical' lighting which reached an extreme form in the SS. Mary of Egypt and Mary Magdalene of the mid-1580's (Scuola di S. Rocco). The lighting of the trunks of the three trees in the middle distance in no. 16 and of the trunk and branches of the windswept tree to the spectator's right of them is much more advanced than in the *Adam and Eve*. As it occurs in a comparable form in the great *Crucifixion* of S. Rocco, which is dated 1565, the present writer would tend to favour a dating for no. 16 not earlier than the 1560's.

DRAWING: Paris, Louvre (no. 5382). Charcoal drawing (Tietze: *Venetian Drawings*, 1738). Study (without the drapery) for the corpse, centre. The figure's left hand, roughly indicated, is truncated by the edge of the sheet. A more carefully drawn detail (corresponding with the form as shown in no. 16) is sketched underneath.[6]

VERSION: A picture of this subject at Leningrad (no. 134 in the Hermitage catalogue of 1891) has been attributed to Tintoretto but seems (on photographic evidence only) no more than a pastiche of various Tintorettesque elements. The upright format, the city walls and to some extent the general disposition seem to derive from no. 16, but the mangled body of the dragon's victim is based on that of the slave in the *Miracle of St Mark*.

PROVENANCE: In the possession of the Rev. W. Holwell Carr in 1821, when exhibited by him at the British Institution (46). Before that, said to have belonged to 'R. Westall'—presumably Richard Westall, R.A.[7] On account of the correspondence of the dimensions, almost certainly identical with a picture sold at Prestage's, London, 2nd February, 1764,[8] where stated to have come from 'the Cornaro Family', and identified with one mentioned by Ridolfi (1648) in the possession of 'Signor Pietro Corraro Senatore'[9] and by Boschini (1660) as in 'Casa Corer'.[10] Corraro and Correr are variants of the same name, but Cornaro is distinct, and assuming that the references are to the same picture it could be deduced either that it passed from one family to another or that the names were confused. Holwell Carr bequest, 1831.

REPRODUCTION: *Illustrations, Italian Schools*, 1937, p. 350.

REFERENCES: (1) Von Taube von der Issen: *Die Darstellung des Heiligen Georg in der italienischen Kunst*, 1910, p. 4. (2) Von Taube von der Issen, *op. cit.*, p. 57, also cites an instance in an Avignon fresco. (3) What may well have been no. 16 is first recorded in the possession of Pietro Corraro in the seventeenth century (see PROVENANCE). According to Litta, however, no member of the Corraro family during Tintoretto's working career bore the christian name of Giorgio. (4) E.g. Berenson (*Lists*, 1936) 'giovanile', von der Bercken (1942) 'um 1548–58', Tietze (1948) 'from the 1550's'. (5) Gustav Ludwig in *Italienische Forschungen*, vol. IV (1911), pp. 136 ff. (6) The drawing was roughly (and wrongly) labelled 'study for a Prometheus' by A. L. Mayer (*Burlington Magazine*, vol. XLIII, 1923, p. 34). (7) *Essays and Criticisms by Thomas Griffiths Wainewright . . . collected . . . by W. Carew Hazlitt*, London, 1880, p. 179: 'formerly in the hands of R. Westall, Esq., where I once saw it' (this reference kindly communicated by Frank Simpson). In the MS. list in the Gallery archives of the Holwell Carr pictures no. 16 is one of the very few without indication of previous ownership. (8) Lot 143 in the general catalogue, lot 31 in the catalogue of the first day's sale: 'St George killing the dragon, a fine picture particularly mentioned by Boschini, p. 329, and by Ridolfi, vol. 2, p. 45, by Giacomo Tintoretto . . . 5,3 × 3,3'. (9) Ridolfi/Hadeln, II, p. 54: 'Trouasi il Signor Pietro Corraro Senatore vn gratiosissimo pensiero di San Giorgio, che vccide il Drago, con la figliuola del Rè, che impaurita sen fugge, e vi appaiono alcuni corpi de' morti di rarissima forma.' It may be noted that in no. 16 there is only *one* corpse, not several, and that although the princess appears to be running away she is in fact on her knees. These discrepancies need not rule out the identification, however. (10) *La Carta del Navegar Pitoresco*, p. 329: '. . . L'è vn San Zorzi a caualo brauo, e forte, | che de ficon và con la lanza in resta, | E amazza el Drago, e la Rezina resta | Libera dal spauento, e da la morte. | Questo a Casa Corer fè corer tuti.' Boschini specifies that this picture is on a relatively small scale.

1130   CHRIST WASHING HIS DISCIPLES' FEET

79 × 160¾ (2·006 × 4·083).

Considerably damaged. The area where the local damage is most extensive is in the figure on the left (with the torch), the lower part of whose body seems to fade out. Before the restoration of 1956 this area was covered with a small table of later date and the floor entirely over-painted in a biscuit colour with the lines of the tiles 'corrected' so as to be parallel with the lower edge of the picture. The cat and the projecting flap of the skirt of the apostle on the right (wiping his feet) were originally painted on top of the floor, no doubt as an afterthought, and soon wore thin. Only the base and some of the outline of the cat and a little of the outline of this flap are original paint. The figure of Christ is fairly well preserved and is the least damaged major portion of the picture. Cleaned, 1956.

A comparable arrangement of the floor tiles to that revealed by the restoration of 1956 also occurs in Tintoretto's *Last Supper* at S. Polo, Venice, where the horizontals meet the lower edge of the picture at a still sharper angle. It is probable that Tintoretto was trying, in this respect, to follow the precepts of Serlio who gives a scientific demonstration of this principle (*Il Secondo Libro di Prospettiva*, 1618 ed., pp. 42V, 43R). Tintoretto was certainly acquainted with this book, since the architectural background of the Escorial *Foot-washing* is a fairly literal reproduction of Serlio's illustration 'Della Scena Tragica'.

Almost certainly from the church of SS. Gervasio e Protasio (S. Trovaso), Venice. Since its history before the year 1882 is unknown this point cannot be established with complete certainty, but the strong circumstantial evidence is as follows:

1. In the *Riposo* Borghini mentions a *Foot-washing* and a *Last Supper* by Tintoretto in the Capella del Sacramento in the church of S. Trovaso.[1] As the *Riposo* was published within Tintoretto's lifetime (1584) this is good evidence of authenticity.

2. In the Capella del Sacramento at S. Trovaso there is now to be seen (on the right) a *Last Supper*, clearly by Tintoretto, and (on the left) a *Foot-washing*, clearly not by him. The two pictures line the lateral walls of the chapel and on account of their size and shape were obviously designed for it. They are of the same size as each other and also (with the exception of a narrow strip along the top) as no. 1130.[2] Since the latter is acceptable stylistically as Tintoretto's and corresponds in design (as well as in size) with the picture now in S. Trovaso it may be concluded that that picture is a copy painted to replace it.

The church of S. Trovaso was burnt down in September, 1583 and rebuilt.[3] But the Capella del Sacramento which adjoins the extremity of the left transept is clearly in an earlier style of architecture than the body of the existing church. The distinctive architectural style of the chapel includes both sides of the arch separating it from the transept. On the base of the left pilaster of this arch, on the side nearest the transept, is inscribed the date, MDLVI.[4] It may therefore be deduced that the structure of the chapel escaped the fire and its date would give some indication of that of the paintings. Though no greater precision is possible in this matter it may be pointed out that a date not long after 1556 would be stylistically acceptable for no. 1130, the handling of which is hardly more summary than that of the *Miracle of the Paralytic* (church of S. Rocco, Venice) which is documented as dating from 1559.

The date when no. 1130 would have left S. Trovaso is a more difficult problem. No reliance can be placed on the wording of descriptions of the two paintings in the guide books since the authors in many cases reproduced information derived from earlier writers years after it was out of date and in any case could not be relied on to distinguish an original Tintoretto from an old copy.[5] Even the engraving published in Louisa's *Il Gran Teatro delle Pitture e Prospettive di Venezia* (1720) could have been taken from the copy.[6] For this reason the attitude of so thorough a connoisseur of Tintoretto as Ridolfi is the more important. In Venetian churches where there are two paintings by Tintoretto which are obviously a pair he is normally at pains to describe both—e.g. S. Marcuola (*Foot-washing* and *Last Supper*), S. Giorgio Maggiore

(*Last Supper* and *Manna*), Madonna dell' Orto (*Golden Calf* and *Last Judgement*) or S. Cassiano (*Crucifixion* and *Christ in Limbo*). But at S. Trovaso, while describing the *Last Supper* in some detail, he makes no mention of a *Foot-washing*.[7] If this was not an oversight on his part it would follow either that no *Foot-washing* was there when he wrote or else that there was one which he did not consider to be by Tintoretto. In either case there would thus be a possibility that no. 1130 was no longer in S. Trovaso in the mid-seventeenth century. The further possibility that it was removed because of damage sustained in the fire of 1583 is, however, apparently excluded by microscopic examination of the paint.[8]

In the design of no. 1130 may be traced the germ of that of one of Tintoretto's latest works—the *Last Supper* of S. Giorgio Maggiore.

ENGRAVING: By Andrea Zucchi in Louisa's *Il Gran Teatro delle Pitture e Prospettive di Venezia* (1720), no. 45 (see above).

VERSIONS: Venice, S. Trovaso. Copy replacing no. 1130. The other pictures of this subject by Tintoretto are of different designs, viz.: 1. Escorial (almost certainly from S. Marcuola and Charles I's collection). A large-scale copy of this was lot 43 in the Delahante sale (Phillips, 2nd June, 1814). It was unsold on that occasion but bought on the next day by Sir Matthew White Ridley, who presented it to St Nicholas church, Newcastle-upon-Tyne, in 1815, where it still is.[9] A variant of the Escorial picture was in the collection of Lord Farnham, Cavan, Ireland (reproduced in von der Bercken: *Tintoretto*, 1942, pl. 28).[10] 2. Wilton, since at least 1731.[11] 3. Venice, S. Moisé. 4. Venice, S. Stefano. A picture in the Sir Joshua Reynold's sale, 1795 (4th day, lot 90) claimed to be from 'St Emacora' (i.e. S. Marcuola), but need not have been of the same design.

PROVENANCE: From Hamilton Palace. No. 353 at the sale, 24th June, 1882, where purchased, Clarke Fund (see also above).

REPRODUCTION: *Illustrations, Italian Schools*, 1937, p. 349.

REFERENCES: (1) P. 554 (à propos Tintoretto): *In San Geruaso, e Protaso . . . nella Cappella del Sacrameto . . . vi sono due quadri, nell' uno quando Christo laua i piedi agli Apostoli, e nell' altro quando cena con quelli.* (2) The present writer measured the length of the S. Trovaso *Foot-washing* copy and made it 160″ (4·064)—which is virtually the same as no. 1130. He was unable to measure its height, but it is clearly slightly greater than in the case of no. 1130, having an extra strip along the top. The S. Trovaso *Last Supper* is given in the catalogue of the Tintoretto exhibition (Venice, 1937, no. 27) as 2·21 × 4·13. (3) Giulio Lorenzetti: *Venezia* (1926, p. 515). (4) Lorenzetti, *op. cit.*, p. 516 (1956 ed., p. 540), gives the date of the chapel as 1566. This is presumably a misprint, but it was followed by Mayer (*Burlington Magazine*, December, 1936, p. 282). (5) Even Lorenzetti (*op. cit.*, p. 516) does not make the distinction entirely clear. (6) In Louisa's engraving (which is truncated on the left) the figure on the right is shown wearing a kind of turban and his right sleeve falls to the wrist without much interruption in the folds. In both these respects the engraving is nearer to the copy now in S. Trovaso than to no. 1130. The most striking difference between the latter and the engraving is the figure in the left background—in the engraving it is a man (presumably Judas) going out, in no. 1130 a woman coming in. The latter is original paint and painted on the same canvas as the rest of the picture (contrary to what is stated by Mayer, *loc. cit.*). This area of the copy now in S. Trovaso is entirely dark and that picture also appears to contain no cat. (7) Ridolfi/Hadeln, II, p. 39. (8) An examination of samples of paint disclosed undiscoloured madder and copper resinate (both of which brown readily on exposure to heat) and also revealed no blistering, bubbling or charring of the paint. See the National Gallery Report, July, 1956–June, 1958. (9) The copy in the National Gallery library of the Delahante sale catalogue belonged to Lord Colborne (brother of Sir Matthew White Ridley) who annotated it with this information regarding the sale. The date of presentation to St Nicholas, Newcastle, is from the church authorities there. A photograph of the Newcastle picture is in the Gallery archives. (10) Misprinted by von der Bercken, *op. cit.*, p. 109, as 'Lord Lee of Farnham' and by Tietze (*Tintoretto*, 1948, p. 350) as 'Lord Lee of Fareham'. (11) For the Wilton picture see Tancred Borenius, *Burlington Magazine*, vol. 61 (1932), p. 103.

## 1313  THE ORIGIN OF THE MILKY WAY

$58\frac{1}{4} \times 65$ (1·48 × 1·65).

A good deal of (fairly obvious) retouching in the sky and clouds and in the flesh of Juno, Jupiter, the infant Hercules and the two *putti* on the left. The coloured draperies, eagle, peacocks and *putto* bottom right are in fairly good state.

A horizontal line of repaint (clearer in X-ray and infra-red photographs than to the naked eye) covering losses of original paint some seven or eight inches above the base (cutting across Juno's right ankle and the nose of the *putto* in the bottom left hand corner) suggests that the picture has at one time been folded at this point and pressed down. This is the only indication now visible on the picture that a sizeable piece may have been cut from the base,[1] since if a picture is folded horizontally in one place only it would be natural to do so not towards the base but across the centre (as in fact was done when Titian's *Venus and Adonis*, now in the Prado, was sent to Philip II in London—see Crowe and Cavalcaselle: *Titian*, II, 1881, pp. 238 and 509). In point of fact the existing line of repaint corresponds approximately with the centre of the height of the composition as shown in a drawing at Venice inscribed 'Do. Tintoretto' (see DRAWINGS below) of which the upper part reproduces the design of no. 1313 but which also includes a recumbent figure of a woman and flowers at the base.

The full composition is also reproduced in a less accurate sketch copy by Jacob Hoefnagel (Berlin) and in a painted copy (private collection, Munich, in 1929). The fact that Jacob Hoefnagel was court painter to the Emperor Rudolph II from 1602 suggested to Erna Mandowsky[2] that his drawing might be copied from a picture thus described in the 1621 inventory of the Emperor's collection at Prague: '295. Wie die Natur in den Wolken getragen wirdt, undter Ir das fruchtbare Erdtreich, ein schön Stück, von Tentoret'[3] and that this in its turn could be identified with one of the four pictures which Ridolfi specified as painted by Tintoretto for Rudolph II: 'Giove . . . che arreca al seno di Giunone Bacco fanciullo . . .'.[4] The wording of the entry in the 1621 inventory is repeated (with the omission of the artist's name) in a later inventory (after 15th February, 1637) of the Prague pictures,[5] but the picture in question had either left Prague before 1648, when the bulk of the pictures were looted by the Swedish troops, or else was not included in the booty, since it does not seem to figure in the summary inventory (1652) of Queen Christina's collection and is certainly not in the more detailed inventories of 1689 and 1721.

As the pedigree of no. 1313 cannot be traced farther back than the collection of the Marquis de Seignelay, who died in 1690, it cannot be established with certainty that it is identical with the picture in the Prague inventories or that the latter was identical with the one described by Ridolfi. Nevertheless the various factors already mentioned seem to the present writer to render both assumptions probable. No. 1313 is comparable in design and type with Tintoretto's paintings in the *Anticollegio* of the Doge's Palace, dating from shortly before 1578. Juno's hair-style is also consonant with Tintoretto's practice at that time.[6] Rudolph became Emperor in 1576.

Entitled 'L'Alaitement d'Hercule' in the Orléans collection and 'Juno and the Infant Hercules; or, The Origin of the Milky Way' when exhibited at Manchester in 1857. Hyginus (*Poeticon Astronomicon* II, XLIII) quotes various legends accounting for the Milky Way. The probable source for no. 1313, first indicated by Mandowsky (*loc. cit.*), was the *Geoponica*, a Byzantine botanical text-book of which Italian translations had been published at Venice in 1542 and 1549. In chapter XX of book XI of this work (*Historia del Giglio*) it is related how Jupiter, wishing to immortalise the infant Hercules (whose mother was the mortal, Alcmene) held him to the breasts of the sleeping Juno. The milk continued to flow after the child, sated, had stopped drinking, the milk which spilt upwards becoming the Milky Way, the downward stream giving birth to lilies. The latter are clearly visible in the Venice and Berlin drawings and in the painted copy, the recumbent figure next them being identified by Mandowsky with the Earth. Mandowsky also indicated Tintoretto's patron, the learned doctor, Tommaso Rangoni, as the painter's probable adviser for the story, since it is depicted, in a simplified form, on the reverse of his medal.[7] Of the objects held by the *putti* the bow, arrows and torch are common erotic symbols. The net is used by Ripa (*Iconologia*, 1645, pp. 281 and 287) in connection with Deceit which would also fit the present context as regards Jupiter's intention (Juno would not have consented had she been awake), though it is apparent that Hercules' energy has had the effect of awakening his unwitting foster-mother.

A comparable picture by Rubens (Prado, no. 1668) is from a different version of the legend. There is only one stream of milk, and Juno is fully awake, and directing it towards the child. The latter is more probably the infant Mercury.

VERSION: Small painted copy (29¼ × 21″), already mentioned, with the addition of recumbent female figure and flowers at the base, with Ludwig F. Fuchs, Munich, 1929 (photograph in the Gallery archives).

DRAWINGS: Sketch copies, already discussed, in the Accademia, Venice, and Kupferstichkabinett, Berlin. The Venice drawing was first published (by Loeser, *Rassegna d'Arte*, III, p. 177) as Domenico Tintoretto and as a preliminary study for no. 1313. The attribution of no. 1313 to Domenico need not be considered seriously while even the signature ('Do. Tintoretto') on the drawing is doubted by Tietze and Tietze-Conrat (*Drawings of the Venetian Painters*, 1944, p. 268, no. A 1552). The latter authors consider the drawing a copy after no. 1313, perhaps dating from the seventeenth century. The Berlin drawing is stated (in the 1921 catalogue, by Max J. Friedländer, of the Kupferstichkabinett) to be signed 'Ja Hoefnagel'.

ENGRAVING: By P. R. De Launay, jeune (in reverse) in *Galerie du Palais Royal*, vol. 2 (1808).

PROVENANCE: Probably painted for the Emperor Rudolph II (see above). Marked in the 1727 Palais Royal catalogue (by Du Bois De Saint Gelais) as coming from 'M. de Seignelay'—i.e. the Marquis de Seignelay, who died in 1690.[8] Lot 238, Orléans sale, Lyceum, London, 26th December ff, 1798, when bought in by Bryan.[9] In the possession of the Earl of Darnley by 1828, when lent by him to the B.I. (112).[10] No. 298 in the definitive catalogue of the Manchester exhibition, 1857 (lent Lord Darnley). Purchased from the Earl of Darnley, 1890.

REPRODUCTION: *Illustrations, Italian Schools*, 1937, p. 348.

REFERENCES: (1) In the 1727 catalogue of the Palais Royal the dimensions of no. 1313 were already the same as now—'haut de 4 pieds huit pouces, large de cinq pieds un pouce'. This is the same as in the Palais Royal catalogue (vol. 2) of 1808 which contains an engraving showing the picture in its present form. (2) In the *Burlington Magazine*, vol. 72 (1938), pp. 88–93. (3) The 1621 Prague inventory is reproduced as 'Bilaga 1' in 'Kejsar Rudolf II's Konstkammare' by Olof Granberg (1902). The descriptions of pictures in this inventory are generally vague or inaccurate and for this reason the curious wording used in the present instance does not necessarily constitute evidence against the identification. (4) Ridolfi/Hadeln, II, p. 50. Ridolfi's confusion of the infants Hercules and Bacchus would be only a slight error and one for which Mandowsky (*op. cit.*, footnote 3) has an explanation. Hadeln (*loc. cit.*, footnote 3) identifies the picture mentioned by Ridolfi with the 'Jupiter und Semele im plitz, von Tentoreto' which is no. 172 in the 1621 Prague inventory. This is inadmissible as the latter picture is clearly identical with the 'Jupiter und Semelle in Bley' (therefore presumably a cartoon) which is no. 277 in the later Prague inventory (after 15th February, 1637—see reference 5 below). (5) The later inventory reproduced as appendix 1 to 'La Galerie de Tableaux de la Reine Christine de Suède' by Olof Granberg (1897). For the dating of it see p. XV of the 1938 catalogue of the Gemäldegalerie of the Kunsthistorisches Museum, Vienna. (6) Notes by Stella Mary Pearce in the Gallery archives. (7) It was suggested by E. Newton (*Tintoretto*, 1952, p. 169) that no. 1313 was actually painted for Rangoni. The latter is thought to have died in 1577 (Tiraboschi, *Storia della Letteratura Italiana*, vol. VII, 1809 edition, p. 653, also Rodolfo Gallo: *Contributi su Jacopo Sansovino*, in *Saggi e Memorie di Storia dell' Arte*, Fondazione Giorgio Cini, 1957, p. 105). If, therefore, the suggested dating of no. 1313 to precisely that period is justified, as well as the assumption of the Prague provenance, it might be possible to sustain the hypothesis that no. 1313 was intended for Rangoni, but that he died and so it became the nucleus of four pictures painted for Rudolph. Nevertheless, the type of no. 1313 seems to fit it better for a princely destination than for a doctor's household. (8) C. Stryienski (*La Galerie du Régent*, 1913, p. 154) indicates no. 1313 as in the first Orléans inventory of 1724. (9) Annotated copy of the catalogue in the Gallery library has 'Mr Bryan' against this entry. The same information is given by Buchanan (*Memoirs*, I, 1824, p. 132). The date 1792 given as that of Bryan's purchase in the Gallery catalogues of 1915–29 is a mistake. (10) Passavant (*Tour of a German Artist in England*, vol. II (1836), p. 197) specifically connects the picture in the Orléans sale with that in the Darnley collection.

4004 PORTRAIT OF VINCENZO MOROSINI

$33\frac{1}{4} \times 20\frac{3}{8}$ (0·845 × 0·515).

Good condition in general. The face rubbed in parts and retouched. The outline of the face on the spectator's right is 'worried' and there are traces of *pentimenti*. It is possible that the outline of the forehead may have been modified slightly by repaint.

The identity of the sitter is established by comparison with the portrait which figures in the *Resurrection* on the altar of the Morosini funerary chapel in S. Giorgio Maggiore, Venice, and with an inscribed portrait in the Doge's Palace.[1] The pose of no. 4004 corresponds so closely with that of the portrait in the *Resurrection* that it may either have been intended as a study for it or else have been used subsequently for that purpose. The Doge's Palace portrait is dated 1580, and the *Resurrection* documented as *c.* 1585.[2] As the sitter's age in no. 4004 appears similar to that in the other two portraits it may be assumed to be a fairly late work of Tintoretto. Vincenzo Morosini (1511–88), Senator of the Republic, was Prefect of Bergamo in 1555 and *Savio di Terrafirma*. In 1578 he was appointed *Procurator di San Marco de Citra* and in 1584 President of the University of Padua.

The sitter is shown wearing the *Stola d'Oro* over his right shoulder,[3] which was the privilege of the Knighthood of that name. At a later date the head of the Morosini family for the time being was a knight of the *Stola d'Oro* by hereditary right.[4] In the case of Vincenzo it would have been conferred in recognition of special services.

PROVENANCE: Purchased, 1922, by Messrs Agnew from Count Contini, Via Nomentana, Rome.[5] Purchased by the N.A.-C.F. from Agnew, and presented in commemoration of the Fund's Coming of Age and of the National Gallery Centenary, 1924. Exh. National Gallery (N.A.-C.F. Exhibition), 1945–6 (2).

REPRODUCTION: *Illustrations, Italian Schools*, 1937, p. 349.

REFERENCES: (1) Both these portraits are reproduced by D. S. MacColl: *Tintoretto's 'Vincenzo Morosini'* (*Burlington Magazine*, XLIV, 1924, pp. 266–71). The whole picture of the *Resurrection* is reproduced as pl. 227 in Von der Bercken's *Tintoretto* (1942). A further (uninscribed) portrait was reproduced as plate 54 in the catalogue of '*Quattrocento Pitture Inedite*', Venice, 1947. According to Stringa (edition of 1604 of Sansovino's *Venetia, Città Nobilissima* . . ., p. 167) the S. Giorgio altarpiece was started by Tintoretto and finished by his son. A portrait by Jacopo Tintoretto in the Accademia, Venice, identified as representing Battista Morosini, is of similar type and proportions to no. 4004, though slightly larger (repr. Von der Bercken, *op. cit.*, pl. 342). The latter portrait, unlike no. 4004, does not connect with the S. Giorgio altarpiece. (2) Cigogna: *Inscrizioni Veneziane*, IV (1834), p. 350, note 253. (3) According to P. Hélyot (*Histoire des Ordres Monastiques*, vol. 8, 1719, p. 362) the stole should be worn over the *left* shoulder. In the Doge's Palace portrait of Vincenzo Morosini this is the case. But in Tintoretto's portraits in general the rule seems by no means rigid, the stole tending to be worn over whichever shoulder is nearer the spectator in the portrait. The pattern of the embroidery, too, was not fixed. (4) Tentori: . . . *Storia* . . . *di Venezia*, vol. II (1785), p. 363, says the hereditary honour was instigated in favour of Lorenzo Morosini, brother of the Doge Francesco Morosini (died 1694). (5) Information supplied by Messrs Agnew.

Ascribed to JACOPO TINTORETTO

### 1476  JUPITER AND SEMELE

Panel, $9 \times 25\frac{3}{4}$ (0·22 × 0·654). Painted area slightly less.

Good condition in general. Some slight losses from flaking. Some retouching on Semele's body.

Hitherto as Andrea Schiavone. The Tintoretto attribution was first published by E. K. Waterhouse,[1] who pointed out the affinities with six *cassoni* panels at Vienna.[2] The latter, which were themselves formerly attributed to Schiavone, are undoubtedly very similar to no. 1476 both in design and handling, and of the two attributions that to Tintoretto (as an early work) seems the more probable to the present writer.

PROVENANCE: In the collection of Frederick Leighton (later Lord Leighton of Stretton, P.R.A.) by 1876, when exh. by him, R.A. (189) (as Schiavone). Lord Leighton sale, Christie's, 3rd day, 14th July, 1896 (362) (as Schiavone), where purchased.

REPRODUCTION: *Illustrations, Italian Schools*, 1937, p. 327.

REFERENCES: (1) In *Burlington Magazine*, vol. 50 (1927), p. 344. The Tintoretto attribution was confirmed by Berenson (*Lists*, 1957) and by Pallucchini (*Arte Veneta*, 1951, p. 111). (2) Repr. Pallucchini: *La Giovinezza del Tintoretto*, 1950, pls. 101–6.

### Style of TINTORETTO

### 2147  PORTRAIT OF A CARDINAL

$25\frac{1}{4} \times 21$ (0·641 × 0·533).

A line of damage, perhaps caused by a fold, extends nearly vertically up the canvas, a third of the way from the right. The discoloration of the varnish precludes a more detailed estimate of the condition or the authorship.

Lent to Dublin immediately after entering the Gallery and not catalogued until the edition of 1925.

PROVENANCE: Galvagna Coll., Venice. Bought, 1855.

REPRODUCTION: *Illustrations, Italian Schools*, 1937, p. 351.

### After TINTORETTO

### 2900  THE MIRACLE OF ST MARK

$16 \times 23\frac{1}{2}$ (0·406 × 0·597).

Slightly damaged in places by cracking, some of which is bituminous. Sketch copy, apparently dating from the first half of the nineteenth century, of the large picture in the Accademia, Venice. The suggestion, made in earlier editions of the National Gallery catalogue, that it might be the work of Etty would not be impossible, but there is no positive evidence.

REPRODUCTION: Negative in the possession of the Gallery.

PROVENANCE: Lady Lindsay Bequest, 1913.

## Follower of TINTORETTO

### 2161  PORTRAIT OF A LADY

$38\frac{3}{4} \times 31\frac{3}{4}$ (0·984 × 0·807).

Much discoloured by old varnish and engrained dirt. Basic condition of the figure probably sound.

In the 1929 catalogue as 'Veronese School, XVI century'. Purchased as 'Portrait of Pellegrina Morosini, wife of Bartolommeo Capello . . . by Pordenone'.[1] Pellegrina married Bartolommeo in 1544, their children, Vettore and Bianca, being born in 1547 and 1548 respectively. The costume shown in no. 2161 is datable around the middle of the century and would therefore not refute such an identification; but while the provenance from the Capello family would lend it some support it would be necessary to produce further supporting evidence, which is not forthcoming, to confirm it.

Lent in 1857 to Dublin and not catalogued until 1915, when it appears as 'Pellegrina Morosoni [sic], ascribed to Pordenone'. The Pordenone attribution need not be seriously considered. The connection with a certain type of Tintorettesque portrait was first pointed out by J. Wilde who had isolated a group of pictures of this type.[2]

PROVENANCE: Purchased, Venice, 1855, from the heirs of the Signori Capello.

REPRODUCTION: *Illustrations, Italian Schools*, 1937, p. 386.

REFERENCES: (1) National Gallery Report, 1856, p. 28. (2) Cf. his article: 'Wiedergefundene Gemälde aus der Sammlung des Erzherzogs Leopold Wilhelm', Vienna *Jahrbuch*, 1930, pp. 253 ff.

## TITIAN (TIZIANO VECELLIO)
### Active before 1511, died 1576

The form of signature used in his letters is variously Titiano, Tiziano, Tizian, Tician or Ticiano, Vecellio. On such of his pictures as are signed he uses the latinised form, Titianus or Ticianus. The form Titian was already usual in England as early as the seventeenth century. Exceptional forms of his signature—'Tician da Cadore'[1] in connection with the Padua frescoes of 1511, 'Titianus Cadorinus' on the Ancona *Madonna* of 1520, or 'Titianus de Cadore' on the portrait of Granvella (Kansas)—confirm Dolce's statement (1557) that he came from Cadore (Pieve di Cadore, in the Dolomites).

The date of his birth has been the subject of controversy, and cannot be established exactly. The earliest sources, all of which date from the last years of Titian's life, when he was certainly very old, are contradictory, and show that confusion on the subject already existed. Thus, Garcia Hernandez, writing in 1564 to Philip II of Spain, says that 'according to people who have known him for many years' Titian was 'about 90'—therefore born about 1474.[2] In 1567 Thomas de Cornoça, writing likewise to Philip II, refers to Titian as being 85 years old—

therefore born in 1482.[3] Vasari, writing in 1566–7, says that Titian was born in 1480.[4] Soon after Titian's death, Borghini (1584) says that Titian died in 1576, aged 98 or 99—therefore born in 1477 or 1478.[5] In 1622 Tizianello, a collateral descendant of the painter, dedicated an anonymous biography which stated that Titian was born in 1477.[6] This date was followed by Ridolfi.[7] The sense of the context of all three of the earliest of these statements—the two Spaniards' and Vasari's—is that Titian's activity at the time was remarkable for so old a man, from which it may be deduced that Titian's age was already becoming legendary in the 1560's. This aspect colours still more the famous statement by Titian himself in a 'begging letter' of 1571 to Philip of Spain in which he claims to be 95—therefore born in 1476. Paradoxically, the discovery, in 1955, of what purported to be the register of Titian's death in August, 1576, at the age of 103 tilts the balance if anything against the maximum age rather than for it. For this information must have come from Titian's family or his household, and like his letter of 1571 it would have constituted the 'official' figure. The fact that the official figure should thus have increased by three years within the space of five is sufficient in itself to discredit its reliability. It would be permissible to deduce from these conflicting statements that towards the end of his life Titian either did not know his own age exactly or else that he did but exaggerated it.[8] In either case it is clearly impossible, in view of the uncertainty prevailing at so early a date, to come to a firm conclusion now.

The limits for Titian's birth as given in the written sources—ranging from 1473 to 1482 or later—might in theory be narrowed by the existence of a painting datable to a very early period, but in fact this aspect is equally vague, since no precisely datable painting by Titian survives prior to the frescoes of 1511 in the Scuola del Santo at Padua. Dolce[9] says that Titian joined Giorgione in working on the frescoes (now destroyed) of the Fondaco dei Tedeschi, for his share in which Giorgione was paid in 1508. A picture of Tobias and the Angel (Accademia, Venice from Santa Caterina) is problematically linked with a confused reference by Vasari to one painted by Titian in 1507. Vasari also gives a date—1508—to Titian's wood-cuts of the *Triumph of Faith*. The picture at Antwerp of Jacopo Pesaro presented to S. Peter by the Borgia Pope, Alexander VI, is in a different category. Whatever the date of the inscription on it, Titian's authorship can hardly be doubted and the style is considerably less evolved than that of the Padua frescoes of 1511. The event commemorated—the appointment of Jacopo Pesaro as commander of the papal galleys—occurred in 1501, which is thus the earliest possible date for the picture. But its upper limit need not necessarily be fixed, as has been claimed, by the lack of allusion in the picture to the victory which took place in 1502, or even by the fact of Alexander's death which occurred in 1503.

Of Titian's apprenticeship, Dolce[10] reports that he was sent at the age of nine to Venice to study painting where he was taught first by the Zuccati, who were mosaicists, then in succession by Gentile and

Giovanni Bellini of each of whom he tired and finally attached himself to Giorgione. This account, as the earliest and as dating from well within Titian's lifetime, is probably basically reliable, but it should be borne in mind that the star of the Bellini had set to a great extent by the time when Dolce wrote, whereas Giorgione's was still high. In consequence of this it would have done Titian credit to have preferred the latter. As to the evidence of the surviving paintings, the present uncertainty, among the smaller religious pictures and those of secular subjects, which are late works of Giorgione and which early ones of Titian may be regarded as some indication, at least, that in these fields Titian approached Giorgione closely. But in Titian's major religious works of the earlier period the influence of Giorgione is slighter than that of Giovanni Bellini. The transition, in particular, from Bellini's altarpiece of 1513 in the church of S. Giovanni Crisostomo, Venice, to Titian's *Assunta* of 1516–18 is intelligible, at least as regards technique, without presupposing the influence of Giorgione.

The completion of the *Assunta*, though the records of its reception are fragmentary, would have established Titian's reputation as the greatest of Venetian painters, and from then to the end of his life, more than half a century later, his career was a series of spectacular successes, and correspondingly well documented. His activity was not confined to leading commissions within the Republic. His services, whether as portraitist or as painter of mythologies or religious subjects, were competed for by the chief princely families outside the Veneto—the Este (see no. 35 below), the Gonzaga, the Farnese, the Della Rovere and even the French king, François I. The Farnese patronage led to Titian's visit to Rome in 1545. More important still were his relations with the Habsburgs. In 1533 Charles V created him Count Palatine and Knight of the Golden Spur. The Imperial favour thus shown was continued by Charles' successor as King of Spain, Philip II, for whom Titian worked almost exclusively during his last years.

During the seventeenth century Titian's influence, particularly in respect of his development of the 'tonal' method of painting, was to be dominant. Palma Giovane's statement to Boschini that Titian finished his later pictures 'more with his fingers than his brush'[11] constitutes important contemporary evidence of his practice. A tradition was reported by Ridolfi[12] to the effect that Titian was in the habit of touching up students' copies of his originals which then passed as his own work. In addition, he frequently repeated his own designs, often after long intervals of time. The existence of an undoubtedly genuine Titian, therefore, does not necessarily exclude the possibility of his participation in other versions or variants. The high market value of his work at all times since his death provided an inducement to forgery, and in the case of certain early seventeenth-century painters, pre-eminently Padovanino, the border-line between follower and forger becomes obscured. At least one picture possibly in the latter category—no. 3 of this Gallery—is probably identical with one which was in the collection of Charles I as a Titian.

REFERENCES: (1) Reproduced by Bernardo Gonzati: *La Basilica di S. Antonio di Padova*, vol. I (1852), p. CXLIII. (2) Hernandez' letter is reproduced in Crowe and Cavalcaselle: *Titian*, vol. II (1877), pp. 534–5. (3) Quoted by Gronau in his reply to Herbert Cook. This correspondence, which started with Cook's attempt to date Titian's birth as late as about 1489, is reprinted in an appendix to the later editions of Cook's *Giorgione*. An equally polemical attempt to revert to the traditional dating was made by F. J. Mather, Jr., in the *Art Bulletin*, 1938, pp. 13–25. (4) At the beginning of his biography of Titian, Milanesi ed., vol. VII, p. 426. On page 459 of the same volume Vasari lists Titian's works 'infino alla sua età di circa settantasei anni'. Elsewhere (pp. 427–8) Vasari seems to imply that Titian was only 18 when he started painting in Giorgione's manner in the year 1507, but this seems no more than an embroidery of Dolce's account. (5) *Il Riposo*, 1584, p. 529. (6) Ed. of 1819, p. II. (7) Ridolfi/Hadeln, I, p. 152. (8) The first obituary notice in the issue of *The Times* newspaper of Friday, 6th January, 1956 is a modern illustration of a comparable principle. The subject was Mlle. Jeanne Bourgeois, known as Mistinguett. (9) *Dialogo della Pittura* (1557). Ed. of 1735, p. 284. (10) *Op. cit.* (11) Marco Boschini: preface to *Le Ricche Minere* . . . (1674). (12) *Op. cit.*, p. 227.

## 4  THE HOLY FAMILY AND A SHEPHERD

Original (fine grain) canvas ca. 39 × 54¾ (0·99 × 1·37). The first lining canvas projects slightly beyond this all round and has been roughly painted. The original canvas has probably been cut on all four sides—slightly at the bottom and on the left, more at the top and most of all on the right (see VERSIONS below).

Somewhat worn in places, but in general well preserved for a picture of its type and period. Cleaned 1954.

Doubt has been expressed on occasion concerning Titian's authorship of this picture[1] and such is the lack of definition of the painter's early work that some doubt is likely to remain. Nevertheless the most plausible of the alternative candidates proposed is the young Paris Bordon,[2] and the stylistic indications which have been claimed as favouring him are scantier and less convincing than those in favour of Titian.[3] In connection with the latter's claim, several *Holy Family's* both full length and half length have been associated with no. 4,[4] but some of them are not above question as Titian and they are not entirely homogeneous as a group. The most convincing stylistic analogy for the attribution of no. 4 to Titian seems to the present writer to lie in the altarpiece of S. Mark and four other saints (Venice, S. Maria della Salute). This is an undoubted early Titian and shows similarities of disposition, draperies and physiognomical type alike.[5] The fact, not hitherto published, that the Titian attribution for no. 4 dates back at least to the seventeenth century is a further factor (see PROVENANCE).

Described in the 1929 catalogue as 'unfinished', but despite the sketchy treatment of the ass' head there seems no justification for this statement.

VERSIONS: A copy was lot 157, Christie's, 30th April, 1954. A free copy, lot 9, Christie's, 31st October, 1958. A sketch copy inscribed 'Pallazo Borghese nella Vigna' shows more space round the figures than now exists in no. 4 and indicates that the latter has been cut—fairly considerably on the right, rather less at the top and less still on the left and at the bottom. This sketch, apparently of the seventeenth century, seems to have been in the Dolgoroukoff collection, Moscow, in 1907.[6]

PROVENANCE: Identifiable on the strength of the sketch copy (see VERSIONS) with an entry in an unpublished Borghese inventory of 1693 ('nell'Appartamento Terreno che gode il Sig.r Principe di Rossano')—kindly communicated by Paola Della Pergola: '... un quadro grande in tela, la Madonna, e il Bambino e San Giuseppe, un Pastore in ginocchioni No. 334 cornice dorato di Titiano'.[7] Bought in Italy by W. Y. Ottley, 1797–9.[8] Lot 15 ('Palace Borghese') in anonymous (Ottley) sale, 118 Pall Mall, London (January, 1801). W. Y. Ottley sale, Christie's, 16th May, 1801. Lot 45 (again as ex-Borghese), W. Champion sale, 23rd–24th March, 1810, where bought by the Rev. Holwell Carr,[9] by whom bequeathed, 1831.

REPRODUCTION: *Illustrations, Italian Schools*, 1937, p. 352.

REFERENCES: (1) E.g. by Crowe and Cavalcaselle (*Titian*, vol. II (1877), p. 428), Fischel (*Klassiker der Kunst* volume on Titian, 5th edition, p. 305, note to pl. 21), and Tietze (*Tizian*, 1936, Tafelband, pp. 293–4). The latter refers to further sceptics. The Titian attribution has been upheld by Gronau (*Titian*, English edition, 1904, p. 31), Berenson (*Lists*, 1936, p. 491), A. Venturi (*Storia* ..., IX, III, p. 199) and Suida (*Tiziano*, 1933, p. 26). (2) Proposed by K. Oettinger (*Magyar Müvészet*, 1931) and apparently supported by Tietze (*loc. cit.*). (3) The case for Bordon's authorship of no. 4 rests primarily on the signed early altarpiece in the Galleria Tadini at Lovere (repr. in Venturi, *Storia* ..., IX, III, p. 1002) which probably dates from the '20's of the sixteenth century (see Bailo and Biscaro: *Paris Bordon*, 1900, pp. 132–3). If, as seems likely, the *Nativity* by Giovanni da Asola (Duomo, Asola, reproduced and discussed by Fiocco, *Bollettino d'Arte*, anno V (1925–6), vol. I, pp. 198 and 201) derives from no. 4 it would more or less exclude Bordon's authorship of the latter without more ado, as the Asola picture dates from as early as 1518. A picture comparable with it is no. 1377 of this Gallery. (4) Suida (*op. cit.*, pp. 25–6) associates no. 4 with the Prado, Bache, Dresden, Vienna and Louvre half-length *Holy Family's* (his plates XLI, LXXV, LXXXII, LXXXIII, LXXXIV) and with the Bridgewater House full-length *Holy Family* (his plate LXXIX). (5) The Salute picture is usually (and probably correctly) associated with relief from the plague of 1510. This would also be a possible date (i.e. within a few years from 1510) for no. 4. (6) Reproduced (as Anthony Van Dyck and wrongly labelled as at Chatsworth) and discussed by Frizzoni, *Rassegna d'Arte*, VII (1907), pp. 154–5. (7) Probably the first of the two pictures described by Ramdohr (*Ueber Mahlerei und Bildhauerarbeit in Rom* ..., vol. I, 1787, p. 299) as in Palazzo Borghese: *zwei heilige Familien von Tizian. Auf der einen betet ein Hirte den Christ an ... Das Kind ist in einem angenehmen Halbschatten gehalten; auch ist der Hirte sehr wahr und gut gestellet.* (8) W. Buchanan: *Memoirs*, II, pp. 21 and 27. Preface to anonymous (Ottley) sale catalogue has 'purchased ... at Rome ... 1799, 1800'. (9) Redford: *Art Sales*, vol. II (1888), p. 256. Redford's misprint of Champion as 'Campion' was followed in the National Gallery catalogues of 1915–29.

## 34  VENUS AND ADONIS

$69\frac{3}{4} \times 73\frac{3}{4}$ ($1\cdot771 \times 1\cdot872$).

The canvas, exceptionally, has not been trimmed: the original turnover still exists.

The most damaged area is the upper left corner where as a result of scorching[1] the outline of the trees is distorted by repaint and most of the foliage unreliable. The area of sky between Adonis' right arm and the overhanging foliage is almost entirely repainted. Venus' white drapery is retouched from the shoulder to the knee. The lower part of her back is much rubbed due to the fact that this area was covered in the eighteenth century with draperies executed in water-colour. These had been removed by the time the picture was in the Angerstein collection.[2] Most of the sky is worn. The following areas are in reliable condition: the heads of both the principal figures, Adonis' red tunic, the red and pink drapery under Venus, the vase at her feet, Adonis' left hand and the heads of the two hounds on the right.

Cleaned 1924, when much old repaint was removed.

Preliminary drawing with the point of the brush is visible in many places, notably in Venus' shoulder and right arm, in Adonis' right arm (together with ordinary *pentimenti* in the outlines) and in the sky. Infra-red photography reveals further drawing of this kind in Adonis' red tunic.

This design evidently occupied Titian over a period of years and he developed it in different versions. There are, in addition, numerous studio and later replicas and variants, together with old engravings containing further variations. The surviving paintings attributable to Titian himself (with varying degrees of studio assistance) may be classified in two main groups.

1. Nearly square format (breadth only slightly exceeding height). Adonis holds three hounds. Cupid is shown at full length asleep on the left. An upturned vase is shown under Venus' right foot. Examples in the Prado and no. 34 (differing among themselves in minor respects, such as the arrangement of the quiver and bow and in details of the costume).

2. Oblong format. Over-all dimensions considerably smaller. Adonis has only two hounds, both relatively somewhat larger than any of the three in the group 1 pictures. Only the head and shoulders of Cupid are shown. He is awake and clasps a dove[3] and is nearer to the lovers (and therefore on a relatively larger scale) than in group 1. There is no vase. Examples at Washington (ex-Spencer collection) and Metropolitan Museum, New York (Bache collection, ex-Darnley) (again with minor variations among themselves). A third example was at Capodimonte early in the nineteenth century.[4]

Of these pictures the Prado version is documented as finished in 1554. The New York and Washington examples show a later phase of Titian's style.

The course of Titian's thought as illustrated by the development of group 2 from group 1 was clearly directed towards increasing the dominance of the figures over the landscape. Thus both the Cupid and the hounds are shown on a larger scale, thereby shutting out more of the landscape, while the format is changed from square to oblong so as to fit the pattern of the figures more compactly. It would be in accordance with Titian's development of the design, as interpreted in this way, to assume that a still earlier version than group 1 may have existed of up-right format. There are indications that such may have been the case, but they are not conclusive. A version in the Galleria Nazionale, Rome (ex-Torlonia), attributable to Titian's school (showing Adonis in a hat) is in fact somewhat higher than it is broad, and engravings by Martino Rota,[5] Giulio Sanuto and others[6] show an emphatic upright format. But it is impossible to tell how accurate the engravings may be and some of them, at least, would have been done not from the painting but from drawings or *modelli* (see entry for no. 4222, THE TRINITY).

Sanuto's purports to be after the Prado version, but in addition to differing from it in format it shows Adonis' right shoulder draped, as in the Rome picture and as in (nearly square format) versions in the Normanton collection (ex-Queen Christina, Orléans and FitzHugh collections) and in the Heyl sale, Munich, 1930 (ex-Leigh Court) (Adonis' draped right shoulder makes a fleeting reappearance later in the Bache picture). Moreover, other versions showing Adonis with a hat—Dulwich and a sketch copy at Alnwick (ex-Barberini)—are of square or oblong format. Ridolfi[7] says that Titian did a *Venus and Adonis* (apparently for Ottaviano Farnese) during his stay in Rome (in 1545–6), and this date, some eight years before that of the Prado picture, would accord well with the sequence as a date for an hypothetical Ur-version. But it is probable that Ridolfi was confused, since the version which figures in the Farnese inventory of 1680 is described as containing only two hounds and with a Cupid holding a dove. As it was also of oblong format[8] it was certainly one of group 2 (presumably identical with the Capodimonte picture) and therefore executed considerably after Titian's Roman visit.

The date—1554—of the Prado version is relevant to no. 34, since the two belong to the same group and may be assumed to have been painted within a few years, at the most, of each other. But which of the two was the earlier cannot be settled. The retouched condition of the Prado picture precludes any detailed stylistic comparison and the minor variations in the design are inconclusive as regards relative priority.

The fact that the Prado version was for Philip of Spain and therefore presumably mainly autograph does not in principle exclude the possibility of substantial participation by Titian in the execution of no. 34 also. The free under-drawing (as in no. 4452 of this Gallery, q.v.) is in fact characteristic of Titian himself, whose touch is also unmistakable in the draperies on which Venus sits and in the upturned vase. For the rest, the division of labour between Titian and his studio is less clear.

The story of Venus and Adonis is told by Ovid in the tenth book of the *Metamorphoses*, which was probably the literary source which Titian had in mind. This is relevant to the identity of the figure in the clouds which is identified (in the Alnwick version) by Crowe and Cavalcaselle as Apollo. In no. 34, though the details are sketchily painted in this area, the relative proportions of the hips and shoulders unmistakably indicate a woman. The fact that the chariot is drawn by birds also gravitates against Apollo (or against Aurora) as does the fact that Apollo does not figure in Ovid's account. Despite the fact that Ovid alludes in this connection to Venus' car being drawn by swans (to which the birds in no. 34, though sketchily painted, bear little resemblance, if any) and that Venus is already shown in the foreground it is difficult to avoid the conclusion that this figure also is intended for her.[9]

VERSIONS: In addition to those discussed above mention may be made of a version at Melbury (Lord Ilchester) approximating to the Washington picture, a small copy in the Accademia, Venice (no. 554 in the 1928 catalogue), a version by Zelotti at Dresden (no. 182 in the 1930 catalogue) and a variant (oblong shape) at Vienna (distinct from the one which is engraved as A. Schiavone, no. 127 in the *Theatrum Pictorium* and in pl. 17 of the *Prodromus* of 1735, and of which Teniers' copy is in the Johnson collection, Philadelphia). An old copy at Ham House shows the quiver and arrows arranged as in the Prado version. Others are recorded in the collection of the Earl of Wemyss and in the Nostitz collection, Prague (no. 223 in the 1905 catalogue). Another is said to have been in the collection of the King of Holland but was not included in the sale of 1850. Of pictures of this subject (but not necessarily related in design) which are recorded but which are no longer identifiable the following may be mentioned (some of them perhaps mutually identical): 1. No. 21 in an unpublished inventory pre-1649 (? Lord Fielding's pictures) belonging to the Duke of Hamilton. 2. In the collection of Carlo Doria at Genoa (according to the anonymous life of Titian, Venice, 1809, p. 5). 3. Collection of Marchese Serra, Milan (Scanelli: *Microcosmo*, 1657, p. 222). 4. Lomellini Palace, Genoa (A. Hume: *Notices* . . ., 1829, p. 45). 5. Bryan sale, 2nd day, 18th May, 1798, lot 145. 6. Halliday and Clopton sale, 2nd day, 9th May, 1801, lot 95. 7. Prince de Carignan sale, 1742 (Blanc: *Le Trésor de la Curiosité*, vol. 1, 1857, p. 33). 8. Madame Lenglier sale, 1788 (said to have been ex-Charles I and Jabach, see Blanc, *op. cit.*, vol. 2, p. 119).

DRAWING: A sheet of sketches attributed to Domenico Campagnola, from the Bardi and Novak collections (photograph in the Gallery archives) included drawings after the Venus and one of the hounds in a version of no. 34.

ENGRAVINGS: See above. The engraving by Raphael Sadeler (1610) is after the Washington version. The Normanton version was engraved several times when in the Orléans collection.

PROVENANCE: No. 116 in the catalogue of 1783 of Palazzo Colonna, Rome. Acquired by Alexander Day in Italy after the Napoleonic invasion. Offered for sale by Day, 20 Lower Brook St, London, 1800–1, where bought, May, 1801, by Angerstein.[10] Purchased with the Angerstein collection, 1824.

REPRODUCTION: *Illustrations, Italian Schools*, 1937, p. 353.

REFERENCES: (1) See article by Sir Charles Holmes: *Burlington Magazine*, vol. XLIV (1924), pp. 16–22. Part of a further article on the subject, by A. L. Mayer (*Münchner Jahrbuch*, 1925, pp. 274–9), contains nothing of importance. (2) A MS. note (copy in the Gallery archives) made by Sir Abraham Hume reads: 'the present possessor [i.e. Prince Colonna] has thought fit to cover part of her [i.e. Venus'] back with a piece of linen, tho' there was nothing indecent in its appearance, but, I am assured, it is only in water-colours'. Dibdin (*Aedes Althorpianae*, vol. 1, 1822, pp. 13–14) repeats the story of the draping and adds the information that it had since been removed 'as far as it was possible'. There is a photograph in the Gallery archives of a picture belonging in 1922 to Dr Ferdinand Gotti of Florence which purports to be an English copy of no. 34 made in Rome c. 1795. Marks across the lower half of Venus' back might be interpreted as light drapery. Adonis also seems to be wearing a small beard. (3) A copy of this figure, formerly attributed to Padovanino, is no. 70 of this Gallery. (4) Mentioned in a letter of 1804 from Irvine to Buchanan (Buchanan: *Memoirs*, vol. II (1824), p. 153) and engraved by Strange. (5) Bartsch, vol. 16, no. 108, p. 282. (6) Two others, unsigned, are in the British Museum. (7) Ridolfi/Hadlen, I, p. 179. (8) The relevant entry from the Farnese inventory of 1680 is printed by Campori: *Raccolta di Cataloghi*, p. 211, and by Crowe and Cavalcaselle: *Titian*, vol. II (1877), p. 151. (9) In another picture in this Gallery of similar subject and date (no. 1123: Follower of Titian: Mythological Scene) Cupid occurs both in the foreground and background, while Venus is apparently shown twice in the background. Note also Venus in a swan-drawn car introduced by Rubens into his copy of Titian's *Venus Worship* (Stockholm). (10) Buchanan: *Memoirs*, vol. II (1824), p. 4. Also Farington Diary for 7th May, 1801 (vol. I, p. 308).

## 35  BACCHUS AND ARIADNE

69 × 75 (1·75 × 1·9).
Signed on an urn, left foreground, TICIANVS F.

The picture has suffered in the past from blistering and from relining. The most damaged area is the sky, which is covered with innumerable small retouchings. Bacchus' neck and the middle of his cloak are in similar state. Other retouchings, though less numerous, in the flesh and draperies of the other figures. The following areas seem well preserved: most of the foreground, the cheetahs, the distant landscape and the trees.

As regards the textual source Lomazzo[1] mentions no. 35 with other Renaissance representations of Triumphs and then quotes classical writers who cited the return of Bacchus from India as the prototype of the practice of Triumphs in general. Lomazzo proceeds to quote in translation a passage from Catullus[2] as constituting material suitable for illustration in such circumstances. He does not specifically associate this passage with Titian but Ridolfi appends the names Ovid ('Met. li. 8') and Philostratus as well as Catullus as marginal notes to his description of no. 35.[3] This is the earliest recorded opinion that more than one classical writer was drawn on for the subject and this seems in fact to have been the case. The passage of Catullus quoted by Lomazzo specifies in Bacchus' train figures variously waving thyrsi, rending and throwing a mangled heifer's limbs, girt with writhing snakes, thronged round the mysteries borne in dark caskets, beating cymbals and tambourines and playing horns and pipes. The accurate portrayal of all these features in no. 35, with the exception of the pipe player who is not shown, confirms Ridolfi's specification of Catullus as a source. But the meeting of Bacchus and Ariadne does not occur there, and for this the main source seems to have been Ovid; not the *Metamorphoses* as mentioned by Ridolfi, but the *Ars Amatoria*.[4] Here (I, 525–66) Ariadne is described wandering distractedly along the shore, barefoot and clad in an ungirt tunic. She is surprised by Bacchus' train of satyrs and bacchantes and the drunken Silenus on his ass. She is frightened and attempts to flee, but the god himself reassures her. He leaps from his car towards her, promising her marriage and a place among the stars as a constellation. In this passage Bacchus' car is stated to have been drawn by tigers. The cheetahs shown instead in no. 35 introduce the third writer mentioned by Ridolfi, namely Philostratus, who, in the *Imagines*,[5] had specified the πάρδαλις[6] as particularly associated with Bacchus. The detailed programme for no. 35 was probably sent to Titian by Alfonso d'Este himself.[7] Since the sources drawn on were so well known a conflation of them in the written programme would not in any case have been surprising.[8]

The historical events concerning the commissioning of no. 35 may be summarised as follows. A picture called *The Feast of the Gods*, now at Washington, is signed by Giovanni Bellini and dated 1514. Two Bacchanals by Titian, now in the Prado, and no. 35 are of approximately the same dimensions as Bellini's picture[9] and all four came from the studio of Alfonso d'Este in the *Castello* at Ferrara. Titian was in contact with Alfonso from 1516 and repainted part of Bellini's picture, which was certainly the earliest of the four. Although it cannot be established with certainty when he started no. 35[10] (which was apparently the last of the four to be finished) it can be proved that most of the work on it was done, after considerable delay, between the summer of 1522 and the spring of 1523. The documents for the crucial stages of its execution consist of two letters to Duke Alfonso from his agent in Venice, Giacomo Tebaldi (text published by G. Gronau, Vienna *Jahrbuch*, 1928, p. 246).

In the first of them, dated 'the last day of August, 1522', Tebaldi says he had been to Titian's studio on the preceding day and had seen the canvas which then contained ten[11] figures, the chariot and the animals drawing it.[12] At this time little more than the lay-in can have been done as Tebaldi specifies that Titian expects to be able to paint the figures in the existing attitudes—i.e. without further changes. He adds that a few details—heads and landscape—apparently not yet even sketched in, remained to be done, but that this would not take long. Titian's own estimate is that by October the canvas should be ready to transport to Ferrara where he could finish it in ten or fifteen days. Apparently Titian then shelved the work again as in the second letter in question, dated 14th October, 1522,[13] Tebaldi reports to Alfonso that he has that day rebuked Titian for the delay. Titian's defense was that he had had to change two women,[14] but that he should nevertheless be able to transport the canvas to Ferrara by the end of the month and finish it there. Tebaldi adds that he thinks Titian may keep his promise, saying that he is at work in the Doge's Palace in the mornings, but that for the rest of the day he is exclusively occupied with the *Bacchus and Ariadne*. Nevertheless it was not until 30th January, 1523 that the picture was sent to Ferrara,[15] and even then Titian did not accompany it, being on a visit to Mantua. A letter of 3rd February, 1523 from Federico Gonzaga to Alfonso d'Este[16] says that the bearer was Titian who therefore presumably arrived at Ferrara soon afterwards. No more is heard of progress on no. 35, but as Alfonso was already very angry at the delay[17] it is inconceivable that having at last lured Titian to Ferrara he would let him go without completing the picture. As, according to Titian's own words to Tebaldi, there would then have been only ten or fifteen days work still to do and as he would have had no other commitments at Ferrara it can be assumed (even if, as is probable, Titian's estimate was deliberately optimistic) that no. 35 would have been finished some time in the spring of 1523. It must in any case have been finished before August, as by then Titian was back in Venice.[18]

VERSIONS: Various old copies exist, notably at Bergamo,[19] Accademia di S. Luca (Rome),[20] Schloss Celle and Alnwick.[21] A sketch copy, signed 'D. Wilkie' and dated 1820, was lot 83 in an anonymous sale, Christie's, 21st March, 1952. A copy of the figure of Bacchus, attributed 'A. Carracci', was no. 45 in the Northwick catalogue of 1858. Farington (*Diary*, 15th January, 1811) mentions a 'large' copy in enamel by Henry Bone. Crude pastiches of most of the principal figures are included in Turner's picture of the same title (Tate Gallery, no. 525).

DRAWINGS: In an article in the *Gazette des Beaux-Arts*, 1908, I, p. 135, Emil Jacobsen published a drawing in the Uffizi (Saltarelli collection, no. 7383) which he claimed as preliminary studies for no. 35 and for the Andrian Bacchanal (Prado). Nevertheless Hadeln, in his book on Titian's drawings (1924) excluded this one, and Fischel (*Klassiker der Kunst* volume on Titian, p. 307) speaks of it as copied from the paintings, which it pretty obviously is.

ENGRAVINGS: By G. A. Podestà[22] and by Joseph Juster.[23]

PROVENANCE: Mentioned by Lomazzo (1584)[24] as at Ferrara. Appropriated in 1598 and sent to Rome by the Papal Legate, Cardinal Pietro Aldobrandini,[25] when the state of Ferrara passed to the Papacy. Recorded in 1638 as in the Villa Aldobrandini, Rome,[26] and subsequently (as in the same place) by (?) Bellori (1664),[27] Scaramuccia (1674),[28] Rossini (1693)[29] and in *Roma Antica e Moderna* (1765).[30] During this period the ownership had varied with the dynastic changes.[31] The heir of Cardinal Pietro Aldobrandini (d. 1621) appears to have been Cardinal Ippolito Aldobrandini (son of Pietro's sister, Olimpia, who had married another Aldobrandini, Gianfrancesco) on whom, according to Litta, all the riches of the Aldobrandini family had devolved. Cardinal Ippolito, the last surviving Aldobrandini male of the main branch, died in 1638, entailing the estate and leaving as heir his niece, also called Olimpia (daughter of Ippolito's brother, Giorgio) and then her second son (by her second marriage—to Camillo Pamfili) who had to take the name Aldobrandini. When this line too became extinct (in 1760) most of the Pamfili property passed to the Doria Landi while the Aldobrandini inheritance became the subject of a law suit between the Colonna and Borghese families, won by the latter in 1769. The judgment on that occasion was that the Aldobrandini fortune and title should be held by the second son of the head of the Borghese family. The confusion presumably prevailing over the inheritance between the years 1760 and 1769 may account for Volkmann's statement (published in 1770 but presumably referring to some time before)[32] that no. 35 was at the time of writing in the Palazzo Pamfili (i.e. Palazzo Doria). Contrary to what is often stated no. 35 appears never to have hung in the Palazzo Barberini.[33] It was back in the Villa Aldobrandini by 1787[34] and sold from there, probably in 1797 and certainly before May, 1803, when it was in the hands of Alexander Day. Day seems to have been in partnership with the brothers Camuccini.[35] Bought by Irvine for Buchanan, Rome, May, 1806,[36] who had it sent to England and sold it to Lord Kinnaird, 1806 or 1807.[37] Sold to Basely by Delahante, who had apparently purchased it privately before the Kinnaird sale (5th March, 1813).[38] In the possession of the jeweller, Thomas Hamlet, by 1816, who lent it in that year both to the R.A. for copying[39] and to the B.I. (11). Purchased from Hamlet, 1826.

REPRODUCTION: *Illustrations, Italian Schools*, 1937, p. 356.

REFERENCES: (1) *Trattato*, 1584, p. 393. (2) *Carmina*, LXIV, lines 257–65. (3) Ridolfi/Hadeln, I, pp. 141–2. Ridolfi adds that Theseus' ship is visible in the distance. Though this area (on the spectator's extreme left) is at present very indistinct in the painting the engravings of Podestà and Juster show a ship distinctly. Wind (*Burlington Magazine* 1950, p. 85) denies that the ship is Theseus' on the grounds that the sails are white. However, the scale is so small that with "dark Spanish purple" sails against the dark blue sea and the sky the ship would have been almost invisible. (4) This fact was pointed out by Graves H. Thompson ("The Literary Sources of Titian's *Bacchus and Ariadne*" in *The Classical Journal*, March 1956, pp. 259–64) who demonstrated this work as more applicable to no. 35 than is a passage in the *Fasti* (III, 459–516) which had been adduced by E. Wind. The distinction, stressed in the *Fasti* account, between Bacchus' first and second meetings with Ariadne is not drawn in the *Ars Amatoria* version. Wind's argument is contained in his book *Bellini's Feast of the Gods* (1948) which, together with John Walker's *Bellini and Titian at Ferrara* (1956) is in other respects essential to any study of the series of pictures from Ferrara of which no. 35 was one. (5) *Imagines*, I, 15 and 19. (6) Translated as leopard or panther. A letter of 15 November, 1956 to *The Times* newspaper demonstrated that the creatures shown in no. 35 are in fact cheetahs rather than leopards. (7) See correspondence printed in Crowe and Cavalcaselle: *Titian*, I (1877), pp. 181–3. These letters do not specifically refer to no. 35 but are suggestive as regards the probable system adopted. (8) Anyone, Alfonso himself or another, who was able to draw on Catullus, Philostratus and the *Ars Amatoria* may be presumed also to have been well acquainted with the *Fasti* and the *Metamorphoses* and perhaps to have worded the programme for no. 35 in a way which presupposed such knowledge. *Fasti* III 515–16 and *Metamorphoses* VIII 176–82, for instance, describe the jewels in Ariadne's crown turning into stars, the *Fasti* specifying them as nine. Though there are in fact only eight stars in no. 35 the other accounts do not specify a number at all. (9) *Feast of the Gods* 1·7 × 1·88, Prado Bacchanals 1·75 × 1·93 and 1·72 × 1·75, no. 35 1·75 × 1·9. (10) Wind (*op. cit.*) suggests that although the *Bacchus and Ariadne* was (apparently) finished last of Titian's three bacchanals it was designed first. But the evidence he adduces is inconclusive. (11) In the picture in its present state there are in fact eleven figures—six in the foreground (Ariadne, Bacchus, baby faun, bacchante with cymbals, athlete with snakes and faun flourishing bullock's leg) and five in the background (bacchante with tambourine, boy blowing horn, man supporting Silenus, Silenus himself and man bearing cask). If the picture was only a lay-in at the time when Tebaldi saw it the two heads next to Silenus' may not have been differentiated (in Podestà's engraving there is in fact only one in this area, making only ten figures in all; though this is presumably no more than a whim of the engraver's). (12) This letter is paraphrased (but not directly quoted) in an article by G. Campori: *Tiziano e gli Estensi* (*Nuova Antologia*, 1st series, vol. 27, 1874). Crowe and Cavalcaselle and most other writers re-quote from Campori without noticing that he made a mistake in his reading of the document, reading the word 'dece' as 'due', and stating in consequence that apart from the car drawn by animals the picture contained only two figures, the rest not even started. Venturi (*Storia*, IX, iii, 116) quotes the particular sentence accurately but does not reproduce the document *in extenso*. This, however, was done by Gronau (*loc. cit.*). (13) This document is referred to by Venturi (*op. cit.*, pp. 117 and 118) who wrongly gives its location as Mantua instead of Modena. (14) No confirmation of this statement has been forthcoming from the X-ray photographs specially taken in this connection. (15) A bill of that date for carriage is quoted by Crowe and Cavalcaselle (*op. cit.*, p. 258). (16) Crowe and Cavalcaselle, *op. cit.*, p. 281. (17) It emerges from Tebaldi's first letter that Titian was apprehensive of the possibility even of physical violence as a punishment from Alfonso for his excessive procrastination. (18) Letter of 11th August, 1523 from the Gonzaga envoy in Venice (Crowe and Cavalcaselle, *op. cit.*, p. 282). (19) No. 423 in catalogue of 1930, attributed Padovanino. (20) No. 231, attributed N. Poussin. (21) Attributed N. Poussin. Other copies are listed by John Walker: *Bellini and Titian at Ferrara*, 1957, pp. 119–21. (22) Bartsch, XX, p. 172, no. 6. Podestà was active in Rome in the mid-seventeenth century. (23) In *Pitture Scelte . . . da Carla Caterina Patina*, Cologne, 1691, p. 179. (24) *Loc. cit.* (25) Details are given in a contemporary memorandum published by Adolfo Venturi (*La R. Galleria Estense in Modena*, 1882, p. 113). The removal of no. 35 to Rome by Cardinal Aldobrandini was little more than theft. Only five pictures were concerned—the four Bellini/Titian Bacchanals and one by Dosso (perhaps no. 5279 of this Gallery). The memorandum describes no. 35 as *una pittura in quadro di mano di Tiziano dove era dipinto Lacoonte*. Such indeed is how the figure of the satyr towards the right might appear at first sight or, as here, in retrospect (since the picture had already gone when the memorandum was written). Although Titian had certainly not seen the *Laöcoön* group when he painted no. 35 it is by no means impossible that its general appearance was known to him and that it affected the figure in question. At the same time the resemblance may be fortuitous, since the distinctive feature—the serpents writhing round the naked figure—occurs in Catullus. (26) Gasp. Celio: *Memoria fatta dell' habito di Christo*, Naples, 1638, p. 138: *Quella di Bacco che scende dal Carro è di Titiano*—as in the *Casino del Signor Principe Aldobrandini nel Monte detto Magnanapoli*. The Villa Aldobrandini at Rome is sometimes referred to in seventeenth- and eighteenth-century guide-books as above, sometimes as *Giardino Aldobrandini* and sometimes as *Villa Aldobrandini sopra al Quirinale*, but there is no doubt that all refer to the same building. (27) *Nota delli Musei, Librerie, Galerie . . . e Pittura ne' Palazzi, nelle Case . . . di Roma*, p. 6. (28) *Le Finezze*, p. 12. (29) *Il Mercurio Errante*, p. 108. (30) Vol. II, pp. 607–8. The writers referred to above (references 26 to the present one) are merely those who specify the location and at the same time use words which leave no doubt that the picture in question is no. 35. Other writers of the seventeenth and eighteenth centuries are not referred to if their references are vaguer—for example Ridolfi (*Maraviglie*), having described no. 35 (p. 142), later gives its location (p. 178) simply as *da gli heredi del Signor Cardinale Aldobrandino*. It may be pointed out in this place that Vasari, though describing the other Bacchanals at Ferrara, does not speak of no. 35. (31) The information concerning the fortunes of the family, summarised here, is derived from Litta: *Famiglie Celebri* and from the *Enciclopedia Italiana*. (32) *Historisch-Kritische Nachrichten von Italien*, II, p. 297. (33) Nikodemus Tessin (*Studieresor*, 1687–8, ed. Sirén, 1914, p. 168) mentions *vier zimblich grosse Bachanalien vom Titiano* as in Palazzo Barberini and this was repeated by Carla Caterina Patina (*Pitture Scelte*, Cologne, 1691, p. 179) and by various eighteenth-century writers, while Milanesi (ed. of Vasari, VII, p. 434, note 1) and earlier editions of the National Gallery catalogue include the Barberini in the pedigree of no. 35. The grounds for assuming that the pictures in question were copies are (a) the four original Bacchanals have never been together since the second quarter of the seventeenth century. Two were in Spain by 1638 (see W. N. Sainsbury: *Original Unpublished Papers Illustrative of . . . Rubens*, 1859, p. 353), (b) both Rossini (*Il Mercurio Errante*, 8th ed., 1760, p. 93) and the *Roma Antica e Moderna* (1765, II, p. 283) mention four Titian Bacchanals in Palazzo Barberini and *also* (pp. 271 and II, 607, respectively) no. 35 as at the Villa Aldobrandini, (c) Orbaan (*Documenti sul Barocco in Roma*, 1920, p. 512) quotes a Barberini inventory of 1631 which says clearly that there was at that time in Palazzo Barberini a copy of what is certainly no. 35, there stated as belonging to the Aldobrandini: *un quadro d'un baccanario, con un satiretto, che tira la testa di un vitello, copiato dal Maltese da un di Titiano, che hanno li Signori Altobrandini*, width *c.* 6 Roman *palmi*. (34) Ramdohr: *Ueber Mahlerei . . . in Rom*, II, p. 181. The sojourn (in itself a little mysterious) of no. 35 in Palazzo Doria seems at first to be rendered questionable by a curious statement of Ramdohr's (*op. cit.*, p. 163) *à propos* the Villa Aldobrandini that *diese Villa gehört nicht dem Hause Doria, wie H. Dr Volkmann schreibt, sondern dem Hause Borghese*. Unfortunately the reference to Volkmann's book given in this connection by Ramdohr (viz. vol. II, p. 233) is wrong (page 233 of that work is about something quite different) and it is difficult to be sure to which of Volkmann's remarks Ramdohr is referring. In his description of the Villa Aldobrandini (p. 825) Volkmann does not mention the owner. In his description of Palazzo Pamfili (i.e. Doria) on p. 295 (where he locates the *Bacchus and Ariadne*) he gives the owner of the building as *Prinz Doria aus Genua*—which is correct. Although Volkmann's statement that no. 35 hung in Palazzo Doria some time before 1770 is unsupported (for the reference of Titi: *Descrizione*, 1763, p. 320—*alcuni di Tiziano*—and of Chiusole: *Itinerario*, 1782, p. 265—*bei quadri di Tiziano*—to pictures in Palazzo Doria are too vague to constitute evidence either for or against) there seems no adequate reason to doubt it (the picture had, incidentally, very likely hung there earlier, as the building had been bought by Cardinal Pietro Aldobrandini in 1601). It may be relevant to add in this connection that a further Aldobrandini picture (no. 18, Luini, of this Gallery) was recorded in Palazzo Doria in 1759 and 1763, and Bottari (ed. of Vasari, vol. 3, 1760, p. 379, note 1) says he believes the Bellini Bacchanal (which Ramdohr, *op. cit.*—1787—p. 182, recorded in the Villa Aldobrandini and which had come with no. 35 from Ferrara) was then in Palazzo Pamfili (Doria). (35) Buchanan: *Memoirs*, vol. II (1824), pp. 135–6, 142–3 and 153. The evidence for the year 1797 as the date of the sale comes from Waagen's statement (*Galleries and Cabinets of Art . . .*, 1857, p. 467) that the Bellini *Bacchanal*, still at that time the companion of no. 35, was bought in that year by Camuccini. (36) Buchanan, *op. cit.*, II, p. 173. (37) Whitley: *Art in England*, 1800–1820 (1928), p. 212, says the picture had been brought to England in 1806. But Buchanan (*op. cit.*, p. 174) says it was detained in Italy 'for a considerable time' after its purchase in May, 1806, and the Farington Diary (vol. IV, p. 115) describes it, implying a novelty, under the heading 'April 7th, 1807'. (38) In the copy in the Gallery library of the 1813 Kinnaird sale catalogue no. 35 (lot 88) together with two other pictures (now nos. 62 and 194 of this Gallery) is stated to have been sold 'by private contract' to Delahante or Lafontaine. But a letter of 7th July, 1813 from Delahante himself to Penrice (*Penrice Letters*, pp. 30–1) strongly implies that the purchaser was Delahante and not Lafontaine. (39) Whitley: *op. cit.*, p. 254.

## 224 THE TRIBUTE MONEY

Ca. 43 × 40 (1·09 × 1·015).

The original canvas is of irregular shape at the base, being longer on the right than on the left. There is therefore visible on the left (narrowing towards the centre) some of a strip (about six inches wide) of later canvas, most of which was folded over the stretcher when the picture was cleaned in 1937. Judging by Martino Rota's engraving (see ENGRAVINGS below) this strip roughly corresponds in extent with part of the original canvas which would have been cut off.

Some cutting at one or both sides is also possible.[1]

Signed on the pilaster, right:—TITIANVS | .F.

The paint of the signature, examined under a microscope, gives every indication of being original.

Good condition on the whole. The edges are much abraded and the paint in Christ's blue mantle deteriorated.

X-ray photographs reveal *pentimenti* in all three hands and, more particularly, in Christ's head, which was originally farther to the (spectator's) left and somewhat inclined. The fundamental nature of the last-named change, in particular, is a good indication that no. 224 is not a copy.

The textual sources of the incident are Matthew 22, 17–22, Mark 12, 14–17 and Luke 20, 22–25.

No. 224 was purchased from the Soult collection. A note—'se lo llevó el mariscal Soult'—against an entry—'*Christo nuestro Senor*, de medio cuerpo, y un fariseo que le muestra la moneda de César, de mano de *Tiziano*'—in an inventory of pictures given by Philip II to the Escorial in 1574[2] therefore identifies it with that picture. The fact that no. 224 was engraved by Martino Rota who appears not to have been in Venice after 1568[3] suggests that it was painted not later than then. For two reasons it is therefore almost certainly identifiable with the picture of the Tribute Money which Titian told Philip II in a letter of 26th October, 1568 that he had recently finished and despatched to him.[4] It follows from this (and from the genuine signature) that no. 224 was sent out by Titian from his studio as his own work, and suggestions of an independent painter—such as Paris Bordon[5]—as author are therefore inadmissible. The extent of the studio assistance (the existence of which in no. 224 has long been recognised) cannot be authoritatively defined. The feature which is least characteristic of the late Titian is the relative lack of an all-over tone, but some of this may be due to subsequent modifications in the paint—particularly as regards the blue in Christ's mantle. Most of the execution seems to the present writer acceptable as late Titian with the exception of the head of the questioner, his white sleeve, and (in its present state) of Christ's blue mantle. The design of no. 224 evidently served as model for Van Dyck's picture of the same subject (Genoa, Palazzo Bianco)—perhaps via Cornelis Galle's engraving (see below).

VERSIONS: Sedelmeyer sale, Paris, 3rd–5th June, 1907, lot 188—variant (the secondary questioner—extreme left in no. 224—is transferred to the right of the picture and his hat to the chief questioner). A copy combining features of the latter picture and of no. 224 was lot 129, anonymous sale, Christie's, 6th May, 1938. Others recorded at Wentworth Woodhouse and in the Duque de Infantados collection, Madrid.

ENGRAVINGS: By Martino Rota (see above)—Christ's nimbus much enlarged. Another engraving, by Cornelis Galle, is in reverse and with an extra figure on the side of Christ to which His finger points (as in the Sedelmeyer picture though not corresponding with it in other respects).

PROVENANCE: Sent, before 26th October, 1568 from Titian in Venice to Philip II in Spain and given by the latter, in 1574, to the Escorial (see above). Described as in the Escorial sacristy by de los Santos (1657)[6] and Ximenez (1764).[7] One of six pictures from the Spanish royal collections given, *c.* 1810, by Joseph Bonaparte to Maréchal Soult.[8] No. 132 in the sale of the latter's collection, Paris, 19th–22nd May, 1852, where purchased through Woodburn. Exhibition of Cleaned Pictures, National Gallery, 1947, no. 35.

REPRODUCTION: *Illustrations, Italian Schools*, 1937, p. 357.

REFERENCES: (1) Dimensions given in the Philip II inventory of 1574 as '4½ pies × 4"—i.e. roughly 49 × 44'. (2) Printed by Fr. Julián Zarco Cuevas:

*Inventario de las . . . pinturas . . . donados por Felipe II al Monasterio de El Escorial (1571–98)*, p. 139. For date of this part of the inventory see p. 16. (3) Entry in Thieme-Becker. (4) Letter printed by Crowe and Cavalcaselle: *Titian*, vol. II (1877), p. 537. (5) As made in the 1929 catalogue. (6) P. 129 in the English edition of 1760. (7) P. 307 of his *Descripción . . . del Escorial.* (8) Unpublished list of which copy in the possession of the Duke of Wellington.

## 270 'NOLI ME TANGERE'

$42\frac{3}{4} \times 35\frac{3}{4}$ (1·09 × 0·91).

The sky extensively worn and restored. Some wearing also in Christ's body, particularly in the upper part. Titian's use of copper resinate in much of the foliage has resulted in its changing colour from green to brown. Otherwise reasonably good condition.

Cleaned 1957.

X-ray photographs disclose changes made during the painting and others made at a later date. Originally the background consisted of a tree in the middle which was much smaller than the existing one and inclined in the opposite direction. The line of its foliage was subsequently changed by Titian into that of part of the central cloud. The ridge and buildings were on the left, not on the right.[1] Christ was shown striding away from the Magdalen, not taking a step towards her. He may also have been wearing a gardener's hat. At some time after the picture left Titian's hands and before Nicolas Tardieu's engraving was made (published in 1742, see ENGRAVINGS below) the upper portion of the Magdalen's skirt was painted over, and corresponding modifications made to her bodice. Between the date of Tardieu's engraving and that of F. Trier (immediately pre-Revolution, but not published until 1808) a further addition was made in the form of a sapling on the right of the large tree, following the line of Titian's original tree as disclosed by the X-rays. Both these additions were removed in the 1957 restoration.

Catalogued as by Titian since the seventeenth century and accepted as such by the majority of modern writers. G. M. Richter suggested a work of Giorgione subsequently worked on by Titian,[2] and the publication of some X-rays[3] was at first thought to support this theory. Both figures in their present form are clearly recognisable as Titian's, and the landscape, though very Giorgionesque in type, is no more so than in pictures such as the Capitoline *Baptism* or the Ellesmere *Three Ages*, whose attribution to Titian is not in doubt. In view of the fact, moreover, that one of its principal features—the group of buildings—recurs in two further pictures in the same category—the *Sacred and Profane Love* [4] and the background of the Dresden *Venus* [5]—there would seem to the present writer to be no necessity to assume Giorgione's participation.

VERSIONS: 1. Lot 128 in the Hugh A. J. Munro sale, Christie's, 1st June, 1878, where catalogued as 'small replica of the picture bequeathed to the National Gallery by the poet Rogers'. 2. By W. Etty. Exh. Fine Art and Industrial Exhibition, York, 1866 (514)—'copy of the Rogers Titian in the National Gallery'. 3. Cracow, Czartoryski Museum. G. M. Richter (*Giorgio*

*da Castelfranco*, 1937, p. 225) specifies a Hanfstaengl photograph, no. 24,503.
4. Copy (in reverse) of figures, in the English College, Valladolid (photograph in the Gallery archives).

ENGRAVINGS: 1. By Nicolas Tardieu (in reverse). No. 143 in *Recueil d'Estampes*, 1742. 2. By F. Trier (in reverse). No. 17 (Titian) in vol. II of *Galerie du Palais Royal* (1808). 3. By W. Ensom (Crowe and Cavalcaselle: *Titian*, 1877, vol. 1, p. 210, note).

PROVENANCE: Stated in the *Recueil d'Estampes d'après les Plus Beaux Tableaux . . . en France*, 1742 (vol. II, p. 59) that no. 270—which is engraved in that work—had been in the collection of Christoforo and Francesco Muselli at Verona, that it had been acquired by the Marquis de Seignelay (who died in 1690) who had sent agents [6] to Italy to buy it, that it had then belonged to 'M. Bertin' and that at the time of writing it was in the Orléans collection. It is therefore identifiable with Ridolfi's mention (1648) of Titian's *Maddalena con Christo nell' horto* (as belonging to Christoforo and Francesco Muselli) [7] and with a picture catalogued in the Muselli collection in 1662, despite the fact that in the latter the Magdalen is said to have one hand to her bosom. [8] Pierre-Vincent Bertin, the owner after Seignelay, died in 1711. [9] Catalogued on page 477 of Du Bois de Saint Gelais' *Description des Tableaux du Palais Royal* (1727). The Italian pictures in the Orléans collection were sold in 1792 to the Belgian banker, Walkuers, who sold them to Laborde de Méréville, who fled with them to England [10] where they were bought by Jeremiah Harman who made them over to a syndicate consisting of the Duke of Bridgewater and Lords Carlisle and Gower. [11] A sale was arranged by Bryan who exhibited them in 1798. No. 270 seems to have been lot 119 in the sale at 88 Pall Mall, 26th December, 1798, which in an annotated copy of the sale catalogue in the National Gallery library is marked as bought by Lord Gower. [12] A few of the pictures bought on this occasion by the latter and by the Duke of Bedford reappeared in an anonymous sale (by Coxe, Burrell and Foster), 12th–13th May, 1802. In this sale no. 270 was lot 55 (2nd day). Lot 91 ('from the Orléans Gallery') Arthur Champernowne sale, 2nd day, 30th June, 1820, where bought Rogers. [13] Samuel Rogers bequest, 1856.

REPRODUCTION: *Illustrations, Italian Schools*, 1937, p. 352.

REFERENCES: (1) For a discussion of the implications of the X-ray photographs see Cecil Gould in the *Burlington Magazine*, 1958, pp. 44–8. (2) *Burlington Magazine*, vol. 65 (1934), pp. 4–16. Richter's view was supported by Tietze (*Tizian*, 1936, Tafelband, p. 293). (3) In *From the National Gallery Laboratory* by F. I. G. Rawlins (1940). (4) G. M. Richter (*Giorgio da Castelfranco*, 1937, p. 263) suggests that these buildings are 'a recollection of the Rocca di Asolo'. But the photograph of the Rocca which he reproduces does not bear out this statement. If a specific source had to be postulated it seems to the present writer a possibility that it might be not in any Italian building but in Dürer's engravings or woodcuts. A suggestion has been made (in a pamphlet by Cav. Tarelli of Ancona in the Gallery archives) that the background of no. 270 may represent the Porta Capodimonte at Ancona. In connection with possible further borrowings by Titian in no. 270 attention may be drawn to a suggestion by J. Wilde (note in the Gallery archives) that the figure of Christ in its final form is based on that of a Giorgionesque Venus known from an engraving by Marcantonio Raimondi (Richter, *op. cit.*, pl. LXI, bottom right, reproduces this). Richter (*op. cit.*, p. 225) also mentions 'interesting points of contact' with Fra Bartolommeo's picture of the same subject (Louvre). Kenneth Clark (*Landscape into Art*, 1949, p. 60, note 1) postulates an Antique derivation for the first form of Christ's pose. (5) Generally identified with the picture stated by the Anonimo Morelliano to have been started by Giorgione 'ma lo paese et Cupidine forono finiti da Titiano'. The buildings occur again in the background of a Titianesque *putto* (Vienna Academy 466)—see K.

Oettinger in Vienna *Jahrbuch*, 1944, pp. 113 ff. (6) 'Sieurs Forest et Alvarès'. Alvarese is also mentioned in this connection by Bartolommeo dal Pozzo: *Vite de' Pittori ... Veronesi*, 1718, p. 94. (7) Ridolfi/Hadeln, I, p. 198. (8) Muselli catalogue quoted by G. Campori: *Raccolta di Cataloghi*, 1870, p. 178: *Christo NS che in forma d'Ortolano apparisce alla Maddalena ed ella genuflessa in atto d'adoratione posa una mano sopra un vase, e l'altra tiene al petto, in un bellissimo paese, figure di un braccio, di Titiano e in altezza quasi 2 ba e 1½ per l'altra parte.* (9) E. Bonnaffé: *Dictionnaire des Amateurs Français*, 1884, p. 21. (10) Preface to vol. 1 of the *Galerie du Palais Royal* (1808, but with title-page of 1786). Also Charles Blanc: *Le Trésor de la Curiosité*, 1858, vol. II, pp. 148–59, and W. Buchanan: *Memoirs*, vol. 1 (1824), pp. 9–220. (11) Passavant: *Tour of a German Artist in England*, vol. II (1836), p. 179. (12) Passavant adds the name 'Rogers' against the picture—evidently as meaning the owner in his day, not the purchaser at the Orléans sale. (13) Buyer's name from notes in the Gallery archives communicated by a relation of A. Champernowne. Redford (II, p. 257) and Buchanan (*loc. cit.*) mention the identity of the Champernowne picture with the Orléans one.

635 MADONNA AND CHILD WITH SS. JOHN THE BAP-
TIST AND CATHERINE OF ALEXANDRIA

$39\frac{5}{8} \times 56$ ($1\cdot01 \times 1\cdot42$).

Somewhat rubbed in places, particularly in the sky, but condition in general considerably better than with the average Titian. Strips about two inches wide on the left and about an inch wide along the bottom are extensively repainted. It is possible that these are additions of canvas replacing frayed pieces of similar size. But as the weave of the canvas in these areas does not noticeably differ from that of the bulk of the picture it is more probable that the painter himself found he had insufficient space at the left and at the bottom and therefore utilised part of the turn-over of the canvas.

Cleaned 1955.

In the 1861 and 1862 editions of the National Gallery catalogue it is stated that no. 635 is signed and dated 'TICIANUS, 1533'. In editions from 1863 to 1925 inclusive it is said to be 'signed TICIAN'. Before the cleaning of 1955 there was an inventory inscription 'No. 78 Di. Titiǫ' painted at the bottom right corner. This was not old but might have been copied from the back of the original canvas. It was claimed to be an Escorial mark at the time when the picture was bought for the Gallery. In the restoration of 1955 it was covered up. No trace of a signature was found on that occasion and the one variously quoted in the early catalogues is unlikely to have been genuine.

S. Catherine is shown without an attribute but is identifiable by her type.

Two separate attempts have been made to associate no. 635 with contemporary documents but both are inconclusive. Frizzoni[1] identified it with a picture seen by the Anonimo Morelliano in the house of Andrea Odoni in Venice in 1532: *El quadro della nostra donna nel paese, cun el Christo fanziuollo et S. Giovan fanziullo, et S(anta) ... fu de mano de Titiano.*[2] It is more likely, however, that Odoni's picture was one from the Reynst collection which was part of the Dutch gift to Charles II

since the latter also included the Lotto portrait of Odoni himself which
is mentioned by the Anonimo in the same context.[3] The fact that the
Anonimo does not identify the female saint is a further pointer in this
direction since the identity of this figure in the Reynst picture, though
called 'St Elizabeth' in the Charles II inventory, might perhaps (to
judge from the engraving) give rise to uncertainty. An alternative theory
proposes identification of no. 635 with the 'Nostra donna con St
Catherina'[4] on which Titian was working in February, 1530 for the
Gonzaga and which is probably identical with the 'Madonna, con il
bambino in braccio et S. Catterina' of the 1627 Mantua inventory.[5] It
cannot be established that the above painting reached the collection of
Charles I with the other Mantua pictures, while the history of no. 635
is unknown before the 'fifties of the seventeenth century (the existence,
in Van Dyck's Italian sketch book, of drawings after Veronese's in
Palazzo Pisani, Venice on the *verso* of a sheet containing a sketch apparently after S. John in no. 635—see DRAWING below—would not
constitute proof that the painting was in Venice during Van Dyck's
residence in Italy). The omission of S. John in both the latter references
militates against identification of no. 635 with the Gonzaga picture
while the fact that the costumes in no. 635 accord best with a date in
the second half of the 1530's would be an element against the Odoni
and the Gonzaga picture alike.[6]

Some studio assistance is probable. The brush-work of the Madonna's
blue dress, in particular, seems too tame for Titian himself.

VERSIONS: A number of copies exist dating from various periods, none of
note. More interesting are the variants. One of these, acceptable as from
Titian's studio, is in the Pitti gallery, Florence. In this, the Madonna's dress
is red, and there is no angel in the sky. It also shows a later moment in the
episode. Whereas in no. 635 S. John is offering the Madonna a fruit complete
with flower and leaf, in the Pitti variant the Madonna has taken the fruit and
handed it to the Child, while S. John has now taken up a kneeling position on
the right hand side of the picture and has been joined by the lamb. As in no. 635
there is still a flower between the thumb and first finger of the Madonna's
right hand, but as a result of the changes it is now a growing flower which she
is plucking and no longer one attached to the fruit. In a further development
of this theme (picture in an anonymous sale, Christie's, 29th May, 1952, lot 129)
the Child has now jettisoned the fruit and S. John leads on the lamb from the
right, instead of kneeling. A version of the latter picture in a late Titianesque
idiom was in the collection of the late Dr Seymour Maynard in London; another
(attributed to Schiavone and with the addition of S. Joseph) is at Vienna (no. 149
in the 1938 catalogue). A picture from the Reynst collection now at Hampton
Court (no. 112) shows the Madonna as in the Pitti version, but the Child is
different, S. John and S. Catherine are omitted and Tobias and the angel have
replaced the shepherds in the right background. A distant derivative, showing
the Child holding the fruit as in the intermediate versions but with two kneeling
clerics instead of S. John and S. Catherine was in the F. E. Sidney sale (Christie's,
10th December, 1937, lot 64) and shown at Agnew's, London, summer 1939.[7]
For a copy or variant belonging in 1720 to the Duc de Noailles in Paris see
below under PROVENANCE.

DRAWING: Folio 12 of Van Dyck's Italian sketch-book (British Museum).
Apparently after S. John.

ENGRAVINGS: 1. By K. Audran (*A Paris de l'Imprimerie de Herman Weyen . . .*) (in reverse). See reference 12 below. 2. By F. Joubert in the Coesvelt catalogue of 1836.

PROVENANCE: Referred to by Mündler in a note dating from 1856 as being then in the Beaucousin collection in Paris and formerly in the Coesvelt collection.[8] It is therefore identifiable with the picture engraved as plate 16 in the catalogue (printed in 1836) of the collection of W. G. Coesvelt, London, which figured as lots 15 and 47 respectively in the Coesvelt sales, Christie's, 2nd June, 1837 and 13th June, 1840 (bought in on the first occasion and perhaps also on the second).[9] In all three of these catalogues stated to have come from the sacristy of the Escorial and therefore fairly certainly identifiable with a picture included in a batch of forty-one sent in 1656 by Velazquez to the Escorial by order of Philip IV: *Otro del mesmo artífice* [i.e. Titian] *de un Deposorio de Santa Caterina. Está Nuestra Señora sentada en un pays; el Niño echado en su regaço; la Santa arrodillada haciéndole caricias; San Ioan Baptista niño, que trae una fruta á la Vírgen que alarga la mano para tomarla . . . Las figuras menores que el natural. Tiene de alto tres piés y medio, de largo casi cinco.*[10] The same picture was described by Francisco de los Santos and by Andres Ximenez in their works on the Escorial.[11] The date (1764) of the latter work (in which the picture is still specified as in the Escorial sacristy) would seem to preclude the identification proposed by Crowe and Cavalcaselle with a picture in the collection of the Duc de Noailles in Paris in 1720.[12] According to Velazquez' memoir the picture seems to have been one of those presented to Philip IV by the Duke de Medina de las Torres on his return to Spain from Italy. Purchased with the Beaucousin collection, 1860.

REPRODUCTION: *Illustrations, Italian Schools*, 1937, p. 353.

REFERENCES: **(1)** Edition of the *Anonimo Morelliano*, 1884, p. 159. **(2)** For the text of the Anonimo see also Frimmcl's edition, 1888, p. 84. **(3)** See Denis Mahon: *Notes on the 'Dutch Gift' to Charles II, III*, in *Burlington Magazine*, vol. 92 (1950), p. 15. The entry in the Charles II inventory reads: 166. *Titiano. Our Saior. with his feete on a Cusheon the B. Virgin St John and St Elizabeth.* This picture is now lost. **(4)** See Crowe and Cavalcaselle: *Titian*, vol. 1 (1877), p. 446. **(5)** See Luzio: *La Galleria dei Gonzaga*, 1913, p. 115, no. 315. **(6)** Notes by Stella Mary Pearce on the costumes in no. 635 in the Gallery archives. If the Gonzaga picture still exists it is possibly identical with the *Vierge au Lapin* now in the Louvre. This was certainly one of the pictures sold in December, 1665 by the Duc de Richelieu to Louis XIV (see Claude Ferraton: *La Collection du Duc de Richelieu au Musée du Louvre* in *Gazette des Beaux-Arts*, vol. 35 (1949), p. 437). Whether or not it was in Charles I's collection before that cannot be established. As regards no. 635 there must remain a possibility that it was in Charles' collection, since the Prado catalogue states that the Correggio *Noli Me Tangere* has his seal on the back and this picture seems to have been presented to Philip IV of Spain by the Duke de Medina de las Torres with no. 635 (see under PROVENANCE). **(7)** The list of variants could be extended. For example, a Poussin drawing formerly in the Tancred Borenius collection was from a version with S. John on the right and a sleeping hound on the left. Mündler, in his note-book (in the Gallery archives) described a picture in the Patrizi collection, Rome, in 1856: 'School of Titian, a marriage of St Catherine, similar to one in Palazzo Pitti, and to the other, once the property of Mr Coesvelt, now of Mr Beaucousin in Paris.' **(8)** See preceding reference for text of Mündler's note. **(9)** Mentioned as in the Coesvelt collection by Passavant (*Tour of a German Artist in England*, vol. 1 (1836), p. 185). In the Coesvelt catalogue of 1836 it is stated that the collection was 'principally made in countries subjected to the revolutionary disasters which have overwhelmed the South of Europe'. The provenance of no. 635 from the Escorial is therefore not surprising. Some account of the artistic losses of the Escorial at the time of the Napoleonic invasion is given in Fr. Damian Bermejo: *Descripción artistica*

del Real Monasterio de S. Lorenzo del Escorial despues de la Invasion de los
Franceses (1820). (**10**) See *Mémoire de Velazquez sur 41 Tableaux envoyés par
Philippe IV à l'Escurial*. Edited by Baron Ch. Davilier, 1874, pp. 50–3. (**11**) The
first edition of Santos' book was published in 1657. (**12**) Crowe and Cavalcaselle:
*Titian*, I (1877), p. 208. The source of the information is Mariette: *Abecedario*,
vol. V, p. 307, who identifies the Noailles picture with K. Audran's engraving.
Whether in fact this engraving was made from no. 635 or from the Noailles
version (assuming that the two were not identical) cannot be determined.
Ximenez' statement is, however, not necessarily conclusive, as he drew heavily
on his predecessors.

### 1944  PORTRAIT OF A MAN

32 × 26 (0·812 × 0·663).

The face somewhat rubbed in places.[1] The main area of the blue
sleeve well preserved. The tighter portion of the sleeve (adjoining the
sitter's hand) damaged by a network of pin pricks, evidently made in an
attempt to treat flaking paint. The parapet extensively restored.

Cleaned 1949.

Inscribed on the parapet: T (with remains of a triangular dot before
it) .V. (the dots on either side are triangular). Before the 1949 restoration
the inscription read 'TITIANVS. TV.' on the left and '.v.' on the right.
The v on the right was clearly original, having been painted 'wet in
wet'. But of the letters on the left only the T in the TV monogram was in
the same technique. The letters TITIANVS and the v of the TV monogram seem to have been added when the underlying paint was not only
dry but already cracked. During the 1949 restoration these letters were
not removed but were covered up to match the general tone of the
parapet. Whoever amplified the original inscription seems to have
thought that the letters 'TV' stood for 'Titiano Vecellio' or 'Titianus
Vecellius'. Though this form was frequently used by Titian as a signature on documents he very rarely included the word 'Vecellio', even in
an abbreviated form, when signing a picture. Nevertheless, examples do
occur, as in the Uffizi portrait of Lodovico Beccadelli, which is signed
'... Titianus Vecellius ...' or in the Prado *Entombment*, which is signed
'Titianus Vecellius Aeques Caes'. An abbreviated form occurs on the
Dresden *Lavinia with a Feather Fan*—'Lavinia Tit. V. F. AB. EO. P'.
It should be borne in mind that the letter V also occurs in inscriptions
on the parapet of portraits not by Titian—e.g. in the Berlin Giorgione,
which has 'V V', or a portrait formerly in a private collection at Boston
(Mass.), attributed to Cariani, which has 'V'.[2] Nevertheless the assumption that the letters T V, on no. 1944 as on no. 5385 of this Gallery,
were in fact intended by Titian as a signature seems to the present writer
more probable than not.

At the time of its entry into the Gallery no. 1944 was catalogued as
representing Ariosto, whose name had been associated with it (or with
another version) at least as early as the seventeenth century. In fact, the
features shown bear no resemblance to those in authentic portraits of the
poet (see the entry for no. 636, Palma Vecchio). An attempt, first made
by J. P. Richter[3] and subsequently supported by others,[4] to identify

no. 1944 with a portrait, mentioned by Vasari,[5] of a member of the Barbarigo family is hypothetical and inconclusive. The pose of no. 1944, on the other hand, and the angle of the eyes strongly suggest a self-portrait. Rembrandt's self-portrait of 1640 (now no. 672 of this Gallery) and his etched self-portrait of 1639 may in fact owe something to no. 1944 as may Van Dyck's self-portrait with a sun-flower.[6]

There is no authenticated portrait of Titian as a young man or even as a middle-aged one, but those of him in old age show one feature, namely a prognathous bone structure—a huge chin and correspondingly underhung lower lip—which would be relatively unaffected by the symptoms of ageing and which is also present in no. 1944.[7] The costume shown in no. 1944 is similar to that shown in a famous portrait of which several versions are known—e.g. at Leningrad (inscribed 'Dominicus') and in, or formerly in, the collection of the Duke of Grafton.[8] These pictures show the same kind of ruffled shirt as in no. 1944, appearing over the top of a tunic cut on similar lines and with similar enormous sleeves. As both these versions are dated 1512 that would constitute some indication of the date of no. 1944.

Sometimes attributed to Giorgione in the past,[9] but without justification.

VERSION: An old copy, ex-Manfrin collection, in the collection of the Earl of Rosebery at Mentmore. Three other copies are mentioned by Crowe and Cavalcaselle.[10]

ENGRAVINGS: The design engraved by R. van Persijn (in reverse) and De Larmessin (see PROVENANCE below).

PROVENANCE: Perhaps from the collection of Alphonso Lopez and conceivably from that of Sir Anthony Van Dyck. The chief evidence for the Lopez provenance is the Persijn engraving which is inscribed as having been taken from a drawing made by Sandrart in Amsterdam from the original in the possession of Alphonso Lopez.[11] The engraving corresponds closely with no. 1944 (in reverse) except for the legend on the parapet which reads 'TITIANVS. U.' The Lopez painting was due to be sold, with others belonging to him, probably in Paris in mid-December, 1641. A letter, written apparently in November, 1641, asks the addressee, François Langlois, to remind Van Dyck of the Lopez sale, and specifically mentions the excellence of the Titian 'Ariosto'.[12] Van Dyck in fact died (in London) on 9th December, 1641,[13] but an inventory of pictures which had belonged to him, dated 1644, includes an 'Ariosto Poeta' among the Titian's.[14] It is therefore possible that shortly before his death Van Dyck had sent instructions to Paris for the purchase of the picture. But even if the one in his inventory was identical with the Lopez picture (which cannot be proved) it cannot be established with certainty that either was identical with no. 1944 and not a copy.[15] In the possession of the Earl of Darnley before 1824, when lent by him to the British Institution (34). Also lent by Lord Darnley to Manchester, 1857 (236),[16] and to the R.A., 1876 (125) and 1895 (109). Sold to Sir G. Donaldson, 1904, from whom purchased, 1904, with substantial contributions from Lord Iveagh, Mr Waldorf Astor, Mr Pierpont Morgan, Mr Alfred Beit, Lady Wantage, Lord Burton and a grant from H.M. Government.

REPRODUCTION: *Illustrations, Italian Schools*, 1937, p. 354.

REFERENCES: (1) During the restoration of 1949 it was found that the moustaches and beard had been reinforced by later repaint which had changed their outlines and which was therefore removed. (2) Reproduced in Berenson's

*Lists* (1957), pl. 732. (**3**) *Art Journal*, 1895, p. 90. (**4**) E.g. H. Cook (*Giorgione*, 1907, pp. 68–73) and Suida (*Tiziano*, 1933, p. 31). (**5**) Vasari/Milanesi, vol. VII, p. 428. (**6**) Collection of the Duke of Westminster. For the question of Van Dyck's ownership of no. 1944 see below and Jenny Müller-Rostock in *Zeitschrift für bildende Kunst*, 1922, pp. 22 ff. (**7**) For the Titian self-portraits see Gronau in the Prussian *Jahrbuch*, 1907, p. 46. (**8**) The Leningrad version is reproduced and discussed by J. Wilde in the Vienna *Jahrbuch*, 1933, pp. 113–36. The Grafton picture is reproduced as pl. 904 of Berenson's *Lists* (1957). (**9**) E.g. by Cook, *op. cit.* Earlier attributions to Sebastiano del Piombo are recorded by Pallucchini in his monograph on that painter, 1944, p. 185. (**10**) *Titian*, vol. 1, p. 201. (**11**) Sandrart's drawing is probably the one now in the Lugt collection, The Hague. Like the Mentmore painting it has no inscription on the balustrade but the latter is restored in this place and it is not possible to assert that it never bore an inscription. In the Willem Six sale, Amsterdam, 12th May, 1734, lot 154 was 'Het Pourtrait van L. Ariosto, door Sandrart'. (**12**) This letter was first published by Bottari (*Raccolta di Lettere . . .*, 1764, vol. IV, p. 303). It is also printed with a commentary in Hofstede de Groot's *Die Urkunden über Rembrandt* (1906, pp. 116–18). Though the letter is signed Jacopo Stella it was stated by Mariette who owned the original that it was really by Claude Vignon. In either case it would have been written in Paris, and since the writer states in it that he has just inspected the Lopez pictures it would follow that the Lopez sale took place in Paris. It could not have occurred in Amsterdam as stated by Müller-Rostock (*op. cit.*) as the writer asks the addressee to give various messages for him in Holland when he next went there. The letter is undated but must have been written some time in November as the writer of it assumes that Van Dyck, who returned from Paris to London during that month, might still be *en route*. See E. W. Moes in *Oud Holland*, 1894, XII, p. 238. (**13**) From a pocket-book MS. of Nicassius Roussel, who was at Van Dyck's funeral (notice printed in W. H. Carpenter's *Pictorial Notices . . . of . . . Van Dyck* (1844, p. 44)). De Groot (*op. cit.*, p. 118) is therefore wrong in saying Van Dyck died on 11th December. (**14**) Müller-Rostock (*loc. cit.*) who published the inventory assumed that it really dated from the 1630's and that in consequence Lopez had acquired the picture after it had belonged to Van Dyck. W. Stechow (*Art Quarterly*, 1942, p. 143) pointed out that there was no reason to suspect the date 1644. (**15**) G. M. Richter (*Giorgio da Castelfranco*, 1937, p. 225) states that Sandrart copied the painting when it was in the Reynst collection at Amsterdam, and Hoogewerff and van Regteren Altena allege (*Arnoldus Buchelius 'Res Pictoriae'*, 1928, p. 99) that it was in the Van Uffelen collection before that of Lopez. The present writer could find no authority for either of these statements. Hoogewerff and van Regteren Altena (*loc. cit.*) are not justified in suggesting an identification of no. 1944 with a picture seen in the Reynst collection by Buchell. The latter was almost certainly Lotto's Odoni portrait which the authors also mention in this context (see Denis Mahon: *Notes on the Dutch Gift to Charles II, III* in *Burlington Magazine*, vol. 92, 1950, p. 15). (**16**) In provisional catalogue. No. 257 in definitive catalogue.

## 3948  MADONNA AND CHILD

$29\frac{3}{4} \times 24\frac{7}{8}$ (0·756 × 0·632).

Worn and retouched, and at present distorted by the spotty remains of old varnish. In the 1929 catalogue as 'Mother and Child', but the type of composition is that of a Madonna and Child.

Despite damage and unequal cleaning usually now accepted and acceptable as a work of Titian's extreme old age—probably varying, as he frequently did at this period, one of his own earlier designs (see VERSIONS below). Closely comparable in handling with (and in quality rather superior to) the *Madonna and Child with SS. Tiziano and Francis and a Donor* (Titian himself) in the chapel of S. Tiziano in the Chiesa Arcipretale at Pieve di Cadore. The latter picture is mentioned as Titian's by Vasari.

VERSIONS: A picture sold at Sotheby's on 15th December, 1954 (lot 43) appeared to derive from a version of the same design but in a Titianesque idiom of an earlier phase. An old copy was lot 117, Christie's, 6th February, 1953. Another was exported in 1943.[1] A version with S. Joseph and the infant S. John was published as Titian's by Hadeln (*Burlington Magazine*, vol. LIII, 1928, pp. 55–6) but the attribution has found no support.[2] A photograph of a much damaged version of the central group with male figures on each side was in the library of Gustav Glück.[3] A modern version, by Vanessa Bell, was shown in London in 1939 (Storran Gallery).

PROVENANCE: Seen by Waagen, 1850–1,[4] in the collection of Lord Ward (1st Earl of Dudley), by whom exh., Dublin, 1854 (101) and R.A., 1871 (331). Earl of Dudley sale, 25th June, 1892 (89) where bought Mond by whom exh. R.A., 1894 (110) and Grosvenor Gallery, 1913–14 (47). Mond Bequest, 1924.

REPRODUCTION: *Illustrations, Italian Schools*, 1937, p. 351.

REFERENCES: (1) Photographs in the Gallery archives. (2) Hadeln, in his article, introduces as analogy the name of Cézanne, who, to judge from the photograph reproduced, would be as acceptable as Titian as author of the picture. (3) Now in the Gallery archives. (4) *Treasures . . .*, vol. II (1854), p. 235.

## 4452 THE VENDRAMIN FAMILY

81 × 118½ (2·06 × 3·01).

Some compression has occurred on the left during painting—an earlier version of the young bearded man's head is visible through the blue of the sky. The outline of the calf of a leg is visible through the red velvet robe of the left central figure. Infra-red photography discloses further underpainting in this figure which is not visible to the naked eye, namely the calf and thigh of the figure's other leg (his left) resting on the step, together with various scribbles for draperies. *Pentimenti* in the outlines of all three principal figures. X-ray photographs disclose further *pentimenti* in the head of the boy on the extreme left.

Condition unequal. Most of the sky is very worn and extensively re-touched. The following areas are well preserved: the faces of all three adults, the red velvet robe and right hand of the left central figure, the piece of red velvet over the right arm of the kneeling central figure, the little boy with red stockings on the right (including the head of the dog he holds) and the cloth hanging from the altar, together with the ewer and candlestick above it. Of the faces of the other children the two on the extreme right are in reliable state except for the small shadowed areas which are retouched. The face of the central boy in the group on the left is retouched in the nostril and round the eyes. The paint in the face of the boy on the extreme left is 'frizzled' and also retouched.

The persistent (and exaggerated) allegations that no. 4452 was a ruined picture seem to stem from a remark made by Reynolds in a letter to Lord Upper Ossory. Reynolds says that 'to painters' eyes' no. 4452 and 'the picture of Van Dyck at Wilton' were 'hardly worth the name of good copies' since cleaning.[1] It is likely that Benjamin West knew Reynolds' opinion and was influenced by it, since he too links Van Dyck's Wilton *Pembroke Family* (presumably the one Reynolds meant) with no. 4452 as being pictures ruined by cleaning.[2] Something of these rumours reappeared when the picture was acquired by the Gallery in 1929, but they were answered in a letter from Lionello Venturi asserting that the condition was remarkably good.[3]

The cross shown on the altar is a reliquary of the True Cross. It had been presented in 1360 by pilgrims to the Patriarch of Constantinople who had made it over to Philippe de Maizières, Cancelliere of the Kingdom of Cyprus, who had presented it, on 23rd December, 1369, to Andrea Vendramin, Guardiano of the Scuola di S. Giovanni Evangelista, Venice, on behalf of his confraternity.[4] It has been preserved in the Scuola or in the church ever since and is still recognisable as that shown in no. 4452 and, among other pictures, in Gentile Bellini's *Miracle of the Cross* (Venice, Accademia).[5] The last-named picture illustrates the most memorable connection of the cross with the Vendramin family—namely the occasion when the cross fell into a canal but remained miraculously suspended above the water until Andrea Vendramin was privileged to jump in and save it.[6] This fact, and the following entry in part of an inventory made in March, 1569, of the collection of Gabriel Vendramin, leave no doubt of the subject of no. 4452: *un quadro grando nel qual li retrazo le crose miracolose con ser Andrea Vendramin con sette fioli et mesier Gabriel Vendramin con suo adornamento d'oro fatto de man de sier Titian.*[7] The early date of this inventory (i.e. within Titian's life-time) together with its reliable character (this part of it was apparently drawn up by Tintoretto and by Titian's son, Orazio)[8] constitute excellent documentation of Titian's authorship of no. 4452.

Pouncey (*loc. cit.*) has suggested plausibly that no. 4452 may have been commissioned by the Vendramin family for a dual purpose. They would have wished in the first place to commemorate the prowess of an ancestor in rescuing the sacred relic. But the cross in addition had safeguarded the family's commercial interests on an earlier occasion, and for that reason they may well have wished, by means of the picture, to invoke continued protection.

Usually dated too late. Crowe and Cavalcaselle put it around 1560[9] and when Gronau discovered the correct identification he let himself be unduly influenced by the fact that Gabriel Vendramin died in 1552 and proposed a date around 1550.[10] Further research in the Archivio di Stato at Venice has, however, established not only that Gabriel's eldest nephew, Leonardo, predeceased him, dying in October, 1547, but that Andrea died earlier still, in January of that year.[11] Andrea's seven sons were: Leonardo (or Lunardo), born 1523, died 1547, Luca, born 1528, Francesco, born 1529, Bortolomeo, born 1530, Giovanni, born 1532, Filippo, born 1534 and Federico, born 1535. In addition to these seven sons Andrea Vendramin was the father of six daughters.[12]

As regards the identification of the figures in the picture, the man standing left centre in the red velvet robe must be Andrea since he is nearest Andrea's sons and also indicates them with his right hand. The man kneeling, centre, is therefore Gabriel, the rich merchant and eminent collector of works of art. Andrea's eldest son, Leonardo (five years older than the next son) is clearly the bearded figure on the left. Of the remaining six sons the three kneeling in the left foreground are certainly older than the three on the right, so whatever the order within the groups the left would consist of the second, third and fourth sons (Luca, Francesco, Bortolomeo) and the right the three youngest (Giovanni, Filippo and Federico). Andrea Vendramin's death in January, 1547 gives a *terminus ad quem* for at least the start of the picture. But even this is too late, as Andrea's second, third and fourth sons are all shown beardless, and the eldest of these three, Luca, being born in March, 1528, would then have been nearly nineteen. The fashion for wearing beards was so general in the 'forties of the sixteenth century that it can be assumed that a youth would do so as soon as he could, and it is therefore most unlikely that Luca was more than about fifteen when the picture was started.[13] The latest date for it on these grounds is therefore about 1543. From a stylistic point of view this date is also about the earliest possible. The *Ecce Homo* (Vienna) which is dated (i.e. finished) as of that year is usually regarded as marking a new phase of Titian's style and one to which no. 4452 belongs. The two pictures have in fact elements both of design and handling in common which would support the assumption of a similar date of origin. On two grounds, therefore, it is reasonable to suppose that no. 4452 would have been started around the year 1543. As with other of Titian's works there may well have been a delay of some years before it was completed.

VERSIONS: Old copy at Hampton Court by Symon Stone. Another, from the Lady Lucas collection, belonged to Lt.-Col. Pepys-Cockerell in 1929 (photograph in the Gallery archives). A third is at Northwick Park (no. 71 in Borenius' catalogue of 1921). A fourth was in the Neeld collection. A copy made by Gainsborough from an engraving was lot 575 in the Samuel Rogers sale, 2nd May, 1856. A sketch copy (drawing) is at Alnwick (photograph in the Gallery archives).

ENGRAVING: By Bernard Baron, London, 1732 (in reverse, with dedication to the then owner, the 6th Duke of Somerset).

PROVENANCE: Vendramin family, Venice (see above). Apparently remained in Venice until at least 1636[14] and entered the collection in England of Sir Anthony Van Dyck some time between then and his death in 1641.[15] Purchased by the 10th Earl of Northumberland from Van Dyck's executors in the year ending 17th January, 1645-6.[16] In the possession of the Earls and Dukes of Northumberland (and, from 1682 to 1750, of the Dukes of Somerset) in various residences—Suffolk House (1652), Northumberland House (1671, and 1750-1873), Petworth (1671-1750, or earlier), 2 Grosvenor Place, London (1873-*c*. 1900) and Alnwick Castle (*c*. 1900-29)[17]—until 1929, when purchased from the 8th Duke, with the aid of a special Grant and of contributions from Samuel Courtauld, Sir Joseph Duveen, the N.A.-C.F. and the Phillips fund. Exh. B.I., 1818 (86) and 1846 (109), R.A., 1873 (146) and 1930 (168),[18] National Gallery (N.A.-C.F. Exhibition), 1945-6 (15).

REPRODUCTION: *Illustrations, Italian Schools*, 1937, p. 355.

REFERENCES: (1) Letter printed in Leslie and Taylor's *Life of Sir Joshua Reynolds*, II, p. 495. (2) Farington Diary, vol. VIII, p. 179. Reynolds and West were not to be the last Presidents of the Royal Academy to utter such sentiments on this topic. (3) Letter to *The Times* newspaper, 1st August, 1929. Waagen (*Treasures*, I, 393) speaks lugubriously of 'this masterpiece' having 'suffered not a little injury' but merely instances 'the right hand of the old man and one hand of the boy on the left'. (4) Giacomo de Mezi: *Miracoli della Croce Santissima della Scuola de San Giovanni Evangelista*, Venice, 1590. See also Philip Pouncey: *The Miraculous Cross in Titian's Vendramin Family*, in *Journal of the Warburg Institute*, vol. II (1939), p. 191. (5) G. M. Urbani de Gheltof: *Guida Storico-Artistica della Scuola di S. Giovanni Evangelista*, Venice, 1895. (6) An account of the event is given by Francesco Sansovino: *Venetia Città Nobilissima . . .*, 1581, p. 100. (7) Printed by Aldo Ravà: *Il 'Camerino delle Antigaglie' di Gabriele Vendramin* in *Nuovo Archivio Veneto*, Nuova serie, tomo XXXIX (1920), p. 117. Attention was drawn to this article by Georg Gronau (*Apollo*, II, 1925, pp. 126 f) who first connected the picture with this entry. Previously it has been known as 'The Cornaro Family'. (8) Ravà, *op. cit.*, p. 181. (9) *Titian*, vol. II (1877), p. 303. (10) *Op. cit.* (11) The following biographical information is from documents (kindly communicated by the Director) in the Archivio di Stato at Venice. Andrea in fact died on 31st January, 1546—i.e. 1547, new style. (12) Documents in the Archivio di Stato, Venice already quoted. (13) This point can be neatly illustrated by studying Moretto's *Feast in the House of Simon* of 1544 (Venice, S. Maria della Pietà). In this picture one of the two young and stylish serving men on the left has a young beard, the other has one just sprouting. (14) Almost certainly identical with a picture mentioned in a letter of 9th September, 1636 from Lord Arundel's son Maltravers as being for sale in Venice (printed in *English Travellers Abroad, 1604–1667* by J. W. Stoye (1952), p. 214): *I have heard that there is a picture of Titian at Venice to bee sould for five or 6 hundred duccatts. I desire that you would enquire diligently after it, and if you like it to give earneste for it, for it is for the King, although his name must not be used. As I heare it hath some 4 or 5 figures in it, drawen after the life of some of the Nobilitye of Vennice.* (15) Recognisable as the first item in an inventory (at Vienna) of Van Dyck's collection: *Tre senatori di Venezia con loro figlioli in un quadro di Titiano* (see Jenny Müller-Rostock in *Zeitschrift für bildende Kunst*, 1922, pp. 22–4). (16) Entry in a document in the Alnwick archives published by Oliver Millar (*Burlington Magazine*, vol. XCVII, August, 1955, p. 255): (year ending 17th January, 1645–6) *for 2 pictures for his LoP. one called the Senators the other the Andromida CCli.* This corrects the date (1656) given for the purchase in the R.A. catalogue (winter exhibition), 1873, which has been widely followed. There can be no doubt of the identity. The picture was already known as 'The Senators'—an unpublished indenture (owned by the Craigie family of Sydney, Australia—photographs in the Gallery library) of 1650 concerning Van Dyck's estate refers to it in those words. See also Richard Symonds' statement 'the great picture of Titian Senators of Venice' when he saw it in the Earl of Northumberland's house in 1652 (*Walpole Society*, 1930, p. 113). A further document in the Alnwick archives (Northumberland MSS. W II 2) of 1656 regularised the sale, ten years before, of the two Titian's from Van Dyck's estate. The present writer is grateful to Mr Oliver Millar for drawing his attention to this. (17) Information received from the Duke of Northumberland at the time of purchase. (18) Also figures as no. 64 in the catalogue of the Burlington Fine Arts Club exhibition of Titian, 1914, but was not in fact exhibited.

5385 PORTRAIT OF A LADY ('LA SCHIAVONA')

47 × 38 (1·18 × 0·97).

Much abraded, particularly in the face, and extensively retouched.

The high lights of the braid in the head-dress, some of the white drapery and the marble relief in fair state.

Inscribed on the parapet: .T. .V.

Of these letters the black strokes and the dots flanking them are of a different texture of paint from the surrounding grey and in places they cover cracks. They are therefore not original. But the paint of the two lighter strokes—part of the vertical of the T and the right arm of the V— gives every sign of being genuine—they were probably intended as the lighter faces of a *trompe-l'œil* 'incised' inscription. It may therefore be concluded that the existing letters T and V (which are recorded as early as 1641—see PROVENANCE below) are the remains of original initials. It seems to the present writer more probable than not that these letters stand for 'Titianus Vecellius', but see the entry for no. 1944, where the same letters occur, for an expression of some reserve. At some stage in the picture's history it seems that clumsy attempts were made to ex- pand the 'T V' into 'TITIANVS'. The two existing letters are very deliberately spaced, dividing the lower portion of the parapet into three approximately equal lengths. The harmony of these intervals would however be broken if the existing T were either used as the first or as the third letter of 'TITIANVS'. Judging by the remains of further letters still visible it looks as though both these possibilities were tried. The space (in which there are faint traces of further letters) between the existing letters T and V would be sufficient to contain the intermediate letters I, T, I, A and N, but the final S after the V would then bring the whole word too far to the right. If, on the other hand, the existing T were used as the third letter there would be too much space between it and the V to account for the three letters I, A and N. Realisation of this seems to have led to an alternative 'improvement'. There are traces not only of another T and an I before the existing T but also of an upright after the existing V. This latter fact suggests that the form 'TIT VEC', which would have solved the problem of symmetry, may have been toyed with at some stage. Consideration of these various factors leads the present writer to conclude that there is no valid reason for supposing that the original inscription ever consisted of more than the letters T and V, probably flanked by dots.[1]

The extensive changes made on the right hand side of the picture are visible to the naked eye where the red of the drapery shows through the grey of the marble. Evidently the raised portion of the parapet with the relief was an afterthought. The lady's left arm would thus have hung down like her right (Sir Charles Holmes thought that her left hand originally rested on a skull, but X-ray photographs give no confirmation of this).[2] The raising of the parapet on the right, which introduced a greater degree of asymmetry into the design, would have left a blank space which was filled by a painted marble relief—apparently of the same lady, but with pseudo-classical hair style and draperies instead of the fashionable ones worn in the main portrait. During the process the artist seems to have transformed some, at least, of the underlying con- tours of the original left sleeve into grains in the marble. Alterations such as these are too common, particularly in Venetian painting, to justify in themselves an assumption that the picture was begun by one artist and finished by another. The type of the portrait, its style and the presence of the initials T V leave no reasonable doubt of Titian's participation. The theory that the picture was started by Giorgione was evolved by Cook[3] by reviving a speculative identification of the sitter with Caterina Cornaro and then identifying the picture with a portrait of Caterina by Giorgione, recorded by Vasari as formerly in the house of Giovanni Cornaro.[4] The pedigree of no. 5385 cannot be traced back farther than shortly before the year 1640 and at this time it is already referred to as 'La Schiavona by Titian'. It is datable around the year 1511 by the costume which is precisely comparable with that in Titian's frescoes of that year in the Scuola del Santo at Padua. As Caterina Cornaro had died in 1510 at the age of fifty-six any portrait of her painted around that date and showing her, as in no. 5385, as a young woman, would constitute an imaginative exercise to which considerations of likeness would scarcely be relevant.[5] Nevertheless the Caterina Cornaro identification is so far-fetched as to be totally unacceptable, and with it goes the main reason for assuming Giorgione's participation. The connection of no. 5385 with Titian's Padua frescoes is so close that there seems no valid reason for doubting his responsibility for the whole of it.[6]

DRAWING: Ugo Monneret de Villard (*Giorgione*, 1904) considered a drawing in the Uffizi (no. 718, rep. in Hadeln: *Zeichnungen des Tizian*, pl. 18) to be a preliminary study.

ENGRAVING: By Alessandro Sala. No. XIX in his *Collezione de' Quadri Scelti di Brescia*, 1817.

PROVENANCE: Mentioned in a letter of 17th November, 1640 (quoted by A. Venturi in his catalogue of the Crespi collection) addressed to Conte Alessandro Martinengo Colleone of Brescia, who had been outlawed in 1634. It appears from this letter that the Count had obtained the picture from a 'mercante di negri'. Described in detail in a related document of 12th August, 1641: *un quadro di pittura detto la Schiavona dal ginocchio in sù, qual tiene la mano su una testa finta in pietra di marmo bianco, et sotto improntato colle lettere T.V. che è di mano di Titiano pittore*. The picture was by this time in the hands of Contessa Giulia Olmo, the wife of Conte Alessandro. In the latter document Contessa Giulia was required to surrender the picture within three days[7] of 12th August, 1641. She had not, however, done so by the 11th November of that year[8] and presumably evaded doing so altogether since Sala's engraving of 1817 states that the picture was then in the possession of Conte Vincenzo Martinengo of Brescia. Recorded by Crowe and Cavalcaselle (*Titian*, vol. II, 1877, p. 58) as belonging to Signor Francesco Riccardi of Bergamo who was the brother-in-law of Conte Venceslao Martinengo Colleoni di Cavernago.[9] By 1900 in the Crespi Gallery, Milan.[10] Sold by Crespi, *c.* 1911–12, to Wildenstein, from whom bought, 1914, by Herbert Cook.[11] Exh. Burlington Fine Arts Club, 1914 (55) (lent Cook), R.A., 1930 (385) (lent Cook). Presented through the N.A-C.F. by Sir Francis Cook, Bart., 1942, in memory of his father, Sir Herbert Cook, Bart.

REPRODUCTION: Negative in the Gallery collection.

REFERENCES: (1) Francesco Malaguzzi Valeri (*Rassegna d'Arte*, 1, 1901, pp. 41–3) reads the inscription as 'TIT V' and assumes that the first two letters though nearly effaced were part of the original lettering. He quotes the restorer, Cavenaghi, as saying 'la scritta è contemporanea', but exactly which part of the 'scritta' is not specified. Cook (catalogue of the Cook collection, vol. III, p. 176) quotes Cavenaghi as considering only the letters T and V as original. (2) Sir Charles Holmes in *Burlington Magazine*, October, 1914. (3) Herbert Cook: *Giorgione*, 1907, pp. 74–81; cf. also an extract from a monograph quoted on pp. 172–7 of vol. III of the Cook catalogue (1915). (4) Vasari/Milanesi, vol. IV, pp. 98–9. (5) The inscribed portrait of Caterina Cornaro by Gentile Bellini (Budapest) is in fact remarkably unlike the sitter in no. 5385. See also portrait by the same artist in his 'Miracle of the True Cross' (Venice, Accademia). The matter is best discussed by Gronau (*Repertorium für Kunstwissenschaft*, 1908, pp. 512–13). Giuseppe Maria Bonomi (pamphlet on no. 5385 published at Bergamo, 1886, p. 13) suggests plausibly that the title of no. 5385 was deliberately changed from 'La Schiavona' to 'Portrait of Caterina Cornaro' to mislead the Venetian authorities in the mid-seventeenth century when they were trying to confiscate the picture (see below under PROVENANCE). A portrait inscribed as of Caterina Cornaro also catalogued in the Cook collection (vol. III, p. 179) together with its replicas and the fancy portrait after Titian (Uffizi) are irrelevant in this context as being posthumous. (6) A. Venturi's attribution to Licinio has found no support and cannot be sustained (*La Galleria Crespi in Milano*, 1900, p. 133). The Giorgione attribution has been revived more recently by J. Wilde (*Festschrift Alexis Petrovics*, Budapest, 1934)—'wahrscheinlich ebenfalls eine Schöpfung Giorgiones'. G. M. Richter (*Giorgio da Castelfranco*, 1937, p. 236) maintained 'Giorgione, finished by Titian'. Holmes (*loc. cit.*) proposed that the alterations in the parapet of no. 5385 were made by Titian much later (about 1540) and Cook used this to the advantage of his theory by claiming that Titian made these changes in what he (Cook) regarded as Giorgione's work at the time when he painted the original of the fancy portrait in the Uffizi. There is however no acceptable evidence in support of this hypothesis and the present writer sees no reason to doubt that the changes were made during the course of painting the picture. (7) Thus Bonomi. Venturi, in the Crespi catalogue, gives 'giorni sei' instead of 'giorni tre' as well as other variations. (8) All this information from G. M. Bonomi, *op. cit.* (9) Bonomi, *loc. cit.* (10) Venturi, *loc. cit.* (11) Cook, *loc. cit.*

## After TITIAN

### 933 A BOY WITH A BIRD

$13\frac{3}{4} \times 19\frac{1}{4}$ (0·35 × 0·49).[1]
So far as can be seen through the present discoloured varnish the paint seems in good condition.

In the 1929 catalogue as Padovanino.

A copy (with the omission of the wings) of the figure of Cupid which occurs in the background of the later versions (e.g., at Washington and New York) of Titian's *Venus and Adonis* (see entry for no. 34). The outline of the leaves has been altered to suit the smaller format and clouds added of a type recalling an earlier phase of Titian's style than the Washington and New York pictures. Such a transformation would not be inconsistent with the methods of a later *pasticheur* and need not imply that there was ever a Titian original exactly corresponding with no. 933 in size and format.[2] The handling of no. 933—so far as it is at present possible to judge it—seems to be of the seventeenth century, though the attribution to Padovanino seems too precise to justify.

PROVENANCE: Jeremiah Harman sale, 17th–18th May, 1844 (lot 65, as 'Titian') where bought Ellis.[3] Wynn Ellis Bequest, 1876.

REPRODUCTION: *Illustrations, Italian Schools*, 1937, p. 262.

REFERENCES: (1) Perhaps originally slightly larger. (2) Suida (*Belvedere*, 1932, Heft 7, pp. 164–6) published a picture in a Swiss private collection as being Titian's original of no. 933. While it is possible that Titian had also made use of this motive or a similar one in an earlier picture now lost (it may be noted that Ridolfi specifies that the Cupid added by Titian to Giorgione's *Venus* had a bird in his hand) it is not found in the earlier versions of the *Venus and Adonis*. (3) Marked copy of the sale catalogue in the Gallery library.

## 3949   PORTRAIT OF A MAN (? GIROLAMO FRACASTORO)

$36\frac{3}{8} \times 28\frac{1}{2}$ (0·92 × 0·724).

The remains of a strip of paper, stuck on, bottom left, read 'ottore Fracastoro'.

Very thin, and disfigured by remains of old, engrained varnish, also (on the face) by old retouches. Strips of the canvas at top and bottom have apparently been pressed down at some time. The outline of the hat was once farther out, towards the right.

Called in the 1929 catalogue 'Girolamo Fracastoro, ascribed to Francesco Torbido'. The Torbido attribution was due to J. P. Richter (catalogue of the Mond collection, 1910) but although it was supported by Berenson[1] and by A. Venturi[2] Richter later[3] admitted that it was hypothetical, apparently depending on the identification of the sitter, the fact that Vasari[4] records portraits of Fracastoro by Titian, Caroto and Torbido and that he (Richter) could not support an attribution to Titian or Caroto. Gronau[5] pointed out the improbability of the Torbido attribution and indicated the Titianesque qualities of the design of no. 3949, in particular the close resemblance to that of the portrait of Tommaso Mosti (Florence, Pitti). Richter's final view,[6] that the picture is a copy after an unidentified Titian, would seem, despite the ( ?) *pentimento* in the hat, the most probable.

The identity of the sitter is a harder problem. The paper still existing on the front of the canvas may well record an old inscription formerly visible on the back of it. Nevertheless, the degree of antiquity of this legend cannot be checked, while the great fame of Fracastoro, in his life time and subsequently, would have caused his name to be hypothetically or spuriously attached to various unconnected portraits.[7] The contemporary and attested portraits of Fracastoro—the woodcut (1538) from the *Hieronymi Fracastorii Homocentrica*, and a portrait medal (in profile)[8] —show long hair and beard, and also a fur collar, as in no. 3949. A different portrait, in profile, illustrating the second edition (1574) of Fracastoro's collected works, shows him with bald head uncovered. Apart from the lack of any object in no. 3949 indicating the sitter's scientific or literary interests, there is therefore nothing against the identification of him with Fracastoro, but equally no means of establishing it.

PROVENANCE: Almost certainly identical with a picture appearing successively as nos. 86, 93 and 66 in the 1824, 1837 and 1852 catalogues respectively of the collection of Conte Teodoro Lechi of Brescia. The description is invariably 'ritratto del celebre Fracastoro' by Titian, described as half-length, bearded, wearing fur, right arm leaning on a support and as measuring 0·9 × 0·73. In a type-script (in the Gallery archives) supplied by Conte Fausto Lechi it is stated that this picture was sold in 1854 to the 'inglese Henfrey'. No. 3949 is listed in the Mond catalogue as having been bought by Ludwig Mond from 'H. Ward, Esq., London' in 1895, so the intermediary history is still obscure. Mond Bequest, 1924.

REPRODUCTION: *Illustrations, Italian Schools*, 1937, p. 359.

REFERENCES: (1) *Lists*, 1936. (2) *Storia* . . ., IX, III, p. 916. Likewise Dirce Viana: *Francesco Torbido detto Il Moro*, 1933, p. 70. (3) *Burlington Magazine*, vol. 48 (1926), p. 216. A letter on the ethics of such attributions appears in the same volume, p. 322. (4) Ed. Milanesi, VII, p. 455, and V, pp. 286 and 295. (5) *Burlington Magazine*, vol. 48 (1926), p. 144. Gronau's attribution to Titian himself cannot be supported. (6) *Loc. cit.* Richter's tentative attribution to Felice Brusasorci may be noted without further comment. (7) A probable example is the portrait formerly in the Fellner collection, Budapest (reproduced in the *Klassiker der Kunst* volume on Palma Vecchio, p. 124) inscribed as representing Fracastoro and as painted by Titian. (8) Both reproduced by E. Schaeffer in the Prussian *Jahrbuch*, vol. XXXI (1910), pp. 132 and 138 (the author's identification of a portrait at Verona attributed to Titian with Fracastoro is questionable). The date of Fracastoro's birth, now apparently established as 1472 (publication of 1953 by R. Brenzoni correcting his earlier publication), would not be inconsistent with the apparent age of the sitter in no. 4939 assuming a Titian original dating from *c.* 1515–30.

## 4222 THE TRINITY

$51\frac{1}{2} \times 38\frac{3}{4}$ (1·31 × 0·985).
Considerably rubbed and largely repainted. The extent of this re-painting is discussed below. Superficially cleaned in 1926.

In the 1929 catalogue as Titian.
'The Trinity' was Titian's own name for the large picture of this design, now in the Prado, which was despatched from Venice to the Emperor Charles V in 1554 and has long been known as 'La Gloria'.[1] The figures of God the Father and of Christ are indistinguishable in themselves, but the one on the spectator's left must be Christ, since otherwise Christ could not be on the right hand of God the Father. Beneath them, on the spectator's left, is the Virgin, with S. John the Baptist behind her. In the foreground are (left to right) Ezekiel (on the eagle), Moses (holding the tables), Noah (holding the ark) and David (with the harp). The female figure between the last two (with her back to the spectator) may be S. Mary Magdalene. Higher up, on the spectator's right, the Emperor Charles V kneels. Behind him are the Empress, Philip II and Mary of Hungary. Below this group the portraits of (?) Pietro Aretino and of Titian himself are introduced (all these portraits are more clearly recognisable in the Prado picture). Titian also said that he had introduced into the latter the portrait of Francisco Vargas, the Emperor's ambassador).[1]

An engraving of Titian's design by Cornelis Cort[2] differs in numerous details from the Prado picture, and since these differences affect the status of no. 4222 it is desirable to tabulate them as follows:

| *Cort's engraving* | *Prado picture* |
|---|---|
| 1. God the Father has His right hand up. He wears a cloak fastened at the neck whose folds are drawn over His knees. He holds a short baton. His orb is large and has no cross. | God the Father has His right hand down. He wears a single voluminous garment. He holds a tall sceptre. His orb is small and has a cross. |
| 2. Christ is shown in profile. His right hand is raised and holds a short baton. The fold of a cloak hangs from His right shoulder and is gathered over His right knee. His orb is large and is on His right knee. It has no cross. | Christ is shown nearly in full face. His right hand is only half raised and holds a long sceptre. No cloak is visible at His shoulders and the draperies at His right knee are probably part of His single garment. His orb is small and on His left knee. It has a cross. |
| 3. The Virgin's veil billows out slightly behind her neck. | The Virgin's veil is gathered round her neck. |
| 4. S. John Baptist's fur-lined cloak is over his left shoulder. | The upper part of S. John Baptist's body is naked. |
| 5. The figure whose head is between the Baptist and the Virgin is bald. | The figure between the Baptist and the Virgin has dark hair. |
| 6. The claws of Ezekiel's eagle rest on a scroll. | There is nothing under the claws of Ezekiel's eagle. |
| 7. Moses is shown in profile. The lowest fold of his loin cloth hangs vertically down. | Moses is looking away from the spectator. The folds of his loin cloth are rounded at the base. |
| 8. Noah's ark has no dove. | Noah's ark has a dove. |
| 9. David looks over his left shoulder. The drapery round his shoulders has a fur lining. The lowest extremity of the loin cloth which falls from his left knee curls back. | David looks over his right shoulder. The drapery round his shoulders has a narrow ermine trimming but no fur lining. The folds of his loin cloth are simple at the base. |
| 10. The head above David's is almost in profile. | The head above David's is nearly three-quarter face. |
| 11. Titian himself wears a turban and a cloak. | Titian is bare-headed and his left arm is also bare. |
| 12. The fingers of ( ?) S. Mary Magdalene's right hand appear to touch the Emperor's drapery. | The fingers of ( ?) S. Mary Magdalene's right hand are clear of the Emperor's drapery. |

| *Cort's engraving* | *Prado picture* |
|---|---|
| 13. The figure on the spectator's left of Titian faces the latter. His features do not resemble those of Pietro Aretino. | The figure on the spectator's left of Titian faces the Trinity. His features resemble those of Pietro Aretino. |
| 14. Philip II is shown in profile. | Philip II is shown three-quarter face. |
| 15. The angel whose arm is round the Empress turns his face towards her. | The angel whose arm is round the Empress faces the Trinity. |
| 16. Angels top right hold small branches with few leaves. | Angels top right hold biggish branches with many leaves. |
| 17. The empty space in the centre shows even rays emanating from the Dove. At the top of the picture clouds cut sharply across the angles to frame the figures of God and Christ. | Half the empty space in the centre is filled by a large cloud from which emanate a few rays. Cherubs' heads fill the top of the picture. There appear to be no clouds there. |
| 18. There are two small cabins in the landscape at the base. | There is only one cabin in the landscape at the base. |

No. 4222, in its present state, corresponds in all respects with the exception of no. 15 with the Prado picture. But X-ray photographs show in each case different forms underneath, and these differences correspond exactly with Cort's engraving. In certain cases the earlier forms show through in the form of *pentimenti*—e.g., in the crownless orb on Christ's right knee, in the Virgin's veil or in the fingers of ( ?) S. Mary Magdalene's right hand.

Cornelis Cort was working for Titian in Venice from 1565 and his engraving of *The Trinity* is dated 1566. But as the Prado picture had left Venice twelve years earlier he must have worked in this case from a drawing or *modello* supplied by Titian.[3] Bearing in mind that no. 4222 originally corresponded with Cort's engraving and that it was altered later the order of events may have been any of the following:

1. Cort could have based his engraving on no. 4222 in its original state. In that case no. 4222 would have been Titian's own *modello*.[4]

2. Cort could have worked from a *modello* by Titian now lost, of which no. 4222 in its original state could have been a copy.

3. No. 4222 in its original state could have been painted from Cort's engraving.

Of these possibilities no. 1 is rendered highly improbable an account of the relative crudeness and un-Titianesque quality of the execution of the original state of no. 4222 as revealed by the X-rays. The second possibility can likewise be virtually eliminated on account of the curious fact that some of the draperies are painted on top of different colours:

the green dress of ( ?) S. Mary Magdalene, for example, is over pink paint, and parts of David's blue drapery and of Christ's robe of the same colour are over red (distinct from the brick-colour ground). In all cases some of the top paint has worn away. These particular colours would be unusual, or even pointless, as underpainting, which in itself would be an unusual technique in a *modello* and almost inconceivable in a copy of a *modello*. It is precisely this factor which tilts the balance in favour of the third possibility—that no. 4222 was originally painted from Cort's engraving. In that case it was almost inevitable that the colours should not correspond with those in the large picture.

The sum of the evidence therefore leads the present writer to conclude that Cort's engraving was made from a sketch or *modello* supplied by Titian and now lost which would have represented an earlier stage in the evolution or would have been sufficiently vague or undefined in certain details to account for the differences between the engraving and the big picture, and that no. 4222 was originally the work of some painter (whose name, working period and nationality are now alike undiscoverable) who had access to Cort's engraving, but not to the Prado picture or to Titian's *modello*. At some stage it would have been ' corrected ' by reference to the original, the forms being altered where they differed (with the exception of the angel whose arm is round the Empress, which was apparently overlooked) and some of the colours changed (they now in fact correspond more or less with those in the Prado picture). The fact that no. 4222 in its present overpainted state superficially resembles the work of Titian whereas the forms disclosed by X-ray photographs appear entirely foreign to him suggests that the transformation was effected by a clever artist who may have been activated by some dishonest intention of uttering the result as Titian's own *modello*. The appearance and style of the top paint suggest that the transformation was made probably not later than the eighteenth century. It must have been done in Spain (where, indeed, the picture is first recorded) but in view of the circumstances and of the amount of damage sustained the identity of the second painter involved is as impossible to discover as that of the first.[5]

ENGRAVING: Cort's engraving is discussed above.

PROVENANCE: Said to have been discovered about 1808 [6] in a gambling house in Madrid by De Bourke, afterwards Danish Minister to London.[7] Brought to London by Wallis.[7] In the collection of Samuel Rogers before 1833.[8] Rogers' sale, 3rd May, 1856 (725), where bought Lord Harry Vane [9] (afterwards Duke of Cleveland) by whom exh. Manchester (*Art Treasures Exhibition*), 1857 (provisional catalogue no. 229), and R.A., 1872 (114). Cleveland sale, 8th March, 1902 (37) where bought Sir William Corry.[9] Corry sale, Claremont, Esher, 25th–28th October, 1926 (285), where bought Mears [10] for Colnaghi. Purchased from Colnaghi, December, 1926 with the aid of the Lewis Fund.

REPRODUCTION: *Burlington Magazine*, vol. L, 1927, p. 52.

REFERENCES: (1) See letter from Titian to the Emperor, dated 10th September, 1554 (reproduced by Crowe and Cavalcaselle, *Titian*, vol. II (1877), pp. 507–8). (2) Reproduced in an article by Sir Charles Holmes, *Burlington*

*Magazine*, vol. L (1927), p. 52. (3) Alfred Stix (Vienna *Jahrbuch*, XXXI (1913–14), p. 340) quotes Titian's letter of 1565 (. . . *fatto metter in stampa di rame il disegno della pittura della Trinità*) as referring definitely to a drawing. But the word 'disegno' need only mean 'composition'. (4) This was claimed by Holmes, *loc. cit.*, and supported by Hadeln (letter of 1926 to Otto Gutekunst in the Gallery archives) and by Tietze (*Tizian*, 1936, Textband, p. 211, and in *Die Graphischen Künste*, 1938, p. 10—the latter article gives further references). Holmes' thesis was developed in ignorance of the results of the X-rays with which it is incompatible. The same applies to one advanced by Palma Bucarelli (*Gazette des Beaux-Arts*, 1935, II, pp. 247–8). (5) A. L. Mayer suggested the name of Francisco Rizi as author of no. 4222 and quoted support from F. J. Sánchez Cantón (*Boletín de la Sociedad Española de Excursiones*, 1934, pp. 297–8). In a letter of the same year (copy in the Gallery archives) Mayer also mentioned the names of Pablo Esquert, José Antolínez, Luca Giordano and Cerezo. A. Porcella (*Revisione alla Mostra di Pittura Spagnuola* (1930), p. 9) referred to no. 4222 simply as a Spanish copy of the Prado picture. A copy of the latter is recorded as early as 1635 in the Duke of Buckingham's collection (see *Burlington Magazine*, X, 1906–7, p. 379). (6) Mrs Jameson: *Companion to the . . . Private Galleries . . . in London*, 1844, p. 402. (7) This information from the Samuel Rogers' sale catalogue. (8) Passavant: *Kunstreise . . .*, p. 86. No. 4222 seems to have been offered by Yeates to Penrice in 1814 (*Letters . . . to . . . Thomas Penrice*, n.d., p. 40). (9) Marked copy of sale catalogue in the Gallery library. (10) Marked copy of the sale catalogue in the library of the Victoria and Albert Museum.

## Follower of TITIAN

### 1123 MYTHOLOGICAL SCENE

Panel, 30 × 52 (0·762 × 1·327).[1]

A number of obviously worn passages and retouchings in the flesh and lighter portions of the sky. Draperies and landscape details may be fairly well preserved but the present discoloured varnish makes appraisal difficult.

At Hamilton Palace as Giorgione. Catalogued since entering the Gallery as 'Venetian School' except in the editions of 1901–15 where it appears as 'School of Giorgione'. Other suggestions have been 'Lattanzio Gambara, Beccarruzzi and others of their class',[2] Cariani[3] and Bonifazio.[4] Of these, the last is the only one to merit serious attention, but it is hypothetical and not entirely satisfactory. In nearly every respect no. 1123 seems to depend directly on Titian.

Called 'Venus and Adonis' in earlier editions of the National Gallery catalogue and 'Hippomenes and Atalanta' by Waagen[5] and Crowe and Cavalcaselle.[5] The incidents in the background would certainly seem to tell the story of Adonis—those on the left of the main figures being connected with his death and with Venus' lament over his body, those on the right with his birth. In the centre of the latter three episodes Myrrha is apparently being driven from the house by her father when he had discovered that she had been his paramour. On the left she seems to be turning into a tree. On the right the baby Adonis is being born from the tree. Nevertheless it is doubtful if the main figures are Venus and Adonis. The man holds an apple in his right hand, and this suggests that the couple are intended as Hippomenes and Atalanta,

9—V.S.C.

whose story is so closely linked by Ovid with that of Adonis that he interrupts the latter to tell it and then continues with the Adonis story again.[6] On the other hand, Cupid—who is seen in no. 1123 being despatched by Venus in the sky, top right, and about to pierce the lovers in the main scene—does not figure in Ovid's account of the Atalanta story, where Venus intervenes in person.

PROVENANCE: Hamilton Palace. No. 383 ('Giorgione') in the 4th day (24th June, 1882) of the Hamilton Palace sale, where purchased.

REPRODUCTION: *Illustrations, Italian Schools*, 1937, p. 375.

REFERENCES: (1) Approximate dimensions of original panel to which strips about ½″ wide have been added all round and painted over. (2) Crowe and Cavalcaselle: *Painting in North Italy*, vol. III (1912), p. 55. The authors refer to the picture as a 'small canvas' (no. 1123 is on wood) and describe it as Hippomenes and Atalanta. Nevertheless it seems that this is the picture referred to. Waagen also (*Treasures of Art in Great Britain*, vol. III (1854), p. 303) refers to 'Hippomenes and Atalanta accompanied by Cupid, in a landscape.' (3) W. Schmidt in *Repertorium für Kunstwissenschaft*, 1908, p. 117. (4) Berenson (with query) in *Lists*, 1932 and 1936. In his 1957 edition he lists it as a 'Giorgionesque painting'. (5) *Loc. cit.* (6) Metamorphoses X.

## Imitator of TITIAN

### 3   A CONCERT

39 × 49¼ (0·99 × 1·25).
Flesh areas much worn and made up. Thicker paint of the green-blue and red robes better preserved. Heavily discoloured by old varnish. It is open to question whether the notes on the musical score were ever legible. In the picture's present worn state they are not.

In the 1929 catalogue as 'School of Titian'. This type of composition —elaborately dressed figures, usually shown at half length, making music—was pre-eminently associated with the Giorgionesque, the most famous example being the *Concert* in the Pitti. Among such pictures, where the attitude of the characters towards the music is apt to appear half-hearted, it would be very difficult to find a parallel for the vigorous singing, with wide open mouth, of the boy in no. 3, whose appearance in general seems somewhat foreign to the Renaissance.

The costumes shown and the hair-style of the lady would admit of dating in the 1540's (but not earlier) provided that considerable alterations were made later.[1] Even on these grounds however the picture would fit more easily into the idiom of the early seventeenth century when certain Giorgionesque features reappeared, and on the whole the present writer is led to regard it as a deliberate imitation of Titian dating from that period. Jacobsen, alone of earlier writers, had proposed so late a dating with his suggestion of 'early Padovanino'.[2] This seems to be on the right track, but such precision, at least in the picture's present darkened state, would be hard to justify.

VERSIONS: An inferior copy at Pommersfelden. Another (with a *trompe-l'œil* frame) was lot 142 anonymous sale, Christie's, 9th March, 1951. A variant (three or four figures instead of five) was at Brunswick in the nineteenth century.[3]

ENGRAVINGS: By H. Danckerts and (in reverse) by J. Gronsveld. See also below under PROVENANCE.

PROVENANCE: History prior to entering the Angerstein collection is uncertain.[4] It corresponds however with a picture catalogued in the collection of Charles I as from Mantua and with two engravings by H. Danckerts and J. Gronsveld.[5] The entry in Bathoe's catalogue of Charles I's collection (p. 99) is as follows: *A Mantua piece, done by Titian. Imprimis, A picture of some five half figures, one whereof being a teaching, another singing, another playing upon a bandore, the fourth playing upon a flute, the fifth being a woman listening to the musick, painted upon cloth, half figures so big as the life . . . 3f.3 4f.3.* What is presumably the relevant entry in the Mantua inventory of 1627 reads: *Doi quadri . . . uno dipintovi homini che cantano di musica, mezze figure . . . di mano di Titiano.*[6] The Charles I picture was probably the 'picture of musick by Georgion' in the Commonwealth sale lists.[7] Hendrick Danckerts was active at The Hague 1645–53, in Italy 1653–7 and later in England. Johannes Gronsveld was active at Amsterdam from 1679 and died there in 1728. Though in theory there could thus be as many as three replicas of no. 3 there is nothing against the assumption that the Mantua/Charles I picture, the Danckerts picture and the Gronsveld picture were identical with each other and with it. The first part of the equation, indeed, is strongly supported, if not proved, by the fact that Danckerts' engraving is inscribed 'Ex collectione regis Magnae Brittanniae'. Purchased with the Angerstein collection, 1824.

REPRODUCTION: *Illustrations, Italian Schools*, 1937, p. 357.

REFERENCES: (1) Notes on the costumes by Stella Mary Pearce in the Gallery archives. (2) *Repertorium für Kunstwissenschaft*, XXIV (1901), p. 372. Other suggestions had been 'Schiavone or Zelotti' (Crowe and Cavalcaselle, *Titian*, vol. II, 1877, pp. 459–60), 'Florigerio' (R. Longhi, 1929, apparently verbally; a picture at Munich, claimed in the 1929 catalogue of the National Gallery as 'somewhat similar', is attributed to Florigerio) and 'copy after Titian' (Berenson, *Lists*, 1936). E. Tietze, in a letter in the Gallery archives, suggests a derivation from a fifteenth-century Ferrarese picture. (3) Crowe and Cavalcaselle, *History of Painting in North Italy*, vol. III (1912), pp. 53–4. The picture was presumably no. 260 (' ? Giorgione') in the Brunswick catalogue of 1849. (4) The National Gallery catalogues of 1915–29 include the statement 'perhaps from R. Strange Coll., 1771'. The evidence for this eludes the present writer. (5) Crowe and Cavalcaselle, *Titian*, II, p. 460. (6) Alessandro Luzio: *La Galleria dei Gonzaga . . .*, 1913, p. 113; also in Carlo D'Arco: *Delle Arti e Degli Artefici di Mantova*, vol. II (1857), p. 160. (7) Crowe and Cavalcaselle (*History of Painting in North Italy*, vol. III, 1912, p. 41) connect no. 3 with a 'Giorgione' in James II's collection, but the latter was in fact a picture still at Hampton Court ('Master of the Pitti Three Ages'). See in this connection and for the entry in the Commonwealth sale lists, Denis Mahon: *Notes on the 'Dutch Gift' to Charles II, III (Burlington Magazine*, vol. 92, 1950, p. 14).

## VENETIAN SCHOOL, Sixteenth century

### 173 PORTRAIT OF A MAN

Stretcher measures $47 \times 38\frac{1}{2}$ ($1.195 \times 0.977$).

Of this, a strip just under 3″ broad along the base is of later canvas, while strips roughly $1\frac{1}{2}$″ wide (varying) at the sides and top have been crudely overpainted at a later date.

The face appears to be in tolerable condition. The existing heavily discoloured varnish renders difficult an assessment of the state of the rest, though there is certainly an appreciable amount of damage.

In the 1929 catalogue as Jacopo Bassano. Also attributed to Francesco Bassano,[1] Domenico Tintoretto[2] and Beccarruzzi.[3] If the indications of dating—ca. 1585-95—afforded by the costume are correct,[4] this is much too late for Beccarruzzi and rather late for Jacopo Bassano. Of the remaining candidates, Domenico Tintoretto, and Francesco, Gerolamo and Leandro Bassano would all be possibilities, but the condition of the picture and the relative lack of definition of the style of all but Leandro of the artists in question as portraitists precludes a decision.

PROVENANCE: From the collection of Alleyne FitzHerbert, first and last Baron St Helens (1753-1839).[5] Passed to his nephew, Henry Gally Knight, the writer on architecture, by whom presented (with no. 174), 1839.

REPRODUCTION: *Illustrations, Italian Schools*, 1937, p. 22.

REFERENCES: (1) Quoted in the 1929 catalogue. (2) By Morelli, according to J. P. Richter (note in the Gallery archives). (3) By Fiocco (quoted by Arslan: *I Bassano*, 1931, p. 345). (4) Notes by Stella Mary Pearce in the Gallery archives. (5) Letter from Henry Gally Knight in the Gallery archives.

## 272 A COLOSSAL DECORATIVE FIGURE

$59\frac{7}{8} \times 45\frac{5}{8}$ (1·521 × 1·159).

Apparently thinly painted—so far as can be seen through the existing varnish, some of which is almost opaque.

The turn-over of the canvas on the right is incompletely covered with paint, and gives the impression of never having been completely painted, rather than of paint which has existed and has since been rubbed off. As the figure is truncated to the right it is therefore more probable that the continuation was on a separate canvas than that an appreciable amount of the existing canvas has been cut off. In the 1929 catalogue as 'Italian School, 16th century.' Presented as by Pordenone, and accepted as such by Crowe and Cavalcaselle.[1] This type of spandrel figure, however, seems typical of a rather later fashion in the Veneto, and was not uncommon among the followers of Paolo Veronese.[2]

PROVENANCE: Stated (in the MS. catalogue in the Gallery archives) to have come 'from a church in the territory of Venice'. Presented, 1855, by Cavaliere Vallati of Rome.

REPRODUCTION: *Illustrations, Italian Schools*, 1937, p. 176.

REFERENCES: (1) *North Italian Painters*, vol. III (1912), p. 182, note 1, no. 8. (2) Cf. e.g. the frescoes at the Villa Coldogno, near Vicenza (repr. A. Venturi, *Storia* . . ., IX, IV, II, pls. 721-6).

## 595 PORTRAIT OF A LADY

$28\frac{3}{4} \times 22\frac{3}{4}$ (0·73 × 0·578).

Disfigured at present by discoloured varnish, but even through it much retouching is apparent—e.g., the outline of the forehead and the eye-lids, also in the shadows of the neck and in the hand. The background is a net-work of retouches. Hair and much of the dress appear to be in better state.

Purchased as by Zelotti. Tentatively ascribed in the 1929 catalogue to Badile. Both these names can be excluded on account of the costume which is much earlier (ca. 1516–17).[1] Berenson's tentative attribution to Palma Vecchio,[2] supported by Wilde,[3] is not open to this objection but is equally unacceptable to the present writer who is unable to recognise in no. 595 either the conception or the handling of Palma.

A smaller figure, such as Licinio,[4] would seem preferable, but a verdict is the harder to come by on account of the picture's condition.

PROVENANCE: Bought at Rome, 1858, from 'Signor Menchetti'.

REPRODUCTION: *Illustrations, Italian Schools*, 1937, p. 372.

REFERENCES: (1) Notes by Stella Mary Pearce in the Gallery archives. (2) *Lists*, 1936 and 1957 (with query). (3) MS. note (based on photographic evidence only) in the Gallery archives. (4) Oral suggestion by Michael Levey.

1377  ADORATION OF THE SHEPHERDS

Original canvas measures ca. $43 \times 63\frac{1}{4}$ (1·092 × 1·606). At the top a strip c. $2\frac{1}{2}''$ wide has been added.
Worn thin in many places and also damaged by past flaking.

Bequeathed as by Savoldo, and catalogued as such until the edition of 1912 when it first appeared as 'Venetian School, XV–XVI century'.
An attribution to Calisto da Lodi was suggested by E. Jacobsen.[1]

No. 1377 has been related to two other pictures—in the Duomo at Asola[2] (province of Mantua) and at Kansas City (ex-Leuchtenberg)[3]— and all three have been attributed by Berenson to Giovanni da Asola.[4] What the three pictures have in fact in common, apart from the subject and the general system of arrangement, is a dependance on Titian. The Asola picture appears to derive from no. 4 (Titian) of this Gallery, supplemented, as regards details of the background, by another Titian now known from copies and an engraving.[5] The group of the Virgin and Child in the Kansas picture seems to be taken from a Titian now at Washington,[6] while the *putto* in the same picture can be paralleled both in the *Sacred and Profane Love* and in no. 635 of this Gallery. In no. 1377 the infant St John with a lamb is an obvious Titianesque motive,[7] other elements in the picture less so. No. 1377 and the Kansas picture have evident features in common—the two shepherds are almost identical and the St Joseph and much of the background very similar in the two pictures. While it is reasonable to attribute these two pictures to the same hand the present writer is convinced, after inspection of the Asola picture *in situ*, that is not by the artist of no. 1377, and since the attribution of the former picture to Giovanni da Asola appears likely the attribution to him of no. 1377 also would therefore seem to be correspondingly less so. Some anonymous, provincial Venetian around the beginning of the second quarter of the sixteenth century would thus be the author.[8]

PROVENANCE: From the Manfrin collection, Venice.[9] Bequeathed by Sir William H. Gregory, 1892.

REPRODUCTION: *Illustrations, Italian Schools*, 1937, p. 375.

REFERENCES: (**1**) *Repertorium für Kunstwissenschaft*, vol. XXIV (1901), p. 368. (**2**) Repr. G. Fiocco in *Bollettino d'Arte*, anno V, 1925–6, pp. 193–205. (**3**) Repr. Herbert Cook in *Burlington Magazine*, vol. II (1903), pp. 83–4. (**4**) *Lists*, 1936. The attribution of no. 1377 to Giovanni da Asola seems first to have been published by G. Ludwig in the Prussian *Jahrbuch*, vol. XXVI (1905), *Beiheft*, p. 114. The Kansas picture was recently attributed by Fiocco to Francesco Vecellio (*Arte Veneta*, IX, 1955, p. 76). (**5**) Painted versions in the Pitti (Suida, *Tiziano*, pl. XCIV) and at Christ Church, Oxford. Engraving by Luca Bertelli. (**6**) Mellon collection. Repr. Suida, *Tiziano*, pl. LXXXVII. (**7**) An example in a Titianesque picture is Suida, *op. cit.*, pl. LXXXVI (a), also in some of the variants of National Gallery no. 635. (**8**) Stella Mary Pearce, in notes in the Gallery archives on the costumes, favours a dating not earlier than 1525 and very possibly later than 1530. She also points out various irrational features in the Virgin's costume which would be natural if the figure were a partly remembered copy of one in another painting. (**9**) Label on the back. Probably no. 428 in the 1856 Manfrin catalogue ('Adorazione dei Pastori. Girolamo Savoldo. Tela, larghezza 1·61, altezza 1.17'), and no. 104 in the 1872 Manfrin catalogue.

## 3108　A NAVAL BATTLE

Panel, $6\frac{3}{4} \times 15\frac{1}{4}$ (0·171 × 0·387).
Good condition.

Formerly catalogued as 'Italian School, XVI century'.

One of a series of at least four, all from the Manfrin collection.[1] A fifth panel, of identical style and type, but unknown provenance, appeared at auction in 1929.[2] All five pictures were probably painted as part of some furniture, and it is reported by Ridolfi[3] that Andrea Schiavone, to whom no. 3108 was attributed by Berenson,[4] had specialised in this work at the outset of his career. To the present writer, however, the pictures, though of a certain Schiavonesque type, seem too far from the most acceptable examples of Schiavone's secular style (such as the ex-Chatsworth *Psyche* and the Vienna mythologies—see entry for no. 1884) to justify so precise an attribution.

PROVENANCE: Manfrin collection, Venice, in the nineteenth century (see above) from which bought by Sir A. H. Layard, 1880.[5] Layard Bequest, 1916.

REPRODUCTION: *Illustrations, Italian Schools*, 1937, p. 177.

REFERENCES: (**1**) No. 3108 has on the back a Manfrin label on which is written 'A 31'. Also 'No. 24' painted on the wood. A Manfrin label on which was written 'A 30' was on the back of the second picture of the series—Oscar Andersen sale, Sotheby's, 16th November, 1949 (140), panel, $7 \times 15\frac{1}{2}$ (0·178 × 0·394) 'Scipio Africanus receiving turbaned envoys' (existence of the Manfrin label checked by the present writer at the time of the sale). The other two pictures were in the Dr Szeben collection, Budapest, as Bonifazio and ex-Manfrin, 0·165 × 0·44 and 0·165 and 0·38 respectively. The Manfrin numbering was changed more than once. The four pictures in question are clearly identifiable as nos. 24, 25, 32 and 33 of 'Stanza Segnata A' in a MS. catalogue (in the Gallery library) of 1851 and as nos. 22, 23, 29 and 30 in the printed catalogue of 1856. In the 1872 catalogue only three of the pictures appear, one evidently having been sold. The other three are nos. 22, 23 and 24. All pictures in all cases are as Bonifazio, height specified in all cases where it is given as 0·18, width varying from 0·38 to 0·45. (2) A. G. B. Russell sale, Sotheby's, 9th May, 1929, lot 7—'Andrea Schiavone . . . Horatius on the Bridge . . . panel, 10¼ × 21⅛.' (3) Ridolfi/Hadeln, I, p. 248. (4) *Lists*, 1936 and 1957. (5) Layard's MS. catalogue in the Gallery archives.

## 4037 THE STORY OF CIMON AND EFIGENIA

Panel, 26¾ × 47¼ (0·67 × 1·2).

Much damaged by flaking, and extensively repainted. A sizeable piece, clearly, has been cut on the left. The shape which its inclusion would have produced suggests that the picture was designed as part of a piece of furniture.

Hitherto catalogued as 'School of Palma Vecchio' and called 'Nymphs and a Shepherd'. The story of Cimon and Efigenia occurs in the Decameron (fifth day, first story).[1] Cimon, the illiterate son of a rich Cypriot, was sent by his father to live on his country estate. Walking one day from one farm to another Cimon found a young woman asleep near a spring, two maid-servants and a man-servant asleep at her feet. Cimon stopped, resting on his staff, and gazed at her until she woke up, which she did before her servants. In no. 4037 it would have to be assumed that the other two servants and the spring were included in the portion cut off on the left. The fact that the man is shown leaning on his staff and that the woman he was gazing at has just awakened whereas the other has not, being distinctive features of the Decameron story, seem sufficient to justify the identification of the subject. A painting by Rubens (Vienna) can be vouched for as representing the same subject through being catalogued as such as early as 1635.[2]

The attribution to Palma has often been made,[3] particularly in conjunction with a picture of similar type at Frankfurt. Nevertheless J. Wilde seems correct in pointing out that the latter picture is in fact by a different hand.[4] His tentative attribution of no. 4037 to Domenico Mancini on the strength of certain stylistic affinities with the Lendinara *Madonna* signed by that artist seems to have more to commend it than the Palma attribution, but the bad condition of no. 4037 precludes a final verdict.

PROVENANCE: Acquired by Sir Claude Phillips before June, 1907.[5] Bequeathed by him, 1924.

REPRODUCTION: *Illustrations, Italian Schools*, 1937, p. 266.

REFERENCES: (1) The identification suggested by J. Wilde (note in the Gallery archives). (2) Inventory of Duke of Buckingham's pictures (*Burlington Magazine*, vol. 10, 1906–7, p. 379). (3) E.g. by Adolfo Venturi (*Storia*, IX, iii, 423), Gombosi (*Klassiker der Kunst* volume on Palma, 1937, p. 36) and Berenson (*Lists*, 1936). (4) J. Wilde: *Die Probleme um Domenico Mancini*, in Vienna *Jahrbuch* (N.F., vol. 7, 1933, pp. 104 ff). The statement in the National Gallery catalogue of 1929 that no. 4037 combines motives from the Frankfurt picture and from no. 3079 of this Gallery is hardly to be taken seriously. (5) Article by C. J. H[olmes] in *Burlington Magazine*, vol. 11, pp. 188–9. The same writer reverts to the subject in a letter to the *Burlington Magazine*, vol. 47 (1925), p. 272.

# (?) VENETIAN School, Sixteenth century

## 2903　A CONCERT

Canvas, transferred from panel, $35\frac{3}{4} \times 48\frac{1}{2}$ (0·9 × 1·23).

Considerably damaged. The largest area of repaint is the curved portion of the lyre, centre. Obvious repaint also in all three faces, and elsewhere.

Variously attributed to Lotto,[1] 'early Pordenone',[2] Palma and Bonifazio.[3] As 'School of Palma Vecchio' in the 1929 catalogue. Although the debt to Palma is obvious—in particular to such a picture as his *Three Sisters* at Dresden[4]—he is no more acceptable as author than the other three.[5] In point of fact no. 2903 seems to be by the same hand as a female portrait shown at the Giorgione exhibition in Venice in 1955 (no. 125)[6] and there attributed to a Friulan painter. Both pictures show some similarity of type and handling to certain pictures attributed to Licinio but no attested Licinio so summary in treatment is known to the present writer.

PROVENANCE: In St Petersburg in the year 1868.[7] Exh. R.A., 1872 (67) (lent by Sir Coutts Lindsay) and 1888 (124) (lent by Lady Lindsay)—both times as 'The Painter's Daughters' by Palma Vecchio. Lady Lindsay Bequest, 1912.

REPRODUCTION: *Illustrations, Italian Schools*, 1937, p. 266.

REFERENCES: (1) K. Oettinger in *Belvedere*, 1930 (ii), pp. 10 ff. The author of this article claimed that a drawing in the Oppenheimer collection was a study for no. 2903. The drawing in question was sold as Previtali at the Oppenheimer sale (10th, 13th, 14th July, 1936, lot 154). (2) Apparently oral communication from 'Dr Kurth, Berlin' recorded in the Gallery archives. (3) Berenson (*Lists*, 1936 and 1957) as begun by Palma and finished by Bonifazio. (4) The costumes shown in no. 2903 would accord best with a date around 1523-4 (notes by S. M. Pearce in the Gallery archives). If the Dresden Palma is identical, as is usually assumed, with the picture seen by Michiel in 1525 it must naturally have been painted before then. (5) The theory of 'early Pordenone' is automatically excluded by the dating of the costumes to the 'twenties. (6) Ex-collections Manfrin, Malmesbury, Barker and C. Butler. Anonymous sale, Sotheby's, 10th November, 1954 (72). (7) Label on the back saying (in Russian) that it had been transferred from wood to canvas in St Petersburg in 1868.

## 3107　SOLOMON AND THE QUEEN OF SHEBA

31 × 73 (0·788 × 1·854).

Thin in many places, and some repaint.

The figures on the spectator's left, around Solomon, though relatively solid, yet seem for the most part painted on top of the architecture and pavement. The figures on the spectator's right are sketched quickly on top of the background and are quite unfinished. It is therefore questionable whether any figures were originally intended and very probable that the main object of the picture was an essay in assembling different types of pseudo-classical building, perhaps influenced by the illustrations of architectural books, such as Serlio's, and possibly done with a view to theatrical scenery.

In any case no. 3107 is an oddity and correspondingly difficult, or impossible, to attribute. In the 1929 catalogue as 'Venetian School, XV–XVI century'. Suggestions have included Bonifazio, Schiavone, Bordon, Christoph Schwarz,[1] 'Jacopo Stella',[2] Paolo Farinati[3] and Lambert Sustris.[4] The latter has received the most support and, among known painters, appears the least improbable.[5]

PROVENANCE: Bought by Sir A. H. Layard in Madrid in 1872. Ascribed by him to Bonifazio. Layard Bequest, 1916.

REPRODUCTION: *Illustrations, Italian Schools*, 1937, p. 376.

REFERENCES: (1) These four attributions cited by A. Venturi (*L'Arte*, 1912, p. 456). (2) Quoted in a note in the Gallery archives as the opinion of W. Suida and L. Venturi. (3) Recorded in the 1929 catalogue. (4) Opinions recorded in the Gallery archives of R. A. Peltzer, Gamba and Berenson. In the 1957 edition of the latter's *Lists* no. 3107 is included as Sustris. (5) The *Baptism* (Caen), the only signed work of Lambert Sustris, was undergoing prolonged restoration at the time when the present entry was being written and was not available for inspection.

## PAOLO VERONESE
### Born probably 1528, died 1588

His name was Paolo Caliari, called 'Veronese' from his native city of Verona. The date of his birth is deduced from the register of his death on 19th April, 1588, which gives his age as sixty. This agrees with a further register, of 1529, whereby the age of 'Paulo', son of Gabriel di Piero (which was indeed the name of the painter's father) is given as one year. Ridolfi's statement that Veronese was born in 1530 (corrected from 1532 in the original edition) may be due to his assuming that a bust on the painter's grave which gives his age as fifty-eight was made at the time of death rather than two years before it. A further inventory at Verona, of 16th April, 1541, of Gabriel di Piero's family refers to 'Paulo' as already 'depentor' but gives his age as ten years and that of other members of the family also as different from what is stated in the earlier document, which in Paolo's case at least is likely to be the more accurate. A final entry, of 2nd May, 1541, gives 'Paulus' as aged fourteen and as the 'discipulus seu garzonus' of the painter Antonio Badile.[1] No parentage is specified but this also probably refers to Paolo Veronese. Vasari calls him the pupil of Caroto,[2] but Ridolfi,[3] and also Borghini,[4] of 'Antonio Badile suo Zio'. Veronese married Badile's daughter in 1566.[5]

Of Veronese's earliest works, a damaged altarpiece (Verona, Museo, from S. Fermo Maggiore) has been identified with the first work listed by Ridolfi and provisionally dated 1548 or soon after, as being the year when the chapel from which it came was built. More reliably datable are the frescoes from the Villa Soranza, near Castelfranco, one of which bears the date 1551. These are vouched for by Vasari (1568) as the work of Veronese and Zelotti.[6] An altarpiece of the *Temptation of S. Anthony* (Caen, from Mantua cathedral) is documented as finished before March,

1553. Veronese had settled in Venice certainly by the beginning of the year 1555 and perhaps as early as 1553 (the carved decoration of the ceiling of the *Sala del Consiglic de' Dieci* in the Doge's Palace, for which Veronese supplied some of the paintings, contains the Donato arms, presumably referring to the Doge, Francesco Donato, who died in that year). In 1555 Veronese completed the first items in the decoration of the church of S. Sebastiano, which occupied him, on and off, for the next fifteen years and which constitutes the most important of his earlier works. Soon afterwards his contribution (1556–7) to the decoration of the ceiling of Sansovino's *Libreria* was adjudged the best of the seven painters' who participated. From then until the end of his life Veronese shared with Tintoretto (Titian being by this time very old) the status of the leading painter in Venice and was his rival for the most important commissions. In 1573 Veronese was arraigned before the Inquisition in connection with the large *Feast* now in the Venice Accademia.

Ridolfi's statement that Veronese 'riueriua Titiano come padre dell' Arte, & apprezzaua molto il viuace ingegno del Tintoretto'[7] seems a fair general comment on his art. In addition, Domenico Brusasorci, Parmigianino, Moretto and Giulio Romano all appear to have contributed something to his formation. Ridolfi says that Veronese visited Rome with Girolamo Grimani, who is known to have gone there in 1555, 1560 and 1566.[8]

Relatively few of Veronese's surviving paintings are dated or are reliably datable, and all attempts at precision in reconstructing the chronology have met with insuperable obstacles. Though his artistic beginnings are still obscure in some ways, it is clear that as soon as Veronese reached maturity as an artist he evolved not one style but several, corresponding roughly with the nature of the undertaking, whether altarpiece, ceiling, feast subject or mythology. Thereafter he continued to work concurrently in these several styles, within each of which he developed relatively little. Similarities between two of Veronese's pictures, therefore, by no means necessarily imply a similar date of origin, nor dissimilarities a dissimilar one. The *Consecration of St Nicholas*, for example, which is no. 26 of this Gallery and which dates from 1562, has more in common as regards both space composition and tone with a very late work in the same category—the *Miracle of S. Pantalone* of 1587 (Venice, church of S. Pantalone)—than it has with a coeval painting in a different one—the *Marriage at Cana* (Louvre: 1562–3).[9] Phenomena to some extent comparable may be observed within the *œuvre* of Tintoretto, though less extreme in degree, while the more highly organised state of the studio which assisted Veronese in his vast output of vast pictures renders the connoisseurship of his work almost as difficult as its chronology.

A number of surviving paintings are signed as being by the 'heirs of Paolo Veronese'.[10] By this was evidently meant Paolo's brother, Benedetto, and his sons, Carlo and Gabriel, whose collaboration is explained in a letter to Giacomo Contarini[11] and who carried on Paolo's studio after his death. In addition, imitations of Veronese, with or without dishonest intent, started at an early date. The Paduan painter, Alessandro Varotari ('il Padovanino') (1588–1648) is particularly associated with this activity. For Veronese's crucial rôle in eighteenth-century Venetian painting cf. *passim* Michael Levey's forthcoming monograph.

For notes on Veronese's technical procedure see the introduction to Boschini's *Ricche Minere* (1674).

REFERENCES: (1) For the relevant documents connected with the date of Veronese's birth cf. Ridolfi/Hadeln, I, pp. 297, note 1, and 349, note 1, and P. Caliari: *Paolo Veronese*, 1888, pp. 9, note 2, 12, notes 1 and 3, 164, note 4. (2) Ed. Milanesi, V, p. 290, and VI, p. 370. (3) Ridolfi/Hadeln, I, 298. (4) *Il Riposo*, 1584, p. 561, where the form 'Baillo' of the surname is used. (5) Caliari, *op. cit.*, p. 70, note 1. (6) Vasari/Milanesi, VI, p. 370. The fragment with the date (Venice, Seminario) also bears a signature, 'paulus f'. (7) Ridolfi/Hadeln, I, p. 349. (8) Ridolfi/Hadeln, I, p. 310, note 3. (9) Among other examples may be cited the *Feast in the House of Levi* (Venice, Accademia) which is the type of great feast-subject and the *Trinity with SS. Peter and Paul* (Vicenza, Museo, from S. Croce) which is a small upright altar. Both of these appear largely autograph, the former broadly but carefully painted, the latter hastily. The differences between them in general appearance are extreme. Both are dated 1573. Two other works of the same year—the *Adoration of the Kings* (no. 268 of this Gallery) and the *Madonna of the Roses* (Venice, Accademia)—would owe some of their differences from the others to studio assistance. Conversely, Veronese's ceiling style, in particular, developed remarkably little over the years—cf. the similarity between the S. Sebastiano ceilings of the mid-'fifties and the 'Venice Enthroned' of the *Sala del Maggior Consiglio* of the Doge's Palace dating from more than twenty years later. (10) Examples are two of the decorations in the *Sala del Maggior Consiglio* of the Doge's Palace (scenes from the career of Pope Alexander III), an *Adoration of the Shepherds* (Vienna, no. 383 in the 1910 catalogue), two *Baptisms* (Venice, Redentore and New York, cathedral of S. John the Divine) (for the latter picture cf. W. Suida in *Art Quarterly*, VIII, 1945, pp. 175–87) an *Annunciation* (Reggio Emilia, Museo Civico) and a *Last Supper* (Naples, S. Martino). (11) Printed in Caliari, *op. cit.*, pp. 177–8.

## 26 THE CONSECRATION OF S. NICHOLAS

Original canvas *c.* $111\frac{1}{4} \times 67\frac{1}{4}$ (2·825 × 1·708). Narrow strips have been added at the sides and base. The original canvas is missing at the upper corners in triangles whose sides measure *c.* 10″ (0·254) from the corners in both directions.[1]

Always rather summarily painted and now somewhat rubbed and made up, particularly in the sky. At present much darkened.

Superficially cleaned, 1938.

On the death of the Archbishop of Myra in Lycia it was revealed to one of the provincial bishops assembled to elect a successor that a young priest named Nicholas had been divinely chosen and would present himself at the cathedral on the morrow. The prophesy was precisely fulfilled, the newcomer being consecrated Archbishop of Myra on the spot. In 1087 his remains were translated to Bari.

On 30th March, 1562, Paolo Veronese received the balance of payment[2] due to him in respect of work commissioned on 27th December, apparently of the previous year,[3] and specified as consisting of three altarpieces for the altars of SS. Nicholas, Anthony and Jerome in the monastery church of S. Benedetto Po, near Mantua. The three altars were described soon afterwards by Vasari[4] as being the best pictures in the church and again, in greater detail, by Giovanni Cadioli (1763).[5]

Three altarpieces answering to this description are still in position at S. Benedetto, all clearly copies after Veronese. As the S. Nicholas altarpiece corresponds exactly with no. 26 and the SS. Anthony and Paul with a painting in the Walter P. Chrysler collection[6] it can be assumed that the pictures existing in the church are copies put up to replace the originals. Confirmation of provenance from S. Benedetto in respect of no. 26, together with a reference to the original of the S. Jerome altarpiece comes from an entry in the A. Delahante sale catalogue at Phillips, 2nd or 3rd June,[7] 1814, lot 41: 'Veronese: St Jerome . . . together with the Communion of St Jerome, now in the British institution, to which it was a companion in the church of the Monastery of St Benedict, Mantua.' The latter picture, despite the apparent discrepancy in the subject, was certainly no. 26 (see PROVENANCE below). The former was later accidentally destroyed by fire at Yates' Galleries in 1836.[8]

Though there is no indication of when no. 26 would have left S. Benedetto, and therefore no continuity in its history, the fact that it is stylistically acceptable as an original Veronese, together with the existence of the copy *in situ*, can leave no reasonable doubt concerning the provenance. The altarpiece of the Madonna and SS. Anthony and Paul was removed from Mantua during the Napoleonic occupation,[9] but as both no. 26 and the altarpiece of the Madonna and S. Jerome were apparently imported into England by Delahante early in the nineteenth century they had evidently become separated from it, possibly some time before.[10]

PROVENANCE: Erroneously stated in all relevant editions of the National Gallery catalogue (i.e. from 1830 to 1929) to have come from the church of S. Niccolò dei Frari at Venice. The mistake was due to speculative identification of no. 26 with old references to a Veronese of the same subject at S. Niccolò, now in the Accademia, Venice. The provenance which is almost certainly correct, namely S. Benedetto Po, has been discussed above. Said to have been imported into England by Alexis Delahante and sold by him to the British Institution in 1811.[11] Exh. 1812, 1816 (87), 1821 (106) and 1824 (160), B.I., by the Governors of which presented, 1826. Cleaned Pictures Exhibition, National Gallery, 1947 (41).

VERSION: Old copy at S. Benedetto Po (see above).

REPRODUCTION: *Illustrations, Italian Schools*, 1937, p. 380.

REFERENCES: (1) It is probable that this shape was dictated by the original frame. The copy of the Madonna with S. Jerome, still at S. Benedetto, has the upper corners cut and there are indications of the same thing in the published photograph of the Madonna with SS. Anthony and Paul (see text below). (2) The document recording payment published by P. Caliari: *Paolo Veronese*, 1888, pp. 52–3. (3) The reference in the payment document to the original agreement says of it 'sub die vigesima septima m̄s decembris anni proxime decursi milli quingentesimi sexagemi primi iuxta stijllum notariorum, non autem secūdum comunem, usum modo loquendi'. The usage then common in Mantua began the year on 25th December and by this system '27th December, 1561' would be 27th December, 1560, N.S. The notary's use of the words 'proxime decursi' however seems as though the passage can only mean that the 'stijllus notariorum' in this case means 1561 when it says 1561. The resulting implication, that the three altarpieces were all executed within three months, takes some believing. **(4)** 1568. Ed. Milanesi, VI, pp. 490–1. **(5)** *Descrizione . . . di Mantova*, p. 128. **(6)** For discussion and photographs of this picture cf. Lionello Venturi: *Un' opera inedita di Paolo Veronese* in *Commentari*, January, 1950, pp. 39–40. See also the 1956 catalogue of the Chrysler collection exhibited at Portland, Oregon. The *Inventario degli Oggetti d'Arte d'Italia*, VI, *Provincia di Mantova*, 1935, p. 148, mistakenly refers to the copy as representing the Virgin and Child 'e in basso S. Benedetto e altri santi'. In fact there can be no doubt either from this copy or from the photograph published by Venturi of the presumed original that the saints are Anthony and Paul the Hermit, as Cadioli had specified. **(7)** Of two copies of the catalogue in the National Gallery library (both printed) one has '2nd June', the other '3rd June'. **(8)** Whitley: *Art in England*, 1821–1837, 1930, p. 313. In the meantime the picture had figured in the Beckford sale, 26th day, 14th October, 1823, lot 269, and in a final Delahante sale, 29th June, 1830, lot 81. **(9)** Lionello Venturi, *op. cit.*, quotes from a contemporary inventory the entry relating to this picture. **(10)** The *Inventario*, already mentioned, attempts to use the superior quality noted by Cadioli à propos no. 26 as opposed to the other two altarpieces to suggest that the originals of the latter had already been removed by his time and replaced by copies. This is possible, but the fact that later on no. 26 appears to accompany the original of the S. Jerome altarpiece, the original of the SS. Anthony and Paul having got separated, would render it improbable. If all three altarpieces had, as it seems, been painted within the space of three months there would have been unevenness in quality in any case. **(11)** The earliest specific source for the Delahante provenance of no. 26 seems to be Thomas Uwins' evidence in 1850 before the Select Committee on the National Gallery (pp. 7–8 of the printed Minutes of Evidence). He also gave evidence before the 1853 Committee in the same sense. Some more details were given subsequently by Thomas Smith (*Recollections of the British Institution*, 1860, pp. 63–4). Nevertheless, two much earlier references, though vague, are certainly to no. 26, namely Delahante's letter to Penrice of 7th July, 1813 (pp. 28–30 of the printed *Letters . . . to . . . Thomas Penrice*): 'P. Veronese—the companion of the one sold to the Institution' (referring to the Madonna with S. Jerome, discussed above) and a reference, already quoted, in the Delahante sale catalogue of 2nd June, 1814.

## 268 ADORATION OF THE KINGS

140 × 126 (3·55 × 3·2).[1]

Widespread abrasion due to having been stored off the stretcher in the last century (see PROVENANCE). Nevertheless this is local and not general and the affected areas are nowhere large in extent. In the remaining areas the paint is well preserved.

Cleaned 1957.
Dated (on the lowest step, bottom right): M.D.LXXIII.[2]
From the church of S. Silvestro, Venice, where first noted by Sansovino (1581).[3] Three other large pictures by Veronese are also dated 1573, namely the *Feast in the House of Levi* (Venice, Accademia, from SS. Giovanni e Paolo) ('20th April'), *Madonna del Rosario* (Venice,

Accademia, from S. Pietro Martire, Murano) ('December') and *Trinity with SS. Peter and Paul* (Vicenza, Museo, from S. Croce). It is therefore not surprising that studio assistance has long been recognised in no. 268. Most of the handling lacks the brilliance of Veronese's own touch, but the design is evidently his and the tone remarkably unified and characteristic of him.

The present writer would incline to the view that Veronese, having designed the picture in the smallest detail, left most of the execution to his studio but finally spent some time working over parts of it himself. His own touch is unmistakable in the Madonna and Child and in the foremost king. He probably touched up other areas.[4]

DRAWINGS: 1. Haarlem, Teyler's Stichting, B 65. Reproduced, Hadeln: *Venezianische Zeichnungen der Spätrenaissance*, 1926, pl. 32. The figures at the bottom of the sheet are clearly preparatory studies for the Madonna and kings in no. 268. The king in the (vertical) centre of the sheet, however, is seen not from the side, as are both the first and second kings in no. 268, but from the back, his page stretching his right arm (holding the train) almost to the ground. Both these features occur in another version of the subject by Veronese—at S. Corona, Vicenza. Since the altar for which it was painted was constructed between 1572 and 1581 it is possible that Veronese was working on the two versions simultaneously. Nevertheless the upper sketches on the Haarlem sheet, to which the king in question belongs, appear very amorphous and belonging to a primitive stage in the conception. If, as seems likely, the lower sketches represent a later stage, an alternative and perhaps more probable explanation is that the Vicenza picture was painted after no. 268 and that in it Veronese returned as regards the first king to a motive he had toyed with for no. 268 and then abandoned.[5] 2. Formerly Koenigs collection (ex-Wauters). Reproduced Tietze and Tietze-Conrat: *Drawings of the Venetian Painters . . .*, 1944, pl. CLX, 3. Study for the king in the red robe (the second king).[6]

ENGRAVING: Etching by Carlo Sacchi, dated 9th March, 1649.

VERSIONS: Copy on reduced scale (1·6 × 1·4) Madrid, Prado (489). Another, with variations, S. Pierre des Minimes, Clermont-Ferrand (signed Guillaume Rome [apparently] Brionde, 1637). A partial copy with variations was lot 21, anonymous sale, Sotheby's, 23rd February, 1955. Another partial copy was engraved by Sim. Gribelin (1712) as from a painting at Windsor (still in the collection of H.M. The Queen; in 1957 on loan to Somerset House). A copy probably by Francesco Minorello was noted by Mündler in Palazzo Pisani at Este in the mid-nineteenth century.[7] What claimed to be the *modello* is catalogued as in the collection of Giovanni Vianelli, Canon of Chioggia (1790 cat., p. 113).

PROVENANCE: From, and clearly painted for, S. Silvestro, Venice (see above). The interior of the church was completely remodelled in 1836–43[8] and as a result no. 268, together with other works of art, was taken down in the year 1837 and removed to an adjoining room where it was folded twice, horizontally.[9] When the remodelling of the church was finished it was found that the larger pictures no longer fitted. No. 268 was bought in August, 1855, by the dealer Toffoli from whom purchased in November of the same year.

REPRODUCTION: *Illustrations, Italian Schools*, 1937, p. 380.

REFERENCES: (1) Approximate measurements only. It is difficult to determine exactly where the original painted area stops. (2) G. A. Moschini (*Guida per Venezia*, 1815, II, part I, 154) misreads the date as 1571. A. Quadri (*Otto Giorni a Venezia*, I, 1821, 273) follows him in this. (3) Also mentioned by seventeenth- and eighteenth-century writers on Venice and Veronese such as Ridolfi, Boschini, Barri and Zanetti. (4) A note in the Gallery archives records Richter as following Morelli in identifying Bassanesque elements in no. 268. While it can be excluded that either Jacopo Bassano or any of his sons can have participated in the execution of the picture (as was suggested in the 1929 catalogue), certain features in it do seem to indicate some *rapprochement* between the styles of Veronese and Jacopo Bassano. (5) For dates of the construction of the S. Corona altar see E. Arslan: *Vicenza, I, Le Chiese*, 1956, p. 67 (with bibliography). (6) Two more drawings vaguely deriving from no. 268 are at Düsseldorf (Budde 104, as Andrea Sacchi) and the Albertina (Stix-Bum 105). (7) Mündler's note-books in the Gallery archives. (8) G. Lorenzetti: *Venezia e il suo Estuario*, 1956, p. 603. (9) National Gallery Report, 1856, p. 27.

## 294 THE FAMILY OF DARIUS BEFORE ALEXANDER

93 × 187 (2·362 × 4·749).
Unusually good condition for a picture of its size and age.[1] Slight wearing in the sky and in a few other areas. The horizontal line of the seam of the canvas repainted in parts. *Pentimenti* notably on the left, where the two small horses and their groom are lightly painted on top of the pillars, also in the shoulder and upper arm of the halbadier, extreme left. Cleaned 1958.

Quick preliminary sketching in grey with the point of the brush is visible in many of the architectural features, and in the neighbourhood of the balustrade seen through the arch on the left. Traces of it above the half pillars of the colonnade suggest that Veronese had toyed with the idea of a broken entablature. Later restorers in fact fulfilled this, both right and left of the central monument, at the sacrifice of perspective. These restorations were removed in the 1958 cleaning. The architectural features of the central monument or fountain were modified several times. In its present form there is clearly meant to be an appreciable amount of space separating it both from the colonnade in the background and from the balustrade in the foreground. In the angle of the existing colonnade, however, on the spectator's right, it is still possible to trace mouldings which correspond exactly in type and height with the double entablature of the central monument. Between this area and the latter (behind the figures of Alexander and his *entourage*) there are also traces of a single entablature at the lower of the two levels. Evidently the original background to the figures on this side was the stone wall now seen only in the central monument. Further indications that the whole idea of the colonnade, with its greater splendour, was an afterthought come from the presence, as revealed by infra-red photography, of several large-scale heads in the area of sky to the spectator's right of the central monument and by traces of a large pyramidal shape in the sky and balustrade to the left of it.

Always recognised as a superb original. Any studio assistance there may have been would have been the minimum.

Though called by Ridolfi 'la Costanza di Alessandro' there can be little doubt, despite Veronese's usual embroidery of the story in the interests of decoration, that the episode illustrated is the mistake in identifying Alexander after the Battle of Issus. This story is told by Arrian,[2] Quintus Curtius Rufus,[3] Diodorus Siculus[4] and Valerius Maximus.[5] Their accounts differ slightly in details, the common elements being that when, after the battle, Alexander and his bosom friend, Hephaestion, visited Darius' family, the mother of Darius, misled by Hephaestion's greater height, offered him the obeisance due to the victorious monarch. When her mistake was pointed out Alexander magnanimously alleviated her confusion by saying of Hephaestion that he too was Alexander. In no. 294 the most prominent figure, in crimson, would naturally be taken for Alexander. Whether for this reason he is really Hephaestion would, in the circumstances, be an arguable point.[6]

First mentioned by Ridolfi, 1648,[7] as 'in Casa Pisana'. Boschini soon afterwards (1674) specifies the setting as 'Casa Pisana nelle Procuratie di S. Marco'.[8] D'Argenville (1762)[9] prints a story to the effect that Veronese had painted the picture in one of the Pisani country houses as a return for hospitality received. Cicogna (1843) specifies that the country house in question was the Palazzo Pisani at Este[10] where indeed a copy of no. 294 was seen by Mündler in 1857.[11] It has sometimes been assumed[12] that no. 294 was painted for Francesco Pisani who had commissioned of Paolo Veronese in 1555 the *Transfiguration* for the Duomo at Montagnana. This would provide a *terminus ad quem* for dating no. 294 as Francesco died in 1567.[13] Nevertheless no evidence has been published in favour of this assumption and the indications afforded by the various costumes in no. 294 suggest a later dating, perhaps towards the end of the 'seventies.[14] The fact that the colonnade in no. 294 seems to be the same as one in the much-damaged fresco of *S. Sebastian before Diocletian* (Venice, S. Sebastiano)[15] which may date from the later 1550's, would not in itself be sufficient evidence for assuming a similar date of origin for the two paintings.

Although much uncertainty remains concerning the date and the circumstances of the execution of no. 294 it need not be doubted that it was painted for the Pisani family—presumably the S. Polo branch since it came from their *palazzo*. It may incorporate portraits of them.[16]

ENGRAVING: By N. R. Cochin in C. C. Patina: *Pitture Scelte*, 1691.

VERSIONS: Full scale seventeenth-century copy by Francesco Minorello recorded by Mündler in Palazzo Pisani at Este in 1857.[17] Subsequent to the purchase of no. 294 by the National Gallery the former owner decided to have this copy brought to Venice to replace the original in Palazzo Pisani a S. Polo.[18] Small copies at Cassel and in the following sales: Sir Allan Adair, 8th December, 1950 (169), Anonymous, 18th February, 1953 (attr. F. Guardi), and Anonymous, 16th July, 1954. A copy said to be 'at least two hundred years old' was in 1926 in the collection of Francis Carey Lea, Philadelphia. Many owners have claimed at different times to possess the 'sketch' for the picture, among them the Président de Brosses (*Lettres Familières*, 1931 ed., I, 206). Tiepolo's fresco (1743) of the same subject at the Villa Cordellina, Montecchio Maggiore, is a distant derivative. Algarotti later (1751) said he had wished to commission Tiepolo to copy no. 294.[19]

PROVENANCE: Purchased, 1857, from Conte Vettor Pisani, Venice.

REFERENCES: (**1**) C. A. Levi (*Le Collezioni Veneziane* ..., 1900, pp. CCXLVII–CCXLVIII) refers to a restoration by Lattanzio Querena, about the year 1800, who was rumoured to have repainted one of the figures. (**2**) *Anabasis of Alexander*, II, 12. (**3**) *History of Alexander the Great*, III, 12. (**4**) *History*, XVII, 37. (**5**) *Factorum et Dictorum* ..., IV, 7. See also J. P. Richter in *Burlington Magazine*, LXII, 1933, pp. 181 ff. (**6**) Goethe seems to have thought so (*Italienische Reise*, 8th October, 1786). The action of the man on the spectator's right, pointing to himself with his right hand, would make more sense as Alexander than as Hephaestion. The present writer is grateful to Mr Philipp P. Fehl for drawing his attention to this aspect of the problem. (**7**) Ridolfi/Hadeln, I, pp. 337–8. (**8**) *Le Ricche Minere* ..., Breve Instruzione, 56 f. (**9**) *Abrégé*, 1762, I, 262 ff. (**10**) *Inscrizioni* ..., IV, 235. (**11**) Mündler's notes in the Gallery archives. (**12**) E.g. in Bruno Brunelli and Adolfo Callegari: *Ville del Brenta e degli Euganei*, 1931, p. 337. (**13**) Pietro Caliari: *Paolo Veronese*, 1888, p. 25, note 1. (**14**) Notes on the costumes by Stella Mary Pearce in the Gallery archives. (**15**) Reproduced Fiocco: *Paolo Veronese*, 1928, p. 58, fig. 42, and Rodolfo Pallucchini: *Veronese* (in series *I Grandi Artisti Italiani*), 3rd ed., 1953, pl. 25. (**16**) It is possible that research among the genealogy of the Pisani family might identify the patron and thereby narrow the dating of the picture. The detailed article by R. Gallo ('I Pisani ed i Palazzi di S. Stefano e di Stra' in *Archivio Veneto*, vol. XXXIV–XXXV, 1944, published 1945) does not cover this. The same writer, however, in a personal (oral) communication, suggests that the patron may have been Vettor Pisani (b. 1528). (**17**) Mündler's notes in the Gallery archives. (**18**) C. A. Levi: *Le Collezioni Veneziane* ..., 1900, pp. CCXLVI–CCXLVIII. (**19**) Cf. Bottari-Ticozzi, *Raccolta di Lettere*, VII, 1822, 390–1. A Tiepolo 'modèle' of the subject (p. xxvi of the French ed. of the Algarotti catalogue, n.d. but after 1776) was perhaps for the Cordellina fresco.

## 931 S. MARY MAGDALENE LAYING ASIDE HER JEWELS

$46\frac{1}{4} \times 64\frac{3}{8}$ ($1 \cdot 175 \times 1 \cdot 635$).

Much damaged. The canvas plainly shows through in places, notably in the white drapery covering the shoulders of the bearded man with the red cap (his right hand to his chest) towards the spectator's right. The faces of the two men on his left (on the spectator's extreme right) crudely daubed with old repaint. Likewise most of the flutings of the pillar on the spectator's right. Little remains of the Magdalen's left hand; her face also much damaged. The following areas in reasonably good state: Christ's face and clothes, the face of the young man on His left, the face and cloak of the woman on His right, the drapery over the Magdalen's knee, and the cloak of the woman on her left (who draws her attention to Christ).

*Pentimento* in the head of the man on the spectator's right (with his right hand to his cloak). His beard was originally larger, and covered more of his neck.

Partly cleaned, 1936.

The episode represented does not figure in the Gospels.

Catalogued as Veronese from the time when it entered the Gallery until the edition of 1920, when it appeared as 'after Veronese'. As such also in the 1929 catalogue. The unusual *pentimento*, already indicated, would more or less exclude the hypothesis that the picture is a copy, irrespective of other considerations. Of these, it may be noted that it

10+V.S.C.

shows the influence both of the Parmigianino circle[1] and of the early Tintoretto.[2] In addition, it contains many points of contact with acknowledged works of Veronese.[3] On the strength of the latter the present writer accepts it as a Veronese and on the strength of the former as a very early work, associable with the *Anointing of David* (Vienna)[4] and perhaps also with the original of the *Raising of Lazarus* (copy in the Uffizi)[5] and *Presentation in the Temple* (Dresden).[6] Whether such a group follows or precedes in date the earliest dated works, namely the Villa Soranza frescoes of 1551, could be discussed but not settled.

PROVENANCE: Wynn Ellis Bequest, 1876. Called, in a MS. list of the Wynn Ellis pictures, 'Woman taken in Adultery'[7] and therefore presumably identical with a picture of that description noted by Waagen as a Veronese in Ellis' possession,[8] and thus purchased by the latter before the date of Waagen's visit (1850 or 1851).[9] Cleaned Pictures Exhibition, National Gallery, 1947, no. 40.

REPRODUCTION: *Illustrations, Italian Schools*, 1937, p. 385.

REFERENCES: (1) Among other points may be noted the figure of the Magdalen, inspired by works such as Parmigianino's etching of the Virgin Annunciate (repr. Copertini: *Il Parmigianino*, II, 1932, pl. CXIV). Also the curved colonnade in the background which was a normal feature of the Parmigianinesque repertory (cf. the background of his *Marriage of S. Catherine* at Bardi or the *Circumcision*, repr. Copertini, *op. cit.*, pl. CXLV, also a drawing by Bedoli in the Albertina, repr. Fröhlich-Bum: *Parmigianino . . .*, 1921, fig. 136). Above all, the girl in profile (in the background, slightly to the spectator's right of the centre) is of a standard Parmigianinesque type. (2) The system of composition used—with excessive crowding together of the figures and plenty of space round them—though exemplified in the Parmigianino circle, seems closer in no. 931 to Tintoretto's practice in pictures such as the *Miracle of S. Mark* of 1548. (3) For example, the system of draperies used in no. 931 is similar to that in the Montagnana *Transfiguration* among others, while the design as a whole may be considered a foretaste of the Louvre *Supper at Emmaus*. Also, the Parmigianinesque profile of the girl, already indicated, recurs in an almost exactly similar form in Veronese's allegory of *Peace* (Rome, Capitoline). (4) Repr. Fiocco: *Paolo Veronese*, 1928, pl. XI. Formerly attributed to Zelotti and to Farinati. The male figure advancing on the spectator's left of the picture is extraordinarily like several in no. 931. (5) Repr. F. H. Meissner: *Veronese* (Künstler-Monographien series), 1897, pl. 43. Stella Mary Pearce, in notes in the Gallery archives, points out the extreme oddity and inconsistency of nearly all the costumes in no. 931, which in her opinion are entirely contrary to Veronese's normal practice. (6) Repr. Fiocco, *op. cit.*, pl. IX. (7) MS. in the Gallery library. (8) Waagen: *Treasures . . .*, II, 1854, p. 293. (9) Earlier than that nothing definite is known. The 1929 catalogue has 'possibly Campion sale, 1810'. This information clearly derives from an entry in Redford's *Art Sales* (II, 260) but no such sale seems otherwise recorded. An *Adulteress before Christ* by Veronese was in the Prince de Carignan sale, 30th July, 1742 (see Blanc: *Le Trésor de la Curiosité*, II, 1857, pp. 30-3) and was supposed to have turned up again at an anonymous sale in 1791 (source for latter Redford, *op. cit.*). However, the dimensions given in the Carignan sale catalogue—'cinquante-huit pouces sur soixante-douze' are considerably larger than no. 931. A 'Woman taken in Adultery' by Veronese was no. 130, British Institution, 1823, lent William Smith, M.P. It did not figure in a small posthumous sale of the latter's pictures, Christie's, 4th July, 1835.

1041 THE VISION OF S. HELENA

$77\frac{3}{4} \times 45\frac{1}{2}$ (1·975 × 1·156).

The present heavily engrained varnish makes assessment of the state of the paint difficult. A good deal of obvious wearing and repaint in the sky, in the cross and in the *putti*. The arm of the cross which points in the direction of the saint's head was originally inclined downwards at a steeper angle. The top left arm of it seems to have been painted out. S. Helena's face and most of her dress seem to be in good state. *Pentimento* in her right hand.

The identification of the subject with S. Helena is universal and probably correct, but the iconography is unusual. Earlier Venetian representations of S. Helena, such as Cima's at S. Giovanni in Bragora, Venice or Palma Vecchio's (Milan, Brera) had shown S. Helena standing under the cross. Veronese was apparently pleased with the form of presentation as here since he repeated it—his S. Helena in the Vatican gallery, though quite different in design from no. 1041, likewise shows the saint seated and asleep, a *putto* near her holding a cross. Though S. Helena is said to have received Divine guidance in her quest for the cross [1] the essential requisite concerned the exact place in which to dig in order to find it, and to this end the vision shown both in no. 1041 and in the Vatican picture would be useless. Some of the unsuitability of the presentation to the subject may spring from the fact that the design was not Veronese's own and that it was never intended for S. Helena. The immediate source was evidently an engraving, ascribed to a follower of Marcantonio Raimondi, in which the female figure is shown in exactly the same attitude as in no. 1041, even the line of the window and some of the folds of the dress being the same. The apparition in the sky is different, consisting of one adult angel instead of two *putti*, and with a relatively smaller cross. The presence of an animal (called by Bartsch and Passavant a dog, but conceivably intended for a lamb) [2] lying curled up asleep at the saint's feet shows that the subject of the engraving can hardly be S. Helena. It may be an allegory or just possibly a representation of S. Agnes.

The engraving in its turn derives from Parmigianino. If he ever did a painting or other finished work of art of it, it has long since disappeared, but the essentials are preserved in a drawing by him in the Uffizi. [3] This consists of a female figure who corresponds closely (in reverse) with the one in the engraving and who is shown in a similar relation to the window. The seat she sits on (under which is the animal again) is inscribed 'Danae', which may well be a later addition. On the same sheet are some architectural studies which may be unconnected and two flying angels, one of whom is clearly the source (again in reverse) of the angel in the engraving. It is these angels in Parmigianino's drawing which lead back to the earliest stage in the progression, since they are copied, with minor and inessential variations, from two who support the Almighty in Raphael's *Moses and the Burning Bush* (Vatican, ceiling of the Stanza d'Eliodoro). Parmigianino's female figure has the same position relative to the angels as Raphael's Moses and was clearly inspired by that figure —the essentials of the pose are similar, hand (with Raphael both of them) to head and one leg raised—though the connection, being looser, could hardly be demonstrated if the angels in the two works corresponded less closely than they do. Though the function of Parmigianino's drawing is uncertain it is clear that in adapting Raphael's motives he changed the subject, that his own subject (whatever it was) may or may not have been changed in adaptation by the anonymous engraver, and that the latter's subject in its turn was changed by Veronese when he took over the design.

Even without these iconographic peculiarities it is clear that no. 1041 is exceptional in Veronese's *œuvre*, and although for that reason the attribution to him may legitimately be questioned it remains acceptable to the present writer. The fact that Veronese reacted as a young man to the Central Italian influences with which he would have come in contact at Mantua but seems already to have become impervious to them by the time of his visit to Rome might favour a relatively early dating for no. 1041, as being based on a Central Italian idea. Its colouring and technique, too, have much in common with the Vicenza *Madonna and Child with S. Peter and a female Saint* which is undated but certainly fairly early.

It has been claimed that no. 1041 is identical with a picture of the same subject described by Ridolfi as having been in Casa Contarini at Padua.[4] It is true that Ridolfi says that the cross in that picture was supported by two small angels—which would apply to no. 1041 and not to the Vatican picture, which has only one. Nevertheless no positive evidence to support the identification has come to light, nor any certain identification of the remaining pictures described by Ridolfi in the same context.

VERSIONS: A derivative in fresco (with the cross arranged differently and supported by three *putti*) was formerly in the Villa Guarnieri at Romanziol (reproduced by A. Moschetti: *I Danni ai Monumenti e alle Opere d'Arte delle Venezie nella Guerra Mondiale*, 1932, fig. 334, where attributed to Veronese). An old copy at Goodwood is labelled 'Passignano'. Among references to pictures by Veronese of this subject are 'St Helena, held to be Paulo Verrona's' in the posthumous inventory of Rubens' collection [5] and two 'inventions de la Croix par Sainte Hélène' recorded by the Président de Brosses at Rome in the 'Palais des Ursins' and the 'Palais Santa Croce'.[6] A 'St Helena with the Cross from P. Veronese' by C. Jarvis was lot 65 in the latter's sale, 11th March, 1739–40.

PROVENANCE: Stated (in the catalogue of the W. Comyns sale, 1815) to have been the property of the 1st Duke of Marlborough, who died in 1722. Included in the sale (6th June, 1803, lot 60) of pictures formerly the property of the Duke's son-in-law, Francis, 2nd Earl of Godolphin, to whom it had presumably passed by inheritance.[7] Bought on this occasion by 'Mr Comyns'.[8] No. 73 in the latter's sale, 6th May, 1815, where bought Ponsonby.[9] No. 109, anonymous sale (said to be 'Dorrien'),[10] 2nd March, 1816, where bought Lord Yarmouth [11] (later 3rd Marquess of Hertford) by whom exh. B.I., 1819 (30). No. 118 in the sale of the 3rd Marquess' possessions at St Dunstan's, Regent's Park, London, 9th July, 1855, where bought Emery.[12] No. 74 in the Hon. P. Ashburnham sale,

19th May, 1860, where bought 'Monro'.[13] No. 144 in the H. A. J. Munro of Novar sale, 1st June, 1878, where purchased.[14]

REPRODUCTION: *Illustrations, Italian Schools*, 1937, p. 384.

REFERENCES: (1) See *Les Petits Bollandistes*, 3rd May (*Invention de la Sainte Croix*). S. Helena is said to have been about eighty years old at the time. (2) Bartsch: *Le Peintre Graveur*, XIV, no. 460: 'cette belle estampe . . . est attribuée par quelques uns à Marc-Antoine. Le dessein paroit être du Parmesan; mais il y a des auteurs qui le croient de Raphaël'. Passavant (*Le Peintre-Graveur*, VI, 1864, p. 89, no. 122) as by a pupil of Marcantonio. Another state, or other version, omits the angel and has been claimed as the origin of a Beham engraving of the Madonna (Fritz Burger: *Die Deutsche Malerei* (Handbuch für Kunstwissenschaft), I, p. 103). A drawing supposed to be a study for the engraving was bought by H. D. Gronau at the Heseltine sale, 28th May, 1935 (124). (3) 1971 E. There is a photograph of this drawing in the W. Gernsheim series, no. 2971. Passavant (*loc. cit.*) had already drawn attention to this drawing. (4) Ridolfi/Hadeln, I, p. 318, note 5. (5) *Catalogue of the Works of Art in the Possession of . . . Rubens*, ed. Dawson Turner, 1839, p. 4, item 22. (6) *Lettres Familières*, 1931 ed., II, pp. 447 and 468. (7) Recorded in Lord Godolphin's possession by Vertue (*Note-books*, Walpole Society, vol. III, 1933–4, p. 133). (8) Marked copy of the sale catalogue of which photostats in the Gallery library. Seen in the possession of 'Commyn's the picture cleaner in Pall Mall' by Coleridge in 1804 (*Unpublished Letters of S. T. Coleridge*, ed. E. L. Griggs, 1932, p. 317). (9) Redford, II, p. 260. (10) Graves: *Art Sales*, III, 1921, p. 302. (11) Redford, *loc. cit.* (12) Marked copy of the sale catalogue in the Wallace collection. (13) Marked copy of the sale catalogue in the Gallery library. The catalogue says that the picture was 'purchased at the sale of the Duke of Leeds' pictures by the late Marquis of Hertford'. The 'Duke of Leeds' sale' was presumably the one of 6th June, 1803, of pictures formerly belonging to the 2nd Earl of Godolphin. The current but unspecified owner was indeed presumably his great-grandson, the 6th Duke of Leeds, but Lord Hertford did not buy the picture until later. (14) In former editions of the National Gallery catalogue stated to be from a chapel at Venice. No evidence is now available for this statement. Also stated in the earlier editions that it was 'engraved by Bonasoni and others'. The present writer has been unable to confirm the existence of a Bonasone engraving.

### 1318 ALLEGORY OF LOVE, I

$74\frac{3}{4} \times 74\frac{3}{4}$ (1·899 × 1·899).
Thinly painted and consequently rather worn, particularly in the sky. A line of repaint along the horizontal seam of the canvas in the centre.

A number of *pentimenti*, notably in the woman's shoulders and in the head and shoulders of the man on the spectator's right.

The letter slipped by the woman into the right hand of the man on the spectator's left is inscribed: *Ch. ./* ( ?) *mi. p(ossede)* ( ?).[1] Entitled 'Unfaithfulness' in earlier editions of the National Gallery catalogue.

Cleaned 1946.

For commentary and provenance see under no. 1326.

REFERENCES: (1) These letters are faint. The inscription does not seem to have been recorded hitherto. The third letter of the second word may be o.

### 1324 ALLEGORY OF LOVE, II

$73\frac{1}{2} \times 74\frac{1}{4}$ (1·866 × 1·885).[1]
Very good general state: the best preserved of the four.

Some retouching along the central horizontal seam. Many *pentimenti*, notably in the back of the left hand of the woman on the spectator's left of the two, in the left arm of the more prominent woman (next her), in the fingers of the man's left hand, in his chest and left leg, and in the *putto's* right arm, shoulders and right leg.

Entitled 'Scorn' in earlier editions of the National Gallery catalogue. Cleaned 1950.

For commentary and provenance see under no. 1326.

REFERENCES: (1) The binding covers some of the painted area as the turn-over is part of the top canvas.

### 1325  ALLEGORY OF LOVE, III

$73\frac{1}{4} \times 76\frac{1}{2}$ ($1 \cdot 861 \times 1 \cdot 943$).
The sky a good deal rubbed and retouched; much wearing down the right hand edge. Some wearing in the woman's body and in the capital of the pilaster. Otherwise generally good condition.

*Pentimento* round the outline of the head of the principal male figure and in his outstretched arm; also in the outline of his green sash as it crosses his left shoulder.

The subject of the relief on the vault has been convincingly identified by Professor Edgar Wind (personal communication) as the *Continence of Scipio*.[1]

Entitled 'Respect' in earlier editions of the National Gallery catalogue. Cleaned 1951.

For commentary and provenance see under no. 1326.

REFERENCES: (1) See also A. Pigler: *Barockthemen* II, pp. 404–9. In the engravings by Desplaces and by Cathelin and Couché (see ENGRAVINGS below) the scene is clearer though not necessarily accurate. These show the left hand of the seated figure resting on a shield or mirror and (in Desplaces' engraving) another figure behind.

### 1326  ALLEGORY OF LOVE, IV

$73\frac{3}{4} \times 73\frac{1}{2}$ ($1 \cdot 874 \times 1 \cdot 867$).
General condition good. Some wearing in the sky and in the sphere on the left.

Obvious *pentimento* in the left hand and arm of the naked seated female figure.

Entitled 'Happy Union' in earlier editions of the National Gallery catalogue. Cleaned 1946.

The titles hitherto applied to nos. 1318, 1324–6 date only from the period of their entry into the Orléans collection.[1] The general theme is clearly some of the various attributes of love. Professor Edgar Wind (private communication) sees nos. 1324 and 1325 as counterparts. In the former the man is prostrate, watched by the woman; in the latter the reverse. In the former the man is punished by Cupid (with his bow, not with his arrows). The woman is shown *décolletée* and is therefore passionate, but is also associated with chastity (the ermine held by her companion). The subject of no. 1324 would therefore be the pains of love. In no. 1325 the gesture of Cupid with his arrow unequivocally indicates the pleasures of love, but some restraint is imposed by the man on the extreme left. The theme of the remaining two pictures would be similarly complementary, no. 1318 symbolising the strife of love, no. 1326 its peace. In the former the naked woman favours the man in courtly dress (who seems also to be associated with music, as indicated by the *putto* playing near him) to the detriment of the military admirer on the spectator's right. In the latter the olive branch held by both the man and woman stands for peace, the dog for fidelity and the gold chain for conjugal ties.

Nos. 1318, 1324, 1325 and 1326 are identifiable in the inventory made after 15th February, 1637, of the collection at Prague of the Emperor Rudolph II, who died in 1612. They do not figure in the 1621 inventory. Though there would remain nevertheless a possibility that they had been commissioned by Rudolph (with whose taste their erotic subject matter would conform) the point cannot be settled. Borghini (1584) specifies two pictures painted by Veronese for Rudolph,[2] and the 1621 inventory lists six as in his collection, of which at least two seem not to have been painted for him.[3] The existence, in Van Dyck's Italian sketch-book, of sketches apparently after nos. 1318 and 1325 (see DRAWINGS below) is not conclusive evidence that the paintings were in Italy during Van Dyck's travels there (1621–7) as a possibility would remain that the sketches were made from copies, or even from *modelli*.

First suggested in the *Recueil d'Estampes* (1742)[4] that the four pictures were executed for a ceiling. This is plausible enough, as Veronese used this kind of foreshortening in ceiling paintings such as those at S. Sebastiano, Venice and in the Doge's Palace.

Though there is no definite evidence for dating the series the costumes and hair styles shown would accord best with Veronese's practice in the mid-1570's.[5]

Though a varying degree of studio assistance is apparent in all four pictures the homogeneity of the design and of the handling and tone when seen from a distance—which, if they were in fact intended as ceiling decorations, would be the normal viewing range—point to close supervision by a controlling personality, obviously Veronese himself. For this reason glaring disparities in quality are rare, though an example are the two *putti* at the lower left corner of no. 1318, of which the one on the spectator's right is painted in the same delicate technique as the woman's back in the same picture, while the *putto* next him, on the left of all, is more coarsely modelled and different in tone. Passages of out-standingly brilliant execution, such as the woman's back in no. 1318, the more prominent of the two women in no. 1324 or the sheet on which the woman reclines in no. 1325, as well as the glass in the foreground of the same picture, are characteristic of the highest quality of Veronese's own work. But even in the areas which would have been painted by an assistant some finishing touches by the master himself are not to be excluded.[6]

DRAWINGS: Oxford, Ashmolean Museum. Sketch copy (wash) by Delacroix of part of no. 1318 (in reverse). Van Dyck's Italian sketch-book (British Museum, from Chatsworth) contains sketches apparently after nos. 1318 and 1325 on both sides of folio 36 (Cust's pagination).

ENGRAVINGS: In vol. II of the *Recueil d'Estampes* ('Crozat Cabinet') (1742) no. 1318 by Simon Vallée, no. 1324 by Benoist Audran, nos. 1325 and 1326 by Louis Desplaces. In vol. II of the *Galerie du Palais Royal* (1808) no. 1318 by J. A. Pierron, no. 1324 by J. Couché, no. 1325 by Cathelin and Couché and no. 1326 by Beljambe and Cathelin.

PROVENANCE: Nos. 1318, 1324, 1325 and 1326 figure as nos. 453, 451, 455 (probably) and 449 in the inventory of the Rudolph II collection at Prague taken after 15th February, 1637,[7] as nos. 99, 98, 96 and 97 in the 1652 inventory of Queen Christina of Sweden's collection, as nos. 3, 1, 2 and 4 in the 1689 inventory and as nos. 73, 71, 72 and 74 in the 1721 inventory. Rudolph II's collection was looted by the Swedes at the Sack of Prague in 1648 and taken to Sweden. Many of the pictures, including nos. 1318, 1324–6, were taken by Queen Christina to Italy after her abdication in 1654, and after her death were sold (in 1721) to the Duc d'Orléans. In the 1727 catalogue (by Du Bois de Saint Gelais) of the Orléans pictures at the Palais Royal, Paris (pp. 377–80), in which building they adorned the 'Salon Octogone' (Palais Royal catalogue, II, 1808). The Italian pictures in the Orléans collection were sold in 1792 to the Belgian banker, Walkuers, who sold them to Laborde de Méréville, who fled with them to England,[8] where they were bought by Jeremiah Harman, who made them over to a syndicate consisting of the Duke of Bridgewater and Lords Carlisle and Gower.[9] A sale was arranged by Bryan who exhibited the pictures in 1798. Nos. 1318, 1324–6 were apparently lots 169, 181, 243 and 245 of the Lyceum portion of the sale (26th December, 1798), all marked 'not sold' in the copy of the sale catalogue in the Gallery library. Probably lots 26, 34, 42 and (?) 57 in the sale (by Peter Coxe, Burrell and Foster) of 'the remaining part of the Orléans collection of Italian Paintings' at Bryan's Gallery, Pall Mall, London, 14th February, 1800. In the possession of the Earl of Darnley by 1818, when lent by him to the B.I. (nos. 23, 75, 99 and 145). Exh. Manchester, 1857 (nos. 274, 273, 271 and 272 in the provisional catalogue, nos. 287, 288, 285 and 286 in the definitive catalogue), and R.A., 1877 (nos. 103, 115, 126 and 95)—on both occasions lent by the Earl of Darnley, from whom acquired: no. 1318 purchased 1890, nos. 1324 and 1326 purchased 1891. No. 1325 was presented by Lord Darnley, 1891. Cleaned Pictures Exhibition, National Gallery, 1947 (42, 43, 45 and 44).

REPRODUCTIONS: *Illustrations, Italian Schools*, 1937, pp. 382–3.

REFERENCES: (1) Namely, the 1727 catalogue. (2) *Riposo*, p. 563. (3) An inventory of 1567 made by Jacopo Strada in connection with his purchases for Albert V, duke of Bavaria, lists two Veronese's, quoting inscriptions on them ('omnia vanitas' and 'honor et virtus post mortem floret') which identify them with pictures later in the Emperor's collection and now in the Frick collection (see J. Stockbauer: *Die Kunstbestrebungen am Bayerischen Hofe, Quellenschriften für Kunstgeschichte*, VIII, 1874, p. 43). It may be noted that the 1808 Palais Royal catalogue contains a fantastic claim (vol. II, 'XIVeme Tableau de Paul Véronese') that nos. 1318, 1324–6, are part of the decorations at Maser as described by Ridolfi. These are, in fact, frescoes. (4) 'Crozat Cabinet', II, p. 67. (5) Notes by Stella Mary Pearce in the Gallery archives. (6) The 1929 catalogue commits itself to the statement 'nos. 1318 and 1326 wholly by the master's hand', while the catalogue of the 1947 Exhibition of Cleaned Pictures lists nos. 1318 and 1324 as Veronese and 1325 and 1326 as 'studio of Veronese'. Though the present writer's point of view is much nearer to the latter than to the former he regards the whole series as homogeneous to the extent of seeing both autograph and studio execution in all four, only the ratio varying. It must be stressed that the organisation of Veronese's work-shop was clearly very elaborate and that we have no detailed knowledge of it. **(7)** For this date see p. XV of the 1938 catalogue of the Kunsthistorisches Museum, Vienna. The relevant inventories are printed in Olof Granberg: *La Galerie de Tableaux de la Reine Christine de Suède*, 1897. **(8)** See preface to vol. 1 of the *Galerie du Palais Royal* (1808), also Charles Blanc: *Le Trésor de la Curiosité*, 1858, vol. II, pp. 148–59, and W. Buchanan: *Memoirs*, I (1824), pp. 9–220. **(9)** Passavant: *Tour of a German Artist in England*, II (1836), p. 179.

## After VERONESE

### 97 THE RAPE OF EUROPA

Canvas on panel, $23\frac{3}{8} \times 27\frac{1}{2}$ (0·594 × 0·699).

A certain amount of repaint is visible through the present heavily discoloured varnish. Basic condition nevertheless probably quite good.

In all references from the seventeenth century onwards and including editions of the National Gallery catalogue prior to that of 1911 stated to be by Veronese and regarded as the sketch or *modello* for the large picture in the Doge's Palace, Venice. The coarseness of the execution, however, leaves no doubt that it is in fact a copy, differing from the original in various ways—it is in reverse, there are three, instead of four, attendant maidens, a *putto* holds the head of the white bull behind which is an extra bull and there are two, instead of three, flying *putti*. Minor variations include the presence of the drapery in the foreground, the lack of a dog and a different arrangement of the trees and distant figures.

These arbitrary variations and the relatively small size of no. 97 would leave a possibility that it may have been painted with fraudulent intent to 'manufacture' a preliminary sketch for the big picture.[1]

ENGRAVING: By R. De Launay (in reverse), 'XVII$^{eme}$ tableau de Paul Calliari' in vol. II (1808) of 'Galerie du Palais Royal'.

PROVENANCE: Probably no. 657 ('Europa auff einem Weissen oxen') in the inventory (after 15th February, 1637)[2] of the Emperor Rudolph II's collection. No. 12 in the 1689 Queen Christina inventory. No. 5 in the 1721 inventory. Page 369 in the 1727 catalogue (by Du Bois de Saint Gelais) of the Orléans pictures in the Palais Royal. Probably lot 47 in the Orléans sale, by Bryan, 88 Pall Mall, London, 26th December, 1798,[3] where bought 'Mr Willet'.[4] Lot 107, John Willett Willett sale, by Peter Coxe, London, 2nd June, 1813, where bought Holwell Carr,[5] by whom exh., B.I., 1818 (91). The Rev. W. Holwell Carr Bequest, 1831.

REPRODUCTION: Negative in the possession of the Gallery.

REFERENCES: **(1)** Various other versions of the Doge's Palace picture exist, notably large-scale variants in the Capitoline and at Dresden. No. 97 is, however, even farther from these than from the Venice picture. **(2)** For this date see p. XV of the 1938 catalogue of the Kunsthistorisches Museum, Vienna. The relevant inventories are printed in Olof Granberg: *La Galerie de Tableaux de la Reine Christine de Suède*, 1897. **(3)** For details of the vicissitudes of the Orléans collection see the entries for nos. 270 (Titian) of 1326 (Veronese). **(4)** Marked copy of the sale catalogue in the Gallery library. **(5)** Mark (in pencil but probably contemporary) in copy of the sale catalogue in the Gallery library.

10*

# INDEX OF PICTURES WHOSE ATTRIBUTIONS HAVE BEEN CHANGED SINCE THE CATALOGUE OF 1929 AND THE SUPPLEMENT OF 1939

*Note*: The following list includes only those instances where the name of the artist or of the school has been changed—i.e. it does not include a picture changed from 'Titian' to 'Studio of Titian' or similar changes.

# SUBJECT INDEX

## A. SAINTS

S. Agatha:
Sebastiano del Piombo, no. 24

S. Anthony of Padua:
Lotto, no. 2281

S. Bonaventure:
Pordenone, no. 4038

S. Catherine of Alexandria:
Bonifazio, no. 1202;
Style of Bonifazio, no. 3536;
Titian, no. 635

S. Elizabeth:
Style of Bonifazio, no. 3536

S. George:
Ascribed to Palma Vecchio, no. 3079
Tintoretto, no. 16

S. Helena:
Veronese, no. 1041

S. James the Greater:
Bonifazio, no. 1202;
Girolamo da Treviso, no. 623

S. Jerome:
Bonifazio, no. 1202;
Catena, no. 694;
Lotto, no. 2281

S. John the Baptist:
Bonifazio, no. 1202;
Style of Bonifazio, no. 3536;

S. John the Baptist (*contd.*)

Ascribed to Catena, no. 3540;
Sebastiano del Piombo, no. 1450;
Titian, no. 635

S. John Martyr:
Bordon, no. 3122

S. Joseph:
Cariani, no. 1203;
Follower of the Bassano, no. 1858;
Giorgione, no. 1160;
Licinio, no. 3075;
Sebastiano del Piombo, no. 1450;
Titian, no. 4;
Veronese, no. 268

S. Louis of Toulouse:
Pordenone, no. 4039

S. Lucy:
Cariani, no. 1203

S. Mary Magdalene:
Sebastiano del Piombo, no. 1;
Titian, no. 270;
Veronese, no. 931

S. Mark:
After Tintoretto, no. 2900

S. Nicholas of Bari:
Veronese, no. 26

S. Peter Martyr:
Ascribed to Cariani, no. 41

## B. OLD TESTAMENT SCENES AND CHARACTERS

Abraham:
(?) After Francesco Bassano, no. 2148

Sheba, Queen of:
(?) Venetian School, sixteenth century, no. 3107

Solomon:
(?) Venetian School, sixteenth century, no. 3107

Tower of Babel:
Leandro Bassano, no. 60

## C. NEW TESTAMENT SCENES AND CHARACTERS:
(N.B. Madonna and Child groups not included, nor either separately except in episodes from the Gospels)

Adoration of the Magi:
Giorgione, no. 1160;
Ascribed to Girolamo da Treviso, no. 218;
Veronese, no. 268

Adoration of the Shepherds:
Follower of the Bassano, no. 1858;
Venetian School, sixteenth century, no. 1377

## C. New Testament Scenes and Characters (*contd.*)

Christ washing His Disciples' Feet:
Tintoretto, no. 1130

Dives and Lazarus:
After Bonifazio, no. 3106

Good Samaritan:
Jacopo Bassano, no. 277

'Noli Me Tangere':
Titian, no. 270

Purification of the Temple:
Jacopo Bassano, no. 228

Raising of Lazarus:
Sebastiano del Piombo, no. 1

Salome:
Sebastiano del Piombo, no. 2493

Tribute Money:
Titian, no. 224

## D. Portraits

Albani:
Cariani, no. 2494

Ariosto, Lodovico (?):
Palma Vecchio, no. 636

Fracastoro, Girolamo (?):
After Titian, no. 3949

Giuliano, Giovanni:
Lotto, no. 1105

Gritti, Andrea:
Catena, no. 5751

Martinengo, Ludovico:
Bartolommeo Veneto, no. 287

Morosini, Vincenzo:
Tintoretto, no. 4004

Nani, Stefano:
Licinio, no. 1309

Titian (?):
Titian, no. 1944

Torre, Giovanni Agostino della, and
Niccolò della:
Lotto, no. 699

Vendramin Family:
Titian, no. 4452

Volta, Giovanni della and family (?):
Lotto, no. 1047

## E. Profane Subjects (excluding portraits)

Adonis:
Titian, no. 34;
Follower of Titian, no. 1123

Alexander the Great:
Veronese, no. 294

Ariadne:
Titian, no. 35

Bacchus:
Titian, no. 35

Boreas, sons of:
Ascribed to Ludovico Pozzoserrato,
no. 5467

Chloe:
Bordon, no. 637

Cimon:
Venetian School, sixteenth century,
no. 4037

Cupid:
Titian, no. 34;
Follower of Titian, no. 1123

Damon:
Ascribed to Previtali, no. 4884

Daphnis:
Bordon, no. 637

Darius, family of:
Veronese, no. 294

Efigenia:
Venetian School, sixteenth century,
no. 4037

Europa:
After Veronese, no. 97

Flora (?):
Palma Vecchio, no. 3939

Ganymede:
Ascribed to Damiano Mazza, no. 32

Harpies:
Ascribed to Ludovico Pozzoserrato,
no. 5467

Hercules:
Tintoretto, no. 1313

Juno:
Tintoretto, no. 1313

Jupiter:
Tintoretto, no. 1313

Justice:
Giuseppe Salviati, no. 3942

Labours of the Months:
Style of Bonifazio, nos. 3109–10

B. PROFANE SUBJECTS (excluding portraits) (*contd.*)

Lucretia:
  Lotto, no. 4256

Mars:
  Palma Giovane, no. 1866

Myrrha:
  Follower of Titian, no. 1123

Semele:
  Ascribed to Tintoretto, no. 1476
Thyrsis:
  Ascribed to Previtali, no. 4884
Venus:
  Palma Giovane, no. 1866;
  Titian, no. 34;
  Follower of Titian, no. 1123

# INDEX OF COLLECTIONS

(N.B. This index does not include all dealers or dealers' agents
or unconfirmed provenance)

# NUMERICAL INDEX

| Inventory number | Present attribution | Inventory number | Present attribution |
|---|---|---|---|
| 2493 | SEBASTIANO del Piombo | 3939 | PALMA Vecchio |
| 2494 | CARIANI | 3942 | Giuseppe SALVIATI |
| 2495 | Ascribed to CARIANI | 3948 | TITIAN |
| 2507 | BARTOLOMMEO Veneto | 3949 | After TITIAN |
| 2900 | After TINTORETTO | 4004 | TINTORETTO |
| 2903 | (?) VENETIAN School, sixteenth century | 4037 | VENETIAN School, sixteenth century |
| 3075 | LICINIO | 4038 | PORDENONE |
| 3079 | Ascribed to PALMA Vecchio | 4039 | PORDENONE |
| 3106 | After BONIFAZIO | 4222 | After TITIAN |
| 3107 | (?) VENETIAN School, sixteenth century | 4256 | LOTTO |
| | | 4452 | TITIAN |
| 3108 | VENETIAN School, sixteenth century | 4884 | Ascribed to PREVITALI |
| | | 5385 | TITIAN |
| 3109 | Style of BONIFAZIO | 5466 | Ascribed to POZZOSERRATO |
| 3110 | Style of BONIFAZIO | | |
| 3122 | BORDON | 5467 | Ascribed to POZZOSERRATO |
| 3536 | Style of BONIFAZIO | | |
| 3540 | Ascribed to CATENA | 5751 | CATENA |